THE MODERN

WONDER BOOK OF KNOWLEDGE

A PAGEANT OF HUMAN PROGRESS

Contents

CONTENTS

The Modern
WONDER BOOK
OF KNOWLEDGE

The thrilling stories of twentieth-
century industry, science, nature,
transportation, communication, and
other marvels of the world.

THE JOHN C. WINSTON COMPANY

PHILADELPHIA
TORONTO

ACKNOWLEDGMENTS

The publishers wish to express their appreciation to Norman Carlisle, Geoffrey Mott-Smith and Arnold Romney for the invaluable assistance they rendered in the preparation of this volume.

The publishers are also grateful to the following sources for the use of the photographs in this book:

All American Aviation, Inc.: Pages 260, 261, 262, 263, 264, 265, 266, 267, 268, 269, 270, 271.

American Airlines: Pages 210, 211, 212, 213, 214, 215, 216, 217.

American Forest Products Industries: Pages 540, 541, 542, 543, 544, 545, 546, 548, 552, 556.

American Telegraph and Telephone Co.: Pages 183, 184, 185, 186, 187, 188, 190, 192, 193, 194, 195, 196, 197.

American Type Founders: Page 654.

American Woolen Company: Pages 325, 331.

Association of American Railroads: Pages 473, 477.

Baldwin Locomotive Works: Page 475.

Baltimore and Ohio Railroad: Pages 456, 474.

Bausch and Lomb Optical Co.: Pages 58, 59.

Bell Aircraft Corp.: Pages 218, 220, 222.

Bituminous Coal Institute: Pages 60, 486, 488, 490, 492, 495, 496, 499, 500, 501, 502, 504.

British Information Service: Pages 459, 460, 463.

Brown Brothers: Page 277.

Californians, Inc.: Page 468.

Canadian Pacific Railway: Pages 461, 481.

Caterpillar Tractor Co.: Pages 527, 533, 534, 535, 536, 537, 538, 547, 566, 568, 569.

Celanese Corporation of America: Pages 323, 327, 329, 330, 333.

Civil Aeronautics Administration: Pages 253, 254.

Columbia Broadcasting System: Pages 139, 141, 142, 143, 145, 146, 147, 148, 149, 153.

Diamond Match Company: Pages 313, 315, 317, 318, 319, 320, 321, 322.

Dodge, J. M., Co.: Page 485.

du Pont de Nemours, E. I., and Co.: Pages 328, 332, 337, 338, 339, 406, 434, 436, 437, 439.

Eastman Kodak Company: Pages 122, 123, 125, 126, 127, 128, 129, 130, 131, 132, 133.

Erie Railroad: Page 484.

Galloway, Ewing: Page 616.

General Electric Co.: Pages 69, 70, 71, 74, 76, 77, 82.

General Electric X-Ray Corp.: Pages 43, 44, 45, 48, 49, 51, 52, 53.

General Motors: Pages 522, 523, 524, 525, 526, 528, 529, 530, 531, 532.

Goodyear Tire and Rubber Co.: Pages 237, 239, 240, 242, 243, 245, 246, 247, 248, 249, 250.

Great Northern: Page 475.

Hammermill Paper Co.: Pages 546, 550, 553, 554.

Harper Brothers: Page 105.

Hood, Harry S.: Page 617.

International Harvester Co.: Pages 557, 558, 559, 560, 561, 562, 564, 565, 570, 571, 572, 573, 574, 575, 576.

International News: Pages 2, 3, 4, 5, 6, 10, 18, 19, 28.

Johns-Manville Asbestos Co.: Pages 286, 288, 289, 290.

Joint Army Navy Task Force: Pages 1, 8.

Lanston Monotype Machine Co.: Page 667.

Lehigh Navigation Coal Co., Inc.: Page 485.

Libby-Owens-Ford Glass Co.: Pages 298, 299, 300, 301, 302.

Lockheed Aircraft Corp.: Page 174.

Louisville and Nashville Railway: Page 441.

McGraw-Hill Publishing Co.: Pages 16-17, 22-23, 25, 27.

Mergenthaler Linotype Co.: Page 665.

Metro-Goldwyn-Mayer: Pages 104, 114, 115, 116, 118, 119, 120, 121.

Miami Daily News: Page 369.

Miller Printing Machinery Co.: Page 668.

Motion Picture Association of America: Pages 103, 105.

FOREWORD

THE MODERN WONDER BOOK OF KNOWLEDGE is designed to present the salient facts about the physical universe and modern civilization and to answer the questions most frequently asked about natural phenomena, science and technology.

The book may be read from cover to cover, with profit, or it may be used for reference. For consecutive reading, the material is presented as a series of "Stories." Each story is complete in itself, but contributory facts may often be found in other stories on related subjects or that have a common historical background. The interrelations are emphasized in some instances by cross references inserted in the text.

A list of all the stories is given in the "Contents"; in addition, the following classifications may also prove useful for reference:

The physical universe: Stars, Ocean, Weather, Lightning.

Natural resources: Coal, Oil, Steel, Minerals, Salt, Lumber, Wildlife.

Power: Atomic Energy, Electrical Power, Rockets, Jet Propulsion.

Structures: Bridges, Tunnels, Dams, Skyscrapers, Steel Ships.

Manufactures: Glass, Cement, Matches, Dynamite, Paper, Textiles, Plastics.

Communication: Telegraph, Telephone, Movies, Radio Broadcasting, Television.

Transportation: Railroading, Airlines, Airways, Air Pick-up.

Applied arts: Photography, Printing.

Specific inventions and discoveries: Telescope, Microscope, X-Rays, Radar, Airships, Helicopter, Gyroscope, Diesel Engine, Farm Machinery, Submarine, Wonder Drugs.

Between the stories are inserted paragraphs in smaller type; these answer many of the frequently asked questions about history, geography, familiar phenomena. For example, "When were the

Olympic games first held?" "What is the hottest place in the United States?" "How fast does sound travel?" "What makes a stick seem to bend in water?" "What is the Nobel Prize?"

A comprehensive index has been included to aid the reader in his quest for knowledge. It is the hope of the editors that this single volume, which is necessarily limited in its scope because of space, will bring both profit and pleasure to the reader.

THE STORY OF ATOMIC ENERGY

The typical "mushroom" formed by the explosion of an atomic bomb.

SHORTLY after nine o'clock on the morning of August 6, 1945, a single American airplane appeared over the city of Hiroshima, Japan. Little attention was paid to it, for its lack of companions seemed to indicate that its purpose was reconnaissance, not attack. But it released a single bomb attached to a parachute. While still about 1,500 feet from the ground, the bomb exploded in a tremendous ball of fire, visible nearly 200 miles away. Sixty percent of the city of Hiroshima simply disappeared. All structures in an area of four square miles were flattened as though by a gigantic steam roller. About 30,000 persons were killed instantly, and tens of thousands more later died of their injuries.

The American government announced that the first "atomic bomb" in history had been unloosed, and called upon the Japanese government to surrender. In the absence of a reply, a second bomb was dropped upon Nagasaki, on August 9, wreaking even greater destruction within a smaller area. The next day, the Japanese government commenced negotiations that led to the termination of the last phase of World War II, the formal articles of surrender being signed on September 2.

The city that was—Hiroshima after the bomb blast of August 6, 1945. Although the buildings were among the most modern in the Japanese Empire, all but a few within an area of four square miles were literally flattened to earth. Radiation caused by the bomb lingered for weeks in some sections of the city.

How Was the Atom Bomb Developed?

It has been said that the two bombs dropped upon Hiroshima and Nagasaki cost a billion dollars apiece, for two billion dollars was expended during 1941-1945 to make the age-old dream of releasing atomic energy a reality. In 1941, a group of scientists persuaded President Roosevelt and other top officials that a method of unlocking the stupendous forces in the atom had at last been found, and that given enough men and material a practical "know-how" could be evolved for the manufacture of bombs hundreds of times more powerful than the 2,000-pound "block-busters." A joint directing staff of American, British and Canadian officials was set up, and the huge "Manhattan Project" got under way. Eventually no less than 125,000 persons were engaged in this project, yet so well was the secret kept that the American public was no less surprised than the enemy countries when the first bomb was released upon Hiroshima.

Three hidden cities grew up, devoted solely to the project, at Oak Ridge, Tennessee, in New Mexico near Santa Fe, and Richland Village near Pasco, Washington. In addition, hundreds of the nation's scientific and industrial concerns contributed vital

Three stages in the development of the "mushroom" cloud, photographed at intervals of twenty minutes over Nagasaki on August 9, 1945.

assistance to the work. The leading scientists of the project were J. Robert Oppenheimer, A. H. Compton, Harold Urey, Niels Bohr, Ernest Lawrence, Enrico Fermi, and Lise Meitner, with Britain and Canada represented by Sir James Chadwick and Dean C. J. Mackenzie.

Working at top speed, the scientists and engineers solved many intricate problems—how to start and control a "chain reaction" of atomic fission, how to extract sufficient quantities of the vital element uranium 235, how to build a bomb safe to handle yet sure of its effect. The success of the undertaking was signalized by the exploding of a trial bomb in the New Mexico desert on July 16, 1945. While a small group of topflight scientists and military experts watched from a post ten miles away, a small bomb fastened to the top of a steel tower burst in a blinding glare

This was Nagasaki. Destruction by the atomic bomb was even more complete than at Hiroshima.

of light. A column of smoke and dust shot up from the ground, mushroomed at the top, and in a few minutes was lost to sight in the stratosphere.

This awesome spectacle marked the culmination of centuries of research and experiment by many generations of scientists. In order to understand what is meant by "splitting the atom" we must learn what scientists have found out about the constitution of matter.

What Is an Atom?

About 2,400 years ago, a Greek philosopher, Democritus, propounded the theory that all matter, everything we can see and touch, is composed of a tremendous number of tiny, indivisible particles. We all know how a piece of iron, for example, can be

Devastated Nagasaki as seen from the ground. It is estimated that eighteen thousand buildings were reduced to rubble like this.

The first atomic bomb ever created was exploded experimentally in the New Mexico desert on July 16, 1945. This view was taken by a telephoto camera six miles away. It is a negative, the darks in the picture actually being light, and vice versa. The black areas seen here were actually brighter than the midday sun.

cut up into smaller and smaller pieces until it is reduced to a fine dust. But Democritus thought that there must be a limit to this process of subdivision; eventually the particles must become so small that they can no longer be split up. He called these supposed tiniest particles "atoms," after the Greek word for "uncuttable."

We now believe that Democritus was right. All matter is composed of tiny particles that are alike in kind, whether they

[6]

form the substance of metal, wood, water, gas, or what-not. But hundreds of years were to pass before his "atomic theory" could be verified.

What Is an Element?

Another ancient theory was that all matter is composed of elements that are of four kinds, resembling "earth, air, fire, and water." Certain abundant substances have been known from prehistoric times—iron, copper, gold, silver, lead, tin, mercury, sulphur, carbon. As more such elements were discovered, it became apparent that the old fourfold classification was meaningless. By 1808, when John Dalton, an Englishman, laid the foundation for modern chemistry, fully 46 different elements were known, and many more were discovered in the ensuing century.

The distinction was early recognized between *elements* and *compounds*. The elements are basic substances like iron, gold, sulphur—although science has discovered that they are neither so homogeneous nor indivisible as was once believed! A compound is a chemical combination of two or more different elements. Water is such a compound—two parts of hydrogen with one of oxygen. Common table salt is a compound of sodium and chlorine.

What Is Atomic Weight?

In the eighteenth and nineteenth centuries, chemists searched for a precise classification of the growing list of known elements. Many groups of these elements have similar properties, that is, they form compounds with much the same other elements, and in some instances look alike and have the same physical characteristics. For example, the metals—iron, gold, silver, tin, lead, mercury, and others—are markedly dense and are impervious to light even when drawn into extremely thin sheets.

At the same time, every element differs in some way from every other, and the most reliable point of difference was found to be in weight. Equal volumes of the elements all have different weights, and these basic weights were called "atomic weights"

A joint United States Navy-Army task force exploded two atomic bombs for experimental purposes at Bikini Lagoon during the summer of 1946. This photo of the underwater blast, July 25, shows a huge column of water hurtling into the air, surmounted by a burst of a lethally radioactive cloud.

because they were imagined to come from the different weights of the component "atoms" of Democritus.

Atomic weights are expressed inrelative terms. The weight of oxygen was arbitrarily fixed at 16. Oxygen, discovered in 1774, was chosen for the standard because it has the widest range of chemical affinity and is found in combination with every active element. With oxygen fixed at 16, the atomic weight of hydrogen, the lightest known element, is about 1, while carbon is 12, nitrogen 14, iron 56, gold 197, lead 207, and so on.

The Bikini blast a few seconds later. At the base, the radioactive cloud has fanned out and is settling down upon the sea.

What Is the Periodic Table?

In 1869, the Russian chemist, Dimitri Ivanovich Mendeleff, made a classification of the elements known as the *periodic table*. He arranged the elements in order of atomic weight, from hydrogen up. He pointed out that the known groups of elements with similar properties, such as the inert gases, the halogens, fit into this table in a regular way. There were certain "holes" in the table, where elements of certain weights and certain properties might be expected to exist if the "periodic" principle persisted throughout the list. One by one these holes have been filled up, by the discovery and isolation of the expected elements. By the time of World War II, only two of the 92 elements (such is the total number predicted by the periodic table) remained to be discovered.

What Was the First Atomic Picture?

The atomic weights of the elements all seemed to be integral multiples of a basic unit. We have noted that with oxygen fixed at 16 the lightest element, hydrogen, has a relative value of 1, while carbon is 12, nitrogen 14, and so on. This fact strongly

The atomic blast cloud soars high above Bikini Lagoon.

suggests that all the elements are built up of particles of exactly the same kind, the elements differing only in the *number* of such particles. So was formed the first "picture" of what an atom actually is.

In this earliest picture, the atom was imagined to be a miniature solar system. There is a *nucleus* in place of the sun, and *electrons* revolve around this nucleus in place of planets. The number of electrons is identical with the *atomic number* of the element (which is its ordinal number in the periodic table). Thus, hydrogen with atomic number 1 has one electron, helium (number 2) has two, and so on. Practically all of the *mass* (weight) of an atom lies in the nucleus.

Electrons are units of negative electricity, and are held in their orbits by a positive charge in the nucleus. It is possible to imagine that all electrons are alike, and so far as we know this is true. But the *nuclei* of elements must differ in some way, since they have different positive charges and different weights.

This broad picture of the atom has been corroborated by all later discoveries. The existence of electrons has been verified in many ways, their size and distance from the nucleus measured. Although an electron is too small to be seen by the most powerful microscope, we can see the track a single electron leaves in darting through a "cloud chamber." But the picture of the inside of a *nucleus* has had to be revised again and again, to take account of new discoveries in atomic behavior and more refined measurements of familiar phenomena.

What Is an Isotope?

From the very beginning, the neat picture of the atom was troubled by the fact that some elements do not have exactly the atomic weights we should expect. They are not exact integral multiples of the weight of hydrogen. Refined measurement has shown more and more such discrepancies.

The mystery has been cleared up, or rather merged with that perrenial mystery, the nucleus, by the discovery of *isotopes*. Isotopes are two or more different forms of the *same element* but with *different atomic weights*. For example, sulphur occurs in no less than five forms, having atomic weights of 32, 33, 34, 35 and 36. Since the sulphur found in nature is invariably a mixture of several of these isotopes, in different proportions, its measured weight runs into decimals instead of being a neat integer.

In the classic picture of the atom, isotopes must be explained by differences in the nucleus that make no difference in the positive charge. But then we have to explain how different kinds of nuclei can exist with the same positive charge.

What Is Radioactivity?

Once the atomic picture was conceived, scientists bent their energies to "getting inside" the nucleus and finding out its composition. The first real knowledge on this point came from the discovery of *radioactivity*.

At the end of the nineteenth century, Prof. Antoine Becquerel, a Frenchman, found that the uranium salts he was investigating made an image on a photographic plate, without the use of visible light. The existence of invisible rays was at once suspected. It was already known that such rays are generated by a powerful electric current passing through a vacuum tube—for in 1895 Prof. Wilhelm Roentgen had announced the discovery of X-rays generated in a tube of the type invented by Sir William Crookes.

Airplane view of Bikini just after the gases liberated by the underwater blast have burst into the air, drawing up a cylindrical column of water.

The task of finding the so-called *radioactive* substance in uranium was undertaken by Pierre and Marie Curie. In 1898 they succeeded in isolating a minute quantity of a new element, which they called *radium*. It was much more radioactive than the original uranium ore.

The next step was to investigate the rays emitted by radium. Sir Ernest Rutherford, a pupil of the great English physicist, Sir J. J. Thomson, found that these rays are of three types, which he called by the first three letters of the Greek alphabet, *alpha, beta,* and *gamma.*

Alpha rays are a stream of positively charged particles, and were soon discovered to be identical with the nuclei of helium. Beta rays are a stream of electrons, negatively charged particles.

[12]

Gamma rays are not material but are waves of pure energy, like X-rays, capable of affecting photographic plates.

Is Transmutation Possible?

The medieval alchemists firmly believed that some day they would discover a magical substance or "philosopher's stone" having the power to transmute one element into another. The spur to their search was the hope of being able to create unlimited quantities of gold out of baser metals. With the inception of modern chemistry the "philosopher's stone" was swept into the discard as idle nonsense.

Then the discovery of radioactivity showed transmutation actually at work in nature! Uranium is radioactive; it gradually loses material particles, electrons and helium nuclei, and so turns into radium; the radiation continues and radium eventually turns into lead!

The dream of the chemists was revived in a new form. We are no longer so keen on changing baser metals into gold. But the change is accompanied by a release of energy—the gamma rays of radium! Energy, the power that turns the wheels of industry, is the real wealth of the earth! Perhaps we can tap a new source of energy to supplement our reserves of oil and coal.

What Is the Source of the Sun's Heat?

Suppose that an iron ball is heated white hot, then sealed in a room full of air. The ball will at once begin to cool, that is, radiate its heat into the air, until eventually the ball and the air will reach the same temperature.

This was early science's conception of the sun. A huge mass of matter had somehow acquired a vast amount of heat and now was engaged in radiating it away for the benefit of its planets. This picture was plausible as long as the sun's age was reckoned in thousands of years. But when the geologists began to say that the sun must be at least two or three billion years old to account for the changes on the surface of the earth, a new problem arose.

[13]

Could a mass hold a large enough initial supply of heat to go on radiating for billions of years? The physicists said no.

The alternative supposition was that the sun draws upon some huge reserve of *potential energy* to maintain its heat. We are familiar with potential energy here on earth. A cold lump of coal looks as inert as a rock. Yet if a small amount of heat is put into it, it begins to burn and eventually gives back a great deal more heat than was put into it. We call this kind of energy, latent in the coal, *potential*.

Perhaps then the sun is a mass of coal or some such material capable of producing heat by oxidation. But here the astronomer steps in. He says, "The spectroscope tells me exactly what elements exist in the sun, at least in its outer regions. They are the same elements as we find on the earth—hydrogen, iron, and so on. I know that there is no huge supply of oxygen such as your theory demands."

The discovery of radioactivity pointed the way to a new theory. In 1905, Dr. Albert Einstein suggested that the heat of the sun is supplied by atomic disintegration. He said, "Let us assume that the entire *mass* of a body is capable of being transformed into energy." He even supplied the formula for calculating the amount of energy:

$$E = mc^2$$

That is, the amount of energy (E) is equal to the product of the mass (m) and the square of the velocity of light (c^2). The constant c, equal to about 186,000 miles per second, is necessarily involved, according to Einstein's theory of relativity, in every formula of celestial physics.

Can All Mass Be Transformed Into Energy

It was indeed a startling idea that the entire mass of a body is *potential energy*. This means that *any* element, if given the necessary initial supply of energy, like the initial heating of a lump of coal, will liberate a much greater amount of energy. The necessary conditions exist in the sun in the form of a very high temperature. Can we on earth create the conditions for the liberation of atomic energy?

Scientists began to work feverishly to answer this question. The nuclei of various elements was bombarded with every kind of ray, every kind of energy, that we know, in the effort to "smash the atom." These experiments revealed much new knowledge about the composition of the nucleus. Before continuing with the history of atom-smashing, let us take note of some of this new knowledge.

What Is Inside the Nucleus of an Atom?

Every nucleus contains one or more *protons*. A proton is identical with the nucleus of a hydrogen atom. The number of protons is the same as the *atomic number* of the element. The atomic number is the ordinal number of the element in the periodic table. For example, hydrogen is number 1, helium 2, oxygen 8, sulphur 16, lead 82, uranium 92.

The proton is a positively charged particle. Outside the nucleus are as many electrons, negative charges, as there are protons. But inside the nucleus are also some particles called *neutrons,* which carry no charge, but contribute to the mass of an atom. The atom of hydrogen alone contains no neutrons. All other elements contain two or more neutrons. For example, helium contains two, so that the atomic weight is 4. Oxygen contains 8, and its atomic weight is 16.

Many of the elements are capable of containing different numbers of neutrons in their atoms, and this variation in neutrons creates isotopes. For example, all forms of sulphur have 16 protons in the nucleus, but the number of neutrons may be 16, 17, 18, 19 or 20, so that the isotopes of sulphur have atomic weights ranging from 32 to 36.

Most of the elements are stable under normal terrestrial conditions. But those from radium, 88, to uranium, 92, are more or less unstable. Protons and neutrons shoot forth from the nuclei in the form of alpha particles. With the loss of positive charge, electrons are released in the form of beta particles. The loss of each proton degrades the atom to that of a lighter isotope and eventually to that of a lower element. The atom finally reaches stability in a form of so-called radium-lead.

1 ATOM PARTS

In Nucleus
- $\oplus$ PROTON, Mass=1 | Electrical charge=+1
- $\bigcirc$ NEUTRON, Mass=1 | Electrical charge=0

In Outer Orbit
- • ELECTRON, Mass=0* | Electrical charge=−1

* Actually $\frac{1}{1850}$ of Proton weight

2 SIMPLEST ATOM

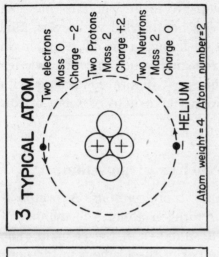

One electron
Mass 0
Charge −1

One Proton
Mass 1
Charge +1

HYDROGEN

Atom weight=1   Atom number=1

3 TYPICAL ATOM

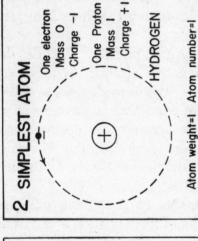

Two electrons
Mass 0
Charge −2

Two Protons
Mass 2
Charge +2

Two Neutrons
Mass 2
Charge 0

HELIUM

Atom weight=4   Atom number=2

4 ATOM SIZE

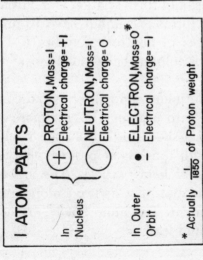

ELECTRON

Most of an atom is mere space

NUCLEUS

$\frac{1}{200,000,000}$ INCH

If the nucleus were a baseball, the electron would be a speck 2000 ft. away

5 ELECTRON ENERGY

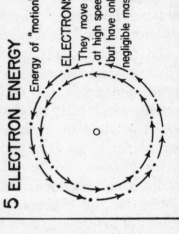

Energy of "motion"

ELECTRONS
They move at high speed but have only negligible mass.

Energy values are relatively small

6 NUCLEAR ENERGY

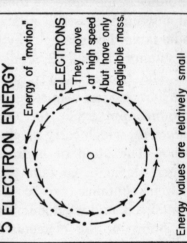

NUCLEUS

Binding energy resists separation of protons and neutrons

In 1 lb. of helium, nuclear energy = electricity enough to run a 100-watt bulb 13,000,000 years.

7 RADIOACTIVITY

RADIUM NUCLEUS

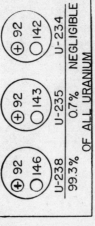

Alpha particles

Beta particles

Gamma rays

Lighter nucleus

Some unstable "heavy" atoms voluntarily split to form other atoms and release usable energy

8 NATURE'S HEAVIEST ATOM

Basic Source of Atomic Energy

92 Electrons

URANIUM 238

92 Protons

146 Neutrons

9 ISOTOPES

Chemically the same element and their nuclei contain the same number of protons. Only the number of neutrons differs. Thus the uranium isotopes are:

+ 92 ⃝ 146	+ 92 ⃝ 143	+ 92 ⃝ 142
U-238	U-235	U-234
99.3%	0.7%	NEGLIGIBLE

OF ALL URANIUM

10 ENERGY RELEASED 11,400,000 kilowatt-hours per pound of U-235

When nucleus of U-235 atom is hit by neutron bullet it explodes to form lighter atoms and spare neutrons whose combined mass is less than mass of U-235. Lost mass is transformed into energy–see Einstein's Law

EINSTEIN'S LAW:

One pound of anything = 11,400,000,000 kw.-hr.

when { mass or energy } converts to { energy or mass }

Applying this law to U-235 split:

Explosion products of one pound of U-235 weigh 0.9990 lb, so 0.001 lb. of the mass is converted into 0.001 x 11,400,000,000 = 11,400,000 kilowatt-hours of energy.

ONE WAY U-235 SPLITS

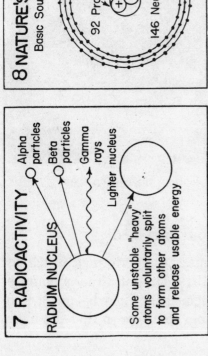

U-235 NUCLEUS

NEUTRON BULLET

BARIUM

NEUTRON "SPARE PARTS"

KRYPTON

11,400,000 kw.-hr. of energy per lb of U-235

Interior of the cyclotron, which develops two million volts.

How Was the Atom Smashed?

The first successful atom-smashing was performed by Ernest Rutherford, a New Zealander, in 1919. He put a tiny amount of radium in a tube filled with nitrogen gas. Then he put a fluorescent screen far enough away from the tube so that the alpha

Dr. Ernest Lawrence and his atom-smashing cyclotron.

particles shooting from the radium could not reach it. He viewed this screen through a microscope from the other side, and detected points of light flashing upon it. These proved to be protons, "blown out" from the nitrogen nuclei by the bombardment of radium rays.

[19]

Rutherford succeeded in *transmuting* one element to another —realizing for the first time the dream of the alchemists! He broke down a fraction of the nitrogen in his tube to oxygen. But his experiments also served to point out a fundamental difficulty in the way of atom smashing. The spaces between the component particles of an atom are comparable with the astronomical spaces between the planets and the sun, the sun and other stars. When a region of such diffuse particles is "bombarded" by a stream of equally diffuse particles, the chances that there will be a collision are of the same order as the chances that two stars will collide— about one in three billion. Probably the only reason we can detect collisions among protons is that the number of protons in a region we can investigate is astronomically huge. But the number of such collisions remains relatively minute, and bombardment with radium rays, for example, is much too feeble a method to produce transmutation on a useful scale.

New machines were invented, such as the cyclotron and betatron, to produce rays thousands of times more intense than those of radium. The construction of giant atom smashers began in 1929. Notable in this field are Dr. Ernest Lawrence, of the University of California, and Dr. J. Van de Graaff, of the Massachusetts Institute of Technology. The cyclotron devised by Lawrence won him the Nobel prize for physics in 1940.

Can Elements Be Stepped "Up" as Well as "Down"?

The first experiments and machines in atom-smashing used bombardment by protons. Such a bombardment may knock some of the protons out of the nuclei of one element and so transmute it into another element of lower atomic number. But can atoms be built up into heavier forms? Dr. Enrico Fermi investigated this question and found an affirmative answer in 1933.

Fermi tried bombarding atoms with a stream of *neutrons*. He found that some of the neutrons were "captured" by the nuclei, which were thereby "stepped up" the atomic scale into heavier isotopes of the element. He found that "neutron capture" is more frequent if the bombarding neutrons are first slowed down, as by passing them through hydrogen.

Experimenting with sixty elements, Fermi found that forty of them could be transmuted upward by the introduction of one slow neutron. The climax came when he added a neutron to uranium 92, and thus created an isotope, uranium 93, an element unknown in nature, the first created by man.

What Is Atomic Fission?

Other scientists joined with Fermi in exploring the new field of "neutron capture." They included Dr. Otto Hahn and Dr. Lise Meitner (who began their work in Germany and continued it in Sweden), Dr. Niels Bohr, and Dr. O. R. Frisch. Working sometimes together and sometimes separately, they made the discoveries that led finally to the realization of the age-old dream —the release of atomic energy on a useful scale.

The vast preponderance of uranium found on the earth has an atomic weight of 238. But there is also an isotope of weight 235, comprising less than one per cent of terrestrial uranium. When U-235 was subjected to neutron bombardment, a strange result was observed. Instead of capturing neutrons, the uranium atoms split into atoms of two other elements, barium and krypton.

Barium has the atomic number 36, krypton 56. The sum is 92, the atomic number of uranium. But the atomic weights of barium and krypton are respectively 91 and 142, which sum to 233, less than the weight of the parent uranium. It is evident that the fission of each U-235 atom releases two neutrons. Here at last was suggested a basis for the long-sought "chain reaction." If a few of the atoms in a quantity of U-235 could be fissioned, perhaps the whole would disintegrate under bombardment of the released neutrons.

How Was the Atomic Bomb Made?

Science had reached the point of verifying the possibility of a "chain reaction," when World War II broke out.

It was still a long step to the practical application of U-235 fission in a destructive bomb. Fifty or a hundred years would probably have been required, at the peace-time rate of scientific

HOW PLUTONIUM IS MADE FROM URANIUM

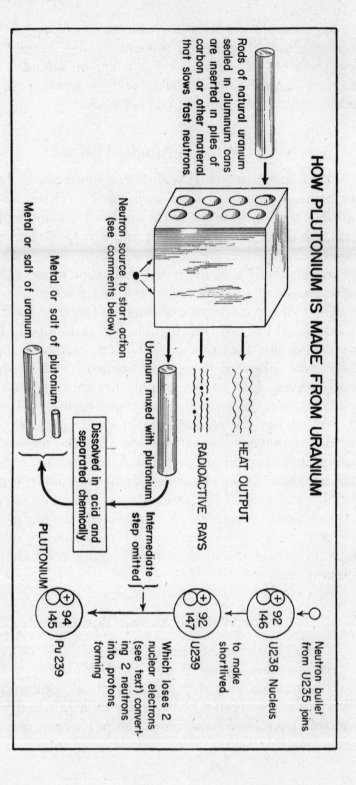

Rods of natural uranium sealed in aluminum cans are inserted in piles of carbon or other material that slows fast neutrons.

Neutron source to start action (see comments below)

Metal or salt of uranium

Metal or salt of plutonium

Uranium mixed with plutonium

Dissolved in acid and separated chemically

Intermediate } step omitted

PLUTONIUM

HEAT OUTPUT
to make shortlived

RADIOACTIVE RAYS

Neutron bullet from U235 joins

(+) 92 146 — U238 Nucleus

(+) 92 147 — U239
Which loses 2 nuclear electrons (see text) converting 2 neutrons into protons forming

(+) 94 145 — Pu 239

Plutonium is a man-made element, No. 94 in the periodic table, heavier than the heaviest natural element, uranium, No. 92. Plutonium can be used as a source of atomic energy, in place of the rare uranium isotope U-235. The diagram shows the process of making plutonium. Although some U-235 is essential to the process, there are several practical advantages to making plutonium instead of isolating U-235. Separating U-235 from U-238 is laborious and costly. But "natural uranium," a mixture of U-238 and a very little U-235, can be used to make plutonium, which can then be separated from the uranium chemically.

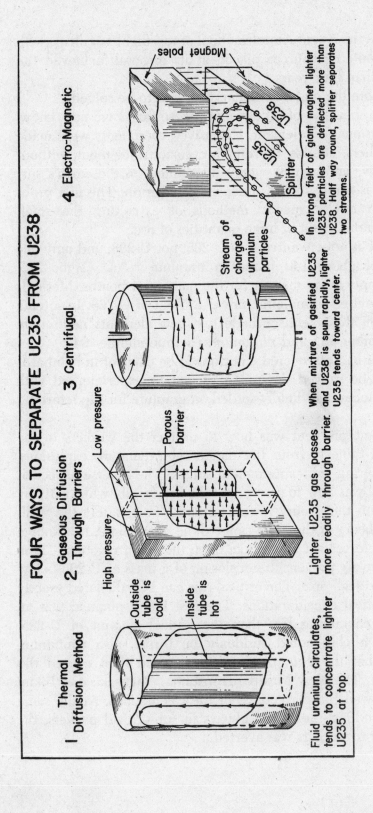

FOUR WAYS TO SEPARATE U235 FROM U238

1 Thermal Diffusion Method

Outside tube is cold

Inside tube is hot

Fluid uranium circulates, tends to concentrate lighter U235 at top.

2 Gaseous Diffusion Through Barriers

Low pressure

Porous barrier

High pressure

Lighter U235 gas passes more readily through barrier.

3 Centrifugal

When mixture of gasified U235 and U238 is spun rapidly, lighter U235 tends toward center.

4 Electro-Magnetic

Magnet poles

U238

U235

Splitter

Stream of charged uranium particles

In strong field of giant magnet lighter U235 particles are deflected more than U238. Half way round, splitter separates two streams.

The difficulty of separating U-235 from U-238 arises from the fact that chemically they are the same, so that chemical methods are inoperative. Physical methods are based primarily upon the very slight difference in weight, amounting to about one per cent.

The four methods here illustrated were all tried in the Manhattan Project. It was found that in any case many stages were necessary to achieve a substantial concentration of pure U-235.

advance. But the Anglo-American pool of top-flight scientists, with almost unlimited resources placed at its disposal, achieved the step in less than four years.

Let us note the major problems that had to be solved.

Uranium, heaviest of all elements, is, so far as we now know, the only "fissionable" element. Extensive experiments were made to utilize others, notably thorium, a radioactive element, without success. Now, uranium is widely distributed on the earth's surface, but it is rarely found in concentrated form. The first problem was to devise speedy methods of extracting the small amount of uranium out of huge quantities of ore.

Next, the isotope wanted was U-235, not U-238, and only one atom out of about 140 found in uranium is of weight 235. Nature's supply is too meager for the making of bombs. Methods had to be devised to manufacture U-235 out of U-238. In solving this problem, the scientists made two new elements *neptunium* (atomic number 93) and *plutonium* (atomic number 94).

As Fermi had discovered, neutrons to be efficient in bombardment, must be slowed down. The scientists experimented with many substances, and finally settled on graphite for the retarding medium.

A constant problem was how to protect the workers in the "Manhattan Project" from the danger of premature explosions, especially during the experimental stages. The reverse aspect of this problem was how to assure that the first bomb, when actually released upon the enemy, would explode. Fortunately the well-developed theory of the atom came to the rescue here. It is known that certain forces act as a brake upon the chain reaction. These forces effectively prevent the explosion of a mass of U-235 below a certain "critical" size. The critical size can be calculated exactly from theoretical considerations. The first bomb planned was an outer shell containing less than the critical amount of U-235, into which a core could suddenly be thrust, also containing U-235, so that the two parts together would then exceed the critical limit. The New Mexico, Hiroshima, Nagasaki, and Bikini tests all showed the correctness of the calculations. At the same time, by handling the U-235 always in sub-critical packets, the chief danger to workers was averted.

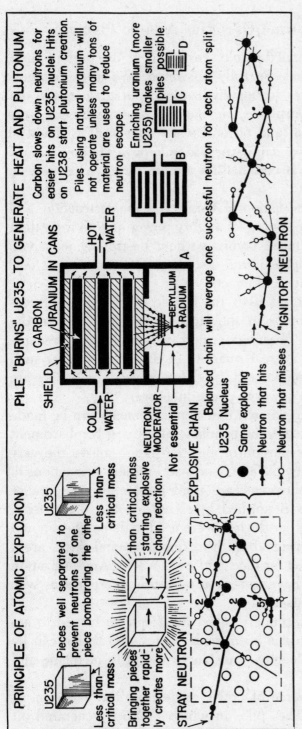

The control of an atomic explosion is relatively easy, for a chain reaction will not occur in a mass of U-235 of less than critical size. To understand what a chain reaction is, imagine that in a given fraction of a second, one million U-235 nuclei are split by neutron bombardment. (There are always enough stray neutrons and cosmic rays in space to start the process, even without the use of a "pilot light" of radium or other substance.) Two million atoms of the lighter elements barium and krypton are created, and at the same time between one and three million neutrons are liberated. These neutrons act as projectiles to smash other U-238 nuclei in the neighborhood. But some are captured by U-238 nuclei, by impurities, and some escape into free space without a collision in the relatively vast atomic "open spaces." To maintain the "chain reaction," no less than one million neutrons, liberated from the million U-235 nuclei, must find targets and split one million more nuclei, and so on. In a mass of uranium below critical size—which can be calculated precisely on statistical probabilities—too many neutrons escape to outer space to maintain the reaction.

To cause an explosion, it is necessary only to bring together enough U-235 suddenly to make a mass greater than the critical. The utilization of a chain reaction to generate heat, however, requires very accurate balance so that the number of nuclei split will not tend to increase beyond control. Hence the need for carbon "moderators" plus a huge mass of natural uranium to reduce the escape of neutrons into free space.

What Peace-time Uses Has Atomic Fission?

This question cannot be fully answered at the present time, and perhaps never can be fully answered. We all know how indispensable is *power* to our civilization. Our great cities, our ships and trains and airplanes, our factories and machinery, were made possible by coal and oil and water power. It is doubtful at this time whether we can harness atomic power to do the same kind of work, but it is certain that atomic power will open up new fields.

The first use of the fission of U-235 was for destruction, and we were interested in taming its mighty power only to the extent of finding a way to make bombs without destroying ourselves. But to harness it for peace-time use we must learn a great deal more about its behavior and effects.

During the summer of 1946, the United States military forces exploded two test bombs in the lagoon of Bikini Atoll in the Pacific. Thousands of observers armed with all kinds of recording devices collected a great quantity of data. Many other such tests will have to be made, and the data analyzed, before we are ready to apply atomic power to peacetime uses.

Scientists have long known that many elements can be made radioactive to some degree by a sufficiently strong bombardment of their nuclei. The explosion of an atom bomb makes the very air and earth radioactive. While X-rays and radium emanations in small, controlled applications, are used in therapy, they cause serious or fatal burns if applied in excess. At the Bikini tests, Geiger counters and other devices were used to detect the amount of radioactivity lingering after the explosions, and some areas were barred to humans for days and even weeks. Any utilization of atomic power will have to reckon with this aftereffect as well as with the explosion itself.

But perhaps the secondary effect itself can be turned to account. The suggestion has been made that U-235 fission can be utilized to create radioactive substances useful in medicine and industry.

There is also a source of power aside from the explosion of concentrated U-235. The "pile" in which U-235 is generated bit

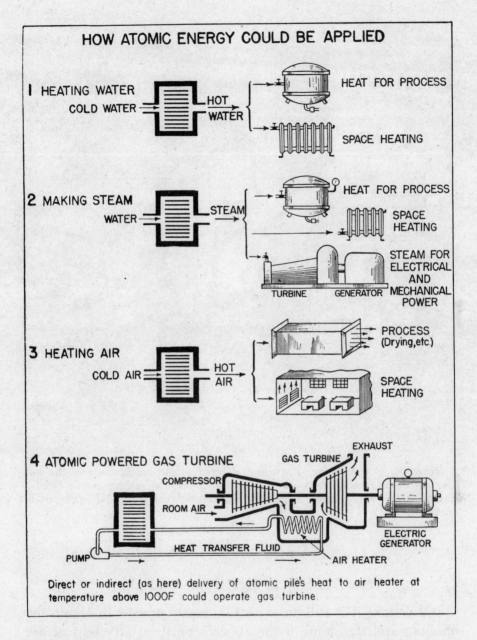

HOW ATOMIC ENERGY COULD BE APPLIED

1 HEATING WATER
COLD WATER → → HOT WATER → HEAT FOR PROCESS / SPACE HEATING

2 MAKING STEAM
WATER → → STEAM → HEAT FOR PROCESS / SPACE HEATING / STEAM FOR ELECTRICAL AND MECHANICAL POWER
TURBINE   GENERATOR

3 HEATING AIR
COLD AIR → → HOT AIR → PROCESS (Drying, etc.) / SPACE HEATING

4 ATOMIC POWERED GAS TURBINE
GAS TURBINE   EXHAUST
COMPRESSOR
ROOM AIR
ELECTRIC GENERATOR
PUMP   HEAT TRANSFER FLUID   AIR HEATER

Direct or indirect (as here) delivery of atomic pile's heat to air heater at temperature above 1000F could operate gas turbine.

by bit from natural U-238 liberates heat. Any source of heat can of course be used for power, by converting water into steam. The question whether a uranium pile can be used as a heater is largely economic. At present it is much more expensive than coal or oil.

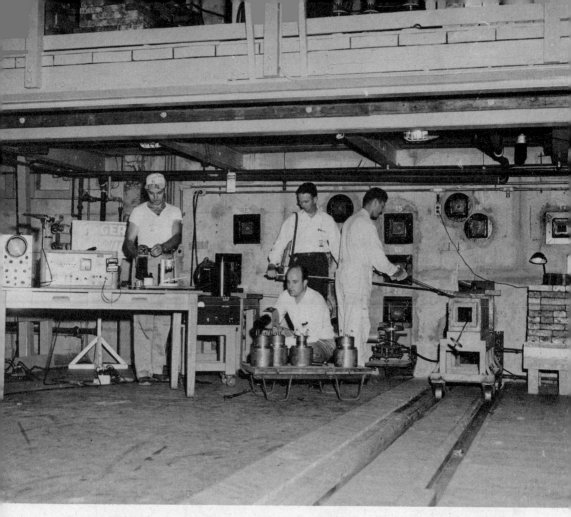

A laboratory at Oak Ridge, Tennessee, devoted to the manufacture of the isotope carbon 14, one of the by-products in the process of making atomic bombs. Carbon 14 is now released to hospitals and research centers to aid in the study of cancer.

How Widely Is Uranium Available?

Of course, it is still an extremely costly process to obtain the uranium and transmute it into U-235. Forty to fifty tons of ore must be refined to obtain one ton of uranium. But workable sources of uranium have been found in many countries.

The chief ore containing uranium is pitchblende. The largest uranium-mining centers are at the pitchblende deposits in Canada's Eldorado mines and the Katanga mine in the Belgian Congo.

The first atomic power plant was built at Oak Ridge, Tennessee. It is a massive concrete box, the thick walls being necessary to absorb the gamma rays and neutron rays emitted by hot uranium. Heat generated by the uranium pile is used to make steam, which drives steam turbines, which in turn drive electric generators. This experimental power plant is expected to answer many questions as to the practicability of utilizing atomic fission as a source of industrial power.

In the United States, uranium is most easily obtained from carnotite, a canary-yellow mineral. Colorado and Utah are the American centers of carnotite.

Pitchblende was mined for centuries at Joachimsthal in eastern Czechoslovakia, and it was from this source that the Curies first isolated pure radium. Production at Joachimsthal stopped soon after 1900. Besides Canada and the Belgian Congo, the only other countries that were producing uranium before World War II were Portugal, Australia, and Sweden.

But sources of uranium are known to exist in Bulgaria, Brazil, England, France, Greenland, India, Madagascar, Norway, Russia, and South Africa.

What Are Infra-Red and Ultra-Violet Rays?

Visible light is one manifestation of what are called "electromagnetic waves." Other manifestations are radiant heat, radio waves, X-rays, cosmic rays. The only difference among all these kinds is in the wave length or frequency. The light we can see lies in a rather narrow band of frequencies, from violet, of shortest wave length, to red, of longest. Waves longer than red light (such as those of radio broadcasting) are called infra-red, while those shorter than violet light (such as X-rays) are called ultra-violet.

When Was "Liquid Fire" First Used in Warfare?

Long before the European war, an inflammable and destructive compound was used in warfare, especially by the Byzantine Greeks. It was poured from caldrons and ladles, vomited through long copper tubes, or flung in pots, phials and barrels. The art of compounding it was concealed at Constantinople with the greatest care, but it appears that naphtha, sulphur and nitre entered into its composition.

What Is "Heavy Water"?

We think of water as H_2O—two volumes of hydrogen combined with one of oxygen. Chemically that is its composition. We have thought of pure water as having a fixed weight; but in 1934 a scientist, Dr. Harold Clayton Urey of Columbia University, after prolonged research, was able to isolate heavy hydrogen atoms, technically called "isotopes," and from these heavy hydrogen atoms he produced pure water that was heavier than any pure water hitherto known. Thus we now have "heavy water." For his researches, Professor Urey was awarded the Nobel Prize in Chemistry in 1934.

What Is the Nobel Prize?

Alfred Nobel (1833–1896), a Swedish inventor of dynamite, left a sum of $9,000,000, the interest on which was to be awarded annually to the man or woman foremost in the cause of peace or in the fields of chemistry, physics, medicine and literature. Each prize amounts to about $40,000. Madame Curie, discoverer of radium, won the award on two occasions. The discoverers of insulin, a remedy for diabetes, Drs. Banting and MacLeod of Canada, won the award in medicine in 1923. Several Americans, including Jane Addams of the Hull House settlement in Chicago, have won the peace prize. The names of many great scientists, Einstein, Michelson, Compton, and others figure in the awards which have been made annually since the beginning of the 20th century.

THE STORY OF ELECTRONICS

A battery of high-voltage rectifiers at a radio transmitting station. These electronic tubes change alternating current into direct current.

T HE STORY of electronics is in general concerned with the flow of electric current, and in particular with the vacuum tube, more accurately known as the "electron valve." Much of this story was written before the name "electronics" was invented. The most important discoveries and inventions in the field of electricity are dealt with in other sections of this book: Electrical Power, Lightning, Telegraph, Telephone, Radio, Radar, Television. Something of the underlying theory of the atom is covered in the Story of X-rays, and above all in the Story of Atomic Energy.

[31]

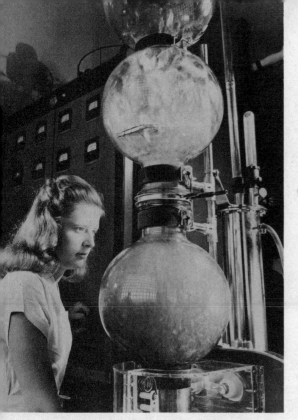

But the electron valve has opened such an extensive vista of new applications that this huge field certainly needs a convenient name, like "electronics."

What Is an Electron?

The atom comprises a *nucleus,* like a central sun, with one or more *electrons* revolving about it like planets. The electron is a charge of negative electricity; whether it is actually a material particle we do not really know, for its mass is infinitesimal compared with that of the nucleus. The latter is positively charged, and the normal atom keeps just enough electrons about its nucleus to make it electrically neutral. Unlike charges attract each other, while like charges repel each other.

An electronic dehydrator, used in the production of penicillin. Radio heat in 30 minutes does the work that requires 24 hours by former heating methods. Speed-up in penicillin manufacture was credited with saving thousands of lives in World War II.

What Is Ionization?

From one cause or another, atoms continually lose one or more electrons, in which state they are called *ions.* The ion is no longer electrically neutral. Its positive charge seeks to seize one of the free electrons floating about in space. Ionization and the recapture of free electrons goes on unceasingly in all matter, usually in helter-skelter fashion. But if all the free electrons are drawn in one direction by a constant excess of positive charge at that point, there is a flow of electrical current. In fact, that is just what an electrical current is, a flow of electrons.

Electronics grew out of the experiments of hundreds of scientists to discover why and how electrical currents flow.

Who Invented the Vacuum Tube?

No one man invented the modern vacuum tube or electron valve. It was the culmination of the work of many men. But we may list some of the most vital contributions.

Thomas Alva Edison, who invented the incandescent electric light, experimented with many substances in search of a suitable filament. In 1883, he discovered what is known as the "Edison effect." A third electrode was sealed by accident into one of his carbon lamps. When the lamp was lighted, a galvanometer showed a current in this third electrode, although it was isolated from the wire filament.

Sir William Crookes experimented with pot-bellied glass tubes from which the air had been exhausted until it was twenty million times thinner than the air we breathe. He sealed the poles of an electric circuit into opposite ends of a tube, and when a high-voltage current was turned on he saw a strange light emanating from the cathode (negative pole). He gave the name "cathode rays" to this phenomenon, but, like Edison, he was unable to explain them.

Wilhelm Konrad Roentgen discovered in 1895 that if cathode rays in a vacuum tube are reflected from the anode, they produce rays of great penetrating force, capable of taking photographs right through solid objects. See "The Story of X-rays."

In 1896, J. J. Thomson, director of the Cavendish Laboratory at Cambridge University, England, announced his discovery of electrons. This not only laid the foundation for the subsequent rapid development of the mod-

The "Klystron," one of the first electronic tubes developed for the wireless transmission of power. Energy from the tube is focused like a light beam with a copper-lined horn. At a demonstration in 1940 this tube lighted up electric bulbs from a distance.

Checking a shipment of high-power radio transmitting tubes for use in naval communications. The invention of the electronic valve made possible a great reduction in the bulk and weight of wireless communication apparatus.

ern theory of the atom, but also explained at once a number of puzzles. The cathode glow is caused by the free electrons forced out of the metal electrode by the force of the electrical current. Years later, the cathode glow was made the basis for an invention familiar to all of us— the "neon sign." The brilliant red, green, blue or yellow lights in glass tubes, so extensively used for advertising signs, are caused by the friction of a stream of electrons passing through the neon or other gas with which the tubes are filled. The voltage of the current is stepped up to the point where the electrons are forced out of the cathode with sufficient velocity to reach the anode, and so fill the whole tube with light.

Who Invented the "Valve"?

The work of Thomson spurred a new era of experimentation. Sir John A. Fleming put the previously useless "Edison effect" to work in 1904-5. He built the Fleming valve, a tube with two electrodes instead of one. This so-called "diode" was and still is the best of all "rectifiers." A rectifier is a device for changing alternating current to direct current. Electrical power can be transmitted over long wire lines only by alternating current, but for some purposes direct current is preferable or essential. If alternating current is fed into the cathode of a vacuum tube, the electrons forced out of it can flow only one way—toward the anode.

An experiment of epochal importance was made in 1906 by Dr. Lee De Forest. He inserted a *grid*, a screen of fine wire, between the electrodes of a Fleming tube. When a small negative potential was impressed upon the grid, its repellent effect on the stream of electrons from the cathode greatly reduced the number that got by to the anode. Conversely, a positive potential in the grid greatly accelerated the flow from cathode to anode.

The first use of this so-called "valve" was to make a galvanometer of great sensitivity. In other words, when the grid is connected to a circuit through which are passing currents much too weak to be detectable by former devices, the effect on the electron-stream in the vacuum tube is so great as to permit very accurate measurement.

Then it was realized that the valve could be used in another

Making final adjustments in cross-pointer indicators. Installed on an airplane dashboard, the indicator responds to guide beams sent out from airports and guides the pilot in blind flying.

way. A weak positive potential in the grid can be *amplified* to relatively huge proportions by its effect on the cathode-anode flow. Dr. Irving Langmuir developed the De Forest tube for this purpose, rearranging the parts and incidentally inventing a mercury vacuum pump far superior to its predecessors. This development of the extremely sensitive amplifying valve made possible at once the transmission of voice by Hertzian waves—that is, radio. All principles of radio had been worked out, but the practical device waited upon a "detector" far more sensitive than was used in wireless telegraphy.

U. S. 785920

How Does the Audion Work?

This basic device, the diode tube with a grid, is called an "audion." The grid, attached sometimes to an antenna, picks up

A tetrode (four-electrode) tube used in controlled relays for switching and similar purposes.

This 1,000-watt mercury vapor lamp produces three times as much light as an incandescent lamp of the same wattage. It quadruples the previously used pressure of the mercury vapor.

A triode (three-electrode) amplifier. The amplifier is the heart of a radio receiver. It "steps up" the faint waves of a broadcast into audible sounds or visible light.

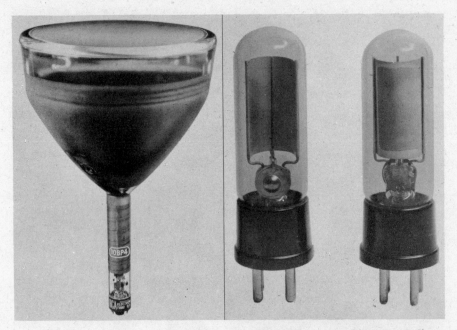

A kinescope or "direct view picture tube" used in television receivers.

The phototube is used to count objects electrically, to grade cigars and beans by color uniformity, and many other purposes based on sensitivity to light.

A battery of radio transmitting tubes, which together represent 100,000 watts of power. The air-cooling fins of each tube carry away enough heat to warm a small house in winter. These giant transmitters are used in beaming intercontinental broadcasts.

[37]

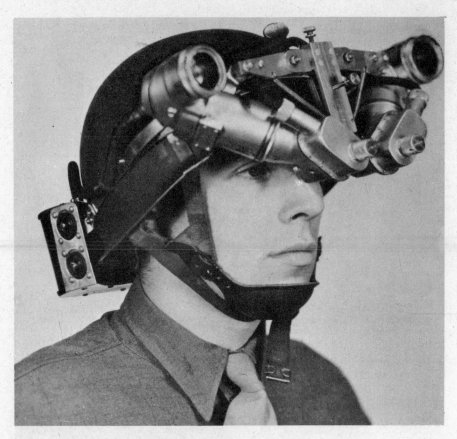

Electronics devised this "snooperscope" to enable American patrols to see in the dark. Mounted on a special helmet, the device picks up infra-red rays and transforms them into frequencies visible to the eye.

the high-frequency waves emitted by a radio transmitter. In wireless telegraphy, the transmitted impulses are all of the same volume—that is, a steady tone of one pitch is sent out. A detector that will pick up this tone at all, even if faint, will serve for wireless communication in a code of dots and dashes. But for voice transmission, the waves transmitted continually vary in volume, corresponding to the rise and fall and the separate sounds of the voice. A more sensitive detector is needed. The grid serves this purpose. Very weak electrical waves, and very slight variations of volume, have a powerful effect on a steady current that is passed through the vacuum tube. This current is used to operate the diaphragm that reproduces the voice in the radio receiver.

What Other Uses Has the Electron Valve?

One of the first applications of the vacuum tube, we have seen, was to produce X-rays. Here, electric current is transformed into light rays. But the vacuum tube can also be adapted to the reverse purpose—to transform light into electric current. A familiar example is the device for opening a door when a person approaching it intercepts a fixed beam of light. This beam is focussed on a selenium cell which is connected in series with a circuit passing through the grid of a valve. The cell varies in conductivity with the amount of light falling upon it, and when the fixed beam is intercepted a marked change occurs in the grid current. This in turn has an amplified effect on a power current passing through the terminals of the tube, sufficient to operate a switch and turn on an electric motor that opens the door.

Another way of converting light to current is to make the cathode of a valve out of light-sensitive material. Then light replaces heat as the stimulator of electronic emission. Variance in the amount of light, and thus in the electron flow, causes a corresponding variance in the flow of current through the grid circuit. This device is used in motion picture projection, to convert the "sound track" on film, which is a band of varying shades of light and dark, into actual sound. It is also the basis of the "scanner" used in television.

The simple diode, without a grid, makes the best rectifier to change alternating into direct current. The triode, or diode with grid, can be made to perform the reverse function by a simple link that feeds part of the outgoing current back to the grid. Then direct current fed in comes out as alternating current. A very im-

The "Antennalyzer," an electronic computing device that determines automatically where antenna towers should be placed in order to direct maximum power in desired directions.

The door opens automatically when the waitress intercepts the fixed beam of light between the two tubes visible on the upright rails.

portant application has been to step up frequencies to millions of cycles per second, far beyond the range of previous methods. Radio transmitters use "oscillators" on this principle, and so can operate at frequencies never touched by wireless telegraph equipment.

Probably one of the largest fields opened up by "electronics" will be the applications of ultra-high-frequency currents. Already they have been utilized to build a radically new type of calculator. All mathematical computations can be reduced ultimately —strange as it may seem—to simple addition. For example, you can multiply any number by 7,593,028 by adding it to itself that number of times. Naturally, that is not a practicable method for the human mind. But circuits of electron valves can be arranged to translate the numbers into electrical impulses, and to "count" the number of impulses in successive additions. The earliest "electronic counters" made could count to 5,000 in less than a second, and later machines are stepping up the pace by hundreds of times.

Another vast field of electronics is the precision control of industrial operations by electron valves. A control circuit is connected to the grid, so that the amount of current flowing through it is governed by time, speed, temperature, or whatever other variable is vital. The circuit operating the machine goes through the tube. Then variations in the grid circuit cause corresponding or compensating changes in the operating current. Already this arrangement has found extensive use in governing motor speeds and controlling tools where great precision is required.

THE STORY OF X-RAYS

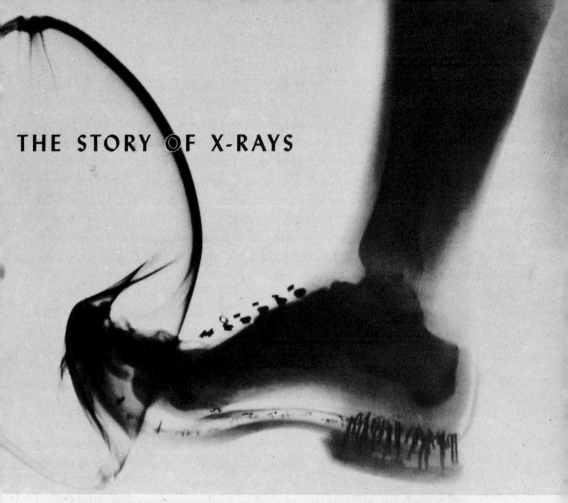

A football just as it is being kicked, caught by the high-speed X-ray camera. Note the metal parts of the shoe and the bones of the foot.

IN A MODEST laboratory at the University of Wurzburg in Bavaria, Germany, an obscure physics professor discovered a mysterious ray, that has the power to penetrate flesh, cloth, wood, and metal. The tall, slender, bearded teacher who discovered this strange ray in November, 1895, was Wilhelm Konrad Roentgen.

Using the mathematical symbol "X" for the unknown quantity, he called his discovery the X-ray.

How Was the Existence of X-Rays Made Known?

When he first came upon the new "wonder ray," so powerful that it could pass through opaque objects, Roentgen told his good friend, Boveri: "I have discovered something interesting, but I do not know whether or not my observations are correct." Except for this remark, he talked to no one about what he had found. For days he locked himself in his laboratory and, without sleep or food, worked out his experiments again and again.

The apparatus used by Roentgen in making his discovery represented the labor of many students and scientists in centuries past. All had contributed something to developing methods of its production, beginning with the creation of high tension currents and continuing on to the study of various effects produced by such currents in a vacuum tube.

Among the scientists who contributed greatly to the discovery of X-rays was the English chemist, Sir William Crookes. Scientists agree that Crookes, with his relatively high vacuum tube, produced X-rays; yet did not actually discover them. It remained for the fifty-year-old Professor Roentgen to discover that the rays emanating from a Crookes tube, when a high-voltage current is sent through it, will penetrate objects opaque to ordinary light and will affect the photographic plate.

It was not till two months after his actual discovery—on January 23, 1896—that Roentgen officially reported his findings in a paper, "A New Kind of Ray," presented to the Physical Medical Society of Wurzburg. His report became news that electrified the world, spreading like wildfire.

Newspapers all over the world published stories, cartoons, and even poems about the new "wonder rays." They printed ghastly skeletons of hands and feet of living persons and extolled the mysterious power of those strange rays which could "see" through almost anything.

Despite attacks on him by some newspapers whose editors felt that his discovery would be harmful to human progress, there were many strong believers in what Roentgen had found. Many medical men foresaw how the sufferings of mankind might be lessened by the use of these new rays. The acclaim of such scientists helped to make Roentgen famous overnight, and he was showered with honors. He was summoned to the Royal Palace at Potsdam, where he dined with Wilhelm II, emperor of Germany and king of Prussia. A government decree bestowed upon

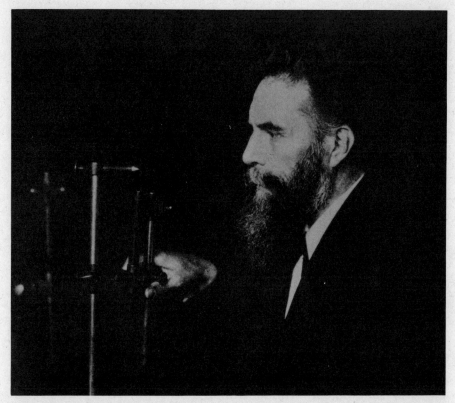

Dr. Wilhelm Konrad Roentgen, professor of physics at the University of Wurzburg, Bavaria, who discovered X-rays in November, 1895. Roentgen was born in 1845 and died in 1923.

him the title of "Excellency." Boulevards and streets were named for him, and monuments were erected in his honor.

Roentgen died in 1923 at the age of 78. He virtually made a gift of his X-ray to humanity, seeking no reward and receiving no monetary gain from the great discovery, except the Nobel prize for physics awarded him in 1901.

How Are X-Rays Produced?

X-rays and the rays of visible light both belong to that class of electromagnetic radiations that stretches from the longest Hertzian or radio waves to the exceedingly short gamma rays of radium and on beyond the cosmic rays. The only difference

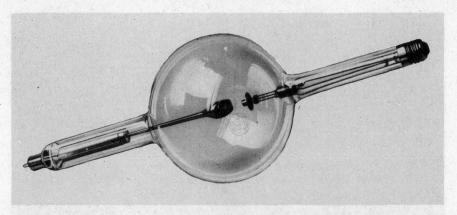

An early type of Coolidge gas tube. Invented by Dr. William D. Coolidge, this type revolutionized the making of radiographic pictures. The electron target is made of tungsten, instead of platinum as in earlier X-ray tubes. With the Coolidge tube, the operator can control the output of X-rays.

among those kinds of waves is in the wave length. X-rays are much shorter than the waves of visible light.

To understand how X-rays are produced, it is first necessary to consider the electron—that negatively charged particle that is one of the fundamental building blocks of matter. So small is the electron that 30,000 trillion trillion (30 followed by 27 zeros) electrons weigh less than an ounce. Yet the electron can be a powerful thing. For when an electron is accelerated by a high electric voltage, it becomes a projectile traveling at an awesome speed. At 50,000 volts an electron attains a velocity of 77,200 miles per second; at 400,000 volts, its speed approximates 155,000 miles per second, or 83 per cent of the velocity of light.

When millions of tiny speeding electrons strike a metal target, they penetrate the very atoms of the metal. And they produce, deep within the atomic structure, dislocations and rearrangements which, in turn, release the radiations we know as X-rays. The faster the electrons are traveling when they hit—that is, the higher the voltage in the X-ray tube—the more penetrating is the radiation.

Roentgen made his discovery while experimenting with a Crookes tube. This is a pear-shaped vacuum tube containing two metal electrodes—a cathode and an anode. Each electrode is connected to one terminal of an induction coil. Electrons shoot

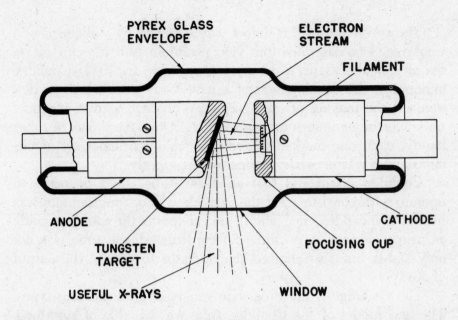

PYREX GLASS ENVELOPE

ELECTRON STREAM

FILAMENT

ANODE

CATHODE

TUNGSTEN TARGET

FOCUSING CUP

USEFUL X-RAYS

WINDOW

Diagram of a modern X-ray tube. The interior is a high vacuum; earlier tubes were filled with gas.

out from the cathode, the negative pole, at speeds of approximately 30,000 miles per second. They travel so fast that most of them cannot turn the corner to get to the anode, the positive pole, but instead hit the glass at the end of the tube. This impact of electrons upon the glass produces the X-rays which Roentgen was first to observe.

How Was the X-Ray Tube Improved?

The early type of tube used to produce X-rays contained a considerable amount of residual gases and was known as a gas tube. Even at its best, this tube produced poor results during much of the pioneer X-ray work. It would function perfectly one day and poorly the next. The debilitation was due largely to the absorption of gases when the metal electrodes inside the tube became heated. The variations in gas pressure were too great to assure steady everyday performance. The addition or subtraction of even a minute percentage of gas greatly modified the tube's behavior.

[45]

The correction of this defect was achieved by William David Coolidge, who later became vice president and director of research for the General Electric Company. In 1913, Coolidge announced the development of a new X-ray tube which revolutionized the making of radiographs. With such a tube, it would no longer be necessary for the radiologist to have a rack of tubes handy, each one marked to indicate what particular set of circumstances was necessary to operate it properly.

Coolidge discovered that an X-ray tube could be made to operate with consistency if the cathode was of tungsten and was heated to incandescence, and if the vacuum in the tube was made as nearly perfect as possible. So constructed, the tube was not only stable but also allowed the operator to control the output of X-rays.

The Coolidge X-ray tube soon superseded all previous types. The first model of the Coolidge tube was capable of sustained, stable operation at voltages as high as 140,000, and later a model was designed for 200,000 volts.

How Are X-Rays Used in Medicine?

No modern hospital is without X-ray equipment, and every physician, surgeon, and dentist depends on the X-ray for diagnosis and prognosis in a large proportion of cases.

In X-ray diagnosis, physicians and surgeons today can examine the skull, the spine, and other bones of the body; they can see that a broken bone is set properly, and how it is knitting; they can find gallstones, kidney stones, and bladder stones. Because tuberculosis of the lungs shows characteristic markings on the X-ray film, the presence of this disease can be accurately detected. X-raying is the one satisfactory method for discovering ulcers and tumors, many of which would otherwise escape detection until too late for treatment.

There are two different methods of X-ray diagnosis. One is known as radiography, whereby a permanent record of the X-ray image of various parts of the body is made on film. The other method is known as fluoroscopy, which affords a means of visual study of the bodily organs in actual operation.

The X-ray in medicine. Checking for tuberculosis by X-ray pictures of the chest. Each patient stands against a panel that holds the recording film. The X-ray tube is back of the funnel-shaped mouthpiece behind the patient. X-raying is now a part of the routine physical examinations made by many companies and government services.

An X-ray film, or radiograph, is like a photograph except that it is fundamentally a shadowgraph rather than a picture produced by reflected light. The "lights and darks" of the film depend upon the differences in density of the tissues situated in the path of the rays. The denser or the thicker the object, the more X-radiation will be absorbed by it, and the less will reach the film. The radiograph is therefore a picture of shadows of different parts, varying according to their respective densities or resistance to X-rays. It is from a highly skilled interpretation of the shadow images that the doctor makes his diagnosis.

The X-ray in dentistry. Dentists rely upon X-rays to detect decay beneath the surface of a tooth. In this picture the dentist holds a piece of cloth-covered film such as is used in making dental pictures. The film is held behind the tooth by the patient's finger. The X-ray machine is swung into position so that the tip of the black cone rests against the cheek or lips directly in front of the film. The picture is made in about three seconds.

X-ray examination by fluoroscopy makes it possible to study the internal organs in motion. The viewing screen is a piece of cardboard treated with chemicals that fluoresce—that is, give off visible light—when exposed to the action of X-rays. If a body is interposed between the source of the rays and the screen, it intercepts some of the rays, according to its thickness or density. Thus a picture of the internal structures of the body, in varying degrees of shadow, is produced upon a background of light.

How Are X-Rays Used in Dentistry?

X-rays play an important diagnostic role in dentistry, too. The usual clinical examination is often inadequate, because it is limited to the visible surfaces of the teeth and the superficial tissues of the mouth. Certain areas of the teeth cannot be examined except by X-rays. The chronic infections at the end of tooth roots which contribute to grave systemic disease rarely give warning by local symptoms or visible changes. Decay in the contact surface of teeth may invade the tooth pulp before being discovered by instrumental examination.

When you have your teeth X-rayed, the radiographs show the state of health of each tooth, down to the bony socket where the root of the tooth is imbedded. They show a cavity which is hidden by another tooth. Or they may show an abscess way down at the tip of a tooth that looks healthy.

How Are X-Rays Used in Therapy?

X-ray units especially designed for therapeutic applications operate at 800,000, 400,000, 250,000, 200,000 and 140,000 volts.

The X-ray in therapy. Certain types of skin diseases and tumors respond to treatment by X-rays. Here a patient is being treated by a million-volt therapy machine whose rays can penetrate deep inside the body.

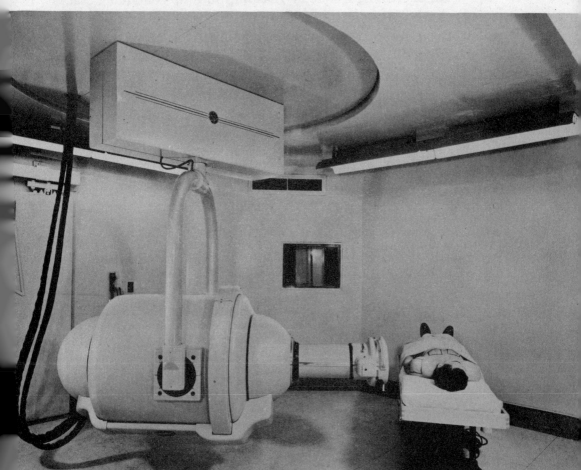

A most effective weapon in the fight against deep-seated cancer is the million-volt X-ray unit, which may be considered the husky glamor boy in the radiation therapy field.

It is estimated that about 300,000 people in the United States have some form of cancer, and, since the cancer disease lasts on an average of two years, 150,000 patients are seen by the medical profession each year. Thousands of cases, especially those involving small cancers, respond effectively to X-ray treatment.

How Are X-Rays Used in Industry?

The use of high-voltage X-rays in industry is not new. Rather, the story is one of early recognition and then a long period of development, leading to efficient, shockproof, high-power apparatus that is in use in our industrial plants from coast to coast.

Much of the pioneering work in the development of X-rays for non-medical purposes was done to further the development of better foundry techniques and, thereby, to insure sound metal castings.

With distressing frequency, castings turn up containing cracks and blowholes. Sometimes there is marked evidence of these defects on the surface, sometimes none at all. More frequently a casting will show slight signs of possible faults on the surface, but the engineer is left in doubt as to whether he is confronted with superficial markings or apparently trifling defects that will widen out into large cracks or cavities. Many important and expensive castings have been scrapped because the engineer dared not risk using them.

An X-ray camera that takes a picture in a millionth of a second. It is capable of making a clear picture of a bullet speeding down the bore of a gun. The electronic tube can be seen mounted on the near side of the machine. Six million watts of electricity are needed to make these high-speed pictures.

Unless X-rays are employed, metal castings of many kinds can only be inspected for hidden defects by destructive methods. The same holds true in inspecting metal welds. A factory director once remarked that destructive methods of inspection are "like striking a match merely to see if it is a good one."

X-rays provide industry with a means of seeing into and learning a great deal about the interior of many articles without destroying or in any way harming them. An important and spectacular industrial tool is the million-volt shockproof X-ray unit. Its rays can penetrate heavy plates of steel. The unit is less than five feet high and three feet in diameter and weighs about 1500 pounds.

The application of fluoroscopy permits production-line in-

The X-ray in industry. Surrounded by 18-inch concrete walls, a million-volt X-ray unit is used to detect flaws in automobile crankshaft castings at the River Rouge steel foundry of the Ford Motor Company. The technician is adjusting the casting before making the exposure. The film holders are in racks beneath the castings.

spection of small aluminum and magnesium castings. Visual X-ray inspection has found its widest industrial use, however, in the food industries. Here it is of tremendous importance that every particle of foreign material, which may have found its way into the product before or during the manufacturing process, be detected and removed.

The X-ray provides an inspection method that may be applied at any stage of processing.

Usually, the products to be inspected are carried on a conveyor belt over the source of X-radiation and under the fluoroscopic viewing screen. Stationed in a darkened booth, or looking through a darkened hood, the operator sees on the screen a brilliant image of the material being carried on the conveyor

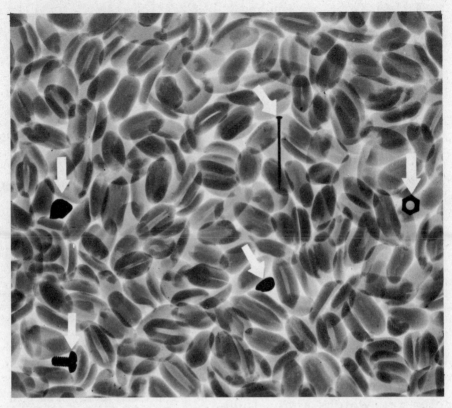

Fluoroscopic X-rays are used for inspection in many food industries. Looking through a darkened hood as the food passes by on a beltline, the operator is able to detect any foreign materials. Shown here is a trayful of peanuts as seen by the operator on a fluoroscopic screen, with several foreign objects visible.

belt. Most foreign objects are markedly different in density from the foodstuff, and so can be immediately detected and removed. Also with many packaged products there is sufficient definition to allow the inspector to detect any shortage in the fill of the container.

California and Arizona citrus growers use X-ray equipment to sort their crops. After one severe frost, X-rays helped California growers to salvage two million boxes of oranges which would have been condemned by ordinary methods. Under the X-ray fluoroscopic viewing screen, it is easy to separate good oranges from bad. A good orange shows uniform density while a bad one shows a mottled pattern.

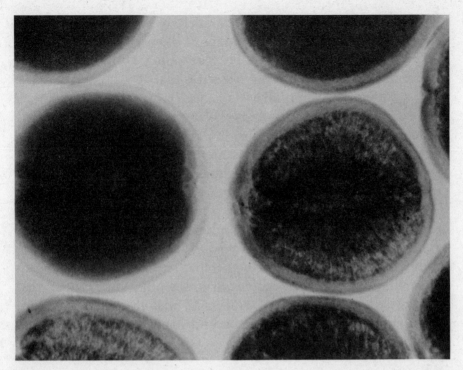

Fruit growers detect unripe fruit by inspection through a fluoroscopic screen. The orange at the right is unripe. At the left is a completely ripe orange.

In What Other Fields Are X-Rays Useful?

X-rays, indispensable to the healing arts and in heavy industry, have also found uses in many strange and unrelated fields.

X-ray equipment has proved to be a master sleuth at Chicago's Museum of Natural History, where a large collection of mummies from Egypt and Peru underwent radiographic examination in their original wrappings. Without damage to the subjects, the X-rays revealed the nature and position of many objects, such as jewelry, pottery, shells.

The use of X-rays to expose forgeries has been widely publicized through a number of celebrated cases. X-rays can prove the genuine as well as the fraudulent. Several years ago an expedition searching for Chinese art treasures unearthed a small black snuff bottle. It was believed to be black jade—a substance

[53]

so rare that the belief was questioned by leading jewelers in Chicago and New York. The opinions of the experts were divided, some believing the bottle to be true jade, with a value of a thousand dollars, while others asserted that it was merely agate with a value of twenty-five dollars. X-rays, which provide a means of "fingerprinting" all crystalline materials, found that the bottle was of true black jade.

Possibly destined for a very important role is the use of X-rays to produce new plant permutations. After a long period of experiment, an enterprising seedman offered American gardeners two new calendulas. One flower is golden, double petaled, the other orange and semi-double. Both were created by the genetic effect of X-rays on seeds. For years, scientists have been bombarding fruit trees, berry bushes, tomato seeds, and string beans with million-volt X-rays. They want to see utilized the action that produces different strains of flowers so that it can also produce grains and vegetables, and cotton and fruits of higher yield and finer quality than before.

What Is the Difference Between Alternating and Direct Current?

An electric current is analogous to a river. What makes a river flow is a difference of level between its source and its outlet. What makes an electric current flow is a difference of *potential* between two ends of a circuit. We measure the difference in *volts,* and we call the higher end of the stream the *negative pole*, the other, the *positive* pole.

A river always flows one way, and so does *direct current.* If we could suddenly raise the outlet of a river higher than its source, we could make the river flow backward. Of course we cannot do that, but we can do the equivalent with an electric current. We can suddenly change the positive pole to the negative and vice versa and so change the direction of flow. A generator does exactly that—reverses the potentials of the poles many times a second, so that the current *alternates* in flow.

Each kind of current has its advantages and disadvantages. Alternating current is much better for the transmission of electrical power over long lines. Direct current is necessary for many processes, such as electroplating. As a rule, therefore, all power lines use alternating current, and any consumer who needs direct current has a *transformer* on his intake line.

What Is an Electromagnet?

An electromagnet is a piece of iron temporarily converted into a magnet by means of a current of electricity sent through a wire which is coiled around it. The wire is usually covered with silk, cotton, gutta-percha or some other insulator, to prevent the current from leaping across, and to compel it to travel through the whole length of the wire.

The more pure and soft the iron is, the stronger will its magnetism be while it lasts, and the more completely will it disappear when the current stops. Steel is less affected than soft iron for the time, but remains permanently magnetized after the current ceases. Electromagnets are usually much more powerful than other magnets of the same size.

The iron which is magnetized by the current passing around it is called the core. It is frequently straight, the wire being wound upon it like thread upon a reel; but very frequently it has the shape of a U or horseshoe, the wire being coiled round the two ends and the bend of the U left uncovered.

What Are Cosmic Rays?

What are termed "cosmic rays" are radiations similar to X-rays, but of greater penetrating power, probably coming from outer space. Experiments have been made which confirm the supposition of scientists that somewhere in the universe a building-up process is going on to replace the tearing-down process of radioactivity. The announcement of this discovery was made by the American physicist, Robert A. Millikan, in 1928; but cosmic rays have been studied since 1912, at first by Hess, then by Kolhorster, and others. It would seem from the new discoveries that this is a changing, dynamic and continuously evolving world instead of a static or merely disintegrating one. All observers are agreed that if there be any directional effect at all in the cosmic rays it is but a slight one; in any case the rays come into the earth nearly equally from all directions. This means that they are either formed out in the interplanetary and interstellar spaces or else in stars that are more or less uniformly distributed throughout the heavens. In both of these localities matter exists under extreme and as yet unexplored conditions. The cosmic rays consist of bands of definite frequency or color, and the general spectral region in which these bands are found corresponds to frequencies 100,000,000,000 times greater than those emitted by the neon lamp. This is why these cosmic radiations are powerful enough to penetrate two hundred feet down into a mountain lake before they are completely absorbed—which means that they are strong enough to pierce a dozen feet of lead! In the study of the rays, Dr. Millikan found new evidence that the seemingly absurd universe of Einstein—a universe which is finite, in which space is curved, in which light comes by the pound, gravitation regarded as a crumpling up of space—is very real.

THE STORY OF THE MICROSCOPE

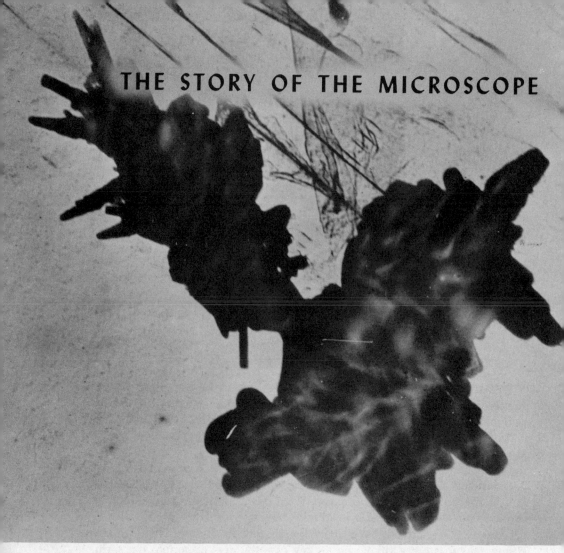

Face powder magnified 50,000 times by the electron microscope.

WHEN William of Orange, that enterprising and daring Dutch nobleman, invaded Merrie England in 1688, there lived in the town of Delft in Holland a nondescript little man who was to invade a whole world and make the exploits of William seem pale by comparison.

Who Made the First Microscope?

This Dutchman, Antony Leeuwenhoek, was merely the janitor of the city hall. The townspeople of Delft thought him a trifle "touched" because he spent all his spare time grinding lenses out of glass. He found childish delight in seeing little things bigger than they appear to the naked eye.

The magnifying properties of glass lenses had been known for many centuries. And a hundred years before Leeuwenhoek, the Dutch Lippershey and the Italian Galileo had put lenses together to make the telescope, which brings the stars, apparently much nearer to the earth. But before Leeuwenhoek no one had been interested in making magnifying lenses to examine all the things on earth that the unaided eye cannot see.

What Did Leeuwenhoek See Through His Lens?

He made more and more lenses, and turned them on everything he came across. One day he chanced to peer through his glass at a drop of clear water from a rain barrel, and what he saw made him jump up and down with excitement. For there, in just ordinary water, were hundreds of infinitely small creatures scurrying feverishly about. That was the first time human eyes had ever beheld the creatures of the little worlds that abound on everything we see and touch—the domains of invisible plants and animals and atoms and molecules.

And so it was that an inconsequential, almost-forgotten little Dutch janitor astonished the learned scientists of his day by inventing the microscope. The importance of this instrument to modern science cannot be overestimated. To mention but one field— medicine scarcely existed as a science until the microscope enabled men to discover the minute organisms and viruses that are the cause of most diseases.

By modern standards Leeuwenhoek's crude instrument was little better than a strong spectacle lens. A hair viewed through it appeared to have about the same diameter as the stick from a lollipop. For a time scientists were content to look at these puny images, but eventually they began to wonder whether still smaller worlds might be nestling unseen against the glass slides of their simple microscopes. So another lens was added to magnify the already magnified image, and the hair began to look like a huge manila rope made up of millions of tiny fibers and scales that were not even visible before.

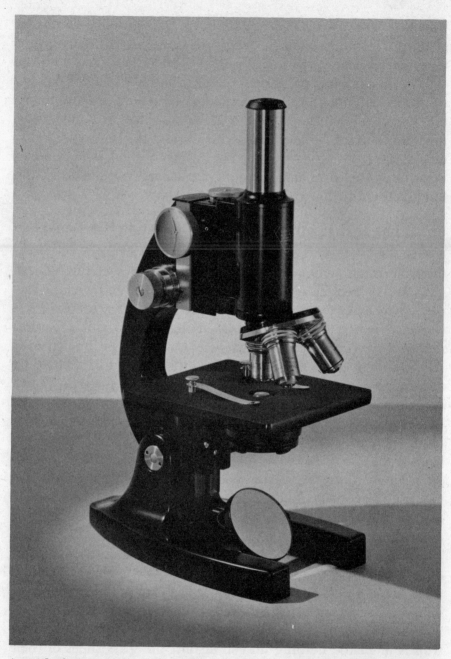

A standard type of laboratory microscope. The tube at the top of the microscope contains the eyepiece which by itself can magnify ten times. The three short tubes just above the platform contain different systems of lenses to allow different degrees of magnification. Only one of the three can be used at a time. The three interchangeable lenses are called objectives.

[58]

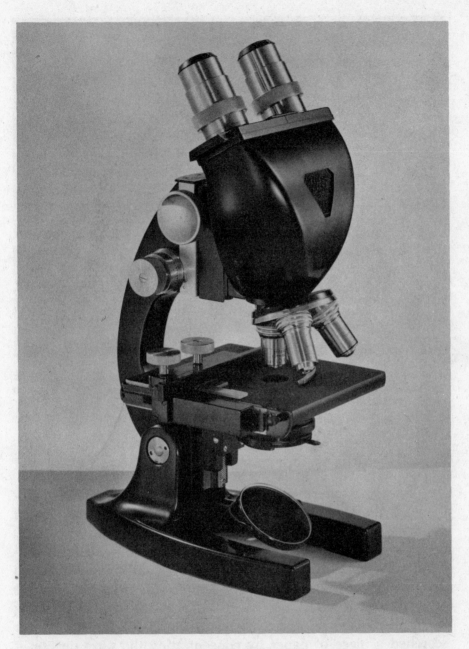

A *binocular microscope. With this type of microscope it is possible to use both eyes at the same time. The three objective lenses have magnification factors of 10, 43 and 97. Only one can be used at a time. The mirror under the platform directs the light into a condenser lens which concentrates it into a narrow beam that goes through the hole in the platform directly into the magnifying lenses of the objective. From the objective the light travels through prisms to the lenses of the eyepieces.*

A paleobotanist examining soft coal under a special industrial microscope. Later he will make a photograph through the microscope of a paper-thin section of coal to record its structure.

What Is the Compound Microscope?

This new two-lens instrument, known as the compound microscope, is the kind used in most schools and laboratories. If you examine such a microscope, you probably will find a small, movable mirror beneath the platform on which the slide is supported. Its purpose is to concentrate light on the specimen, so that the image seen through the eyepiece is brighter. In more expensive microscopes the image is made still clearer by using a so-called condensing lens beneath the slide. Have you ever scorched a piece of paper by concentrating the sun's rays on it with a magnifying glass? The principle of the condensing lens is somewhat the same; it concentrates or condenses the light rays into a small pencil of intensely bright illumination aimed directly at the specimen.

[60]

With all these improvements, the magnifying power of the compound microscope can be increased indefinitely. A mosquito's wing could be made to look like a huge, shining sheet of cellophane 25 feet wide; but the pretty, dark veins in it might cease to look like veins and run together in a meaningless, hazy web. Then if you happen to be interested in the individual veins, that microscope is no more useful than a simpler instrument. What scientists call "useful magnification" is the magnification at which details of the specimen can be distinguished clearly by the human eye. At the useful magnification of the best schoolroom microscope, our imaginary 25-foot mosquito wing shrinks to a mere 4 feet, but at this size every vein, every spot on the wing stands out sharply. In other words, bigness usually is sacrificed for the sake of clarity.

By using tricks, like mounting both the specimen and some of the lenses in cedar oil, the compound microscope can be made about half again as powerful, so the fanciful mosquito wing grows back to 6 feet in width. Only the best professional microscopes are as good as this.

Why Are Quartz Lenses Used?

As laboratory workers kept struggling to get bigger and clearer images in their microscopes, they observed a strange thing. Tiny objects that were invisible in red light leaped suddenly into clear view when the illumination was changed to violet. Some imaginative fellow reasoned that the wave length of the light must make the difference. Red light has long waves; violet light relatively short waves. Apparently, then, if the wave length of the light on the specimen could be shortened further, the microscope should be able to see still smaller objects.

Now this line of reasoning begins to get complicated. If the wave length of violet light is shortened, it ceases to be light in the ordinary sense. The result is ultra-violet radiation, which is invisible. Glass lenses are hungry for ultra-violet; in fact, they like it so well that they simply absorb it, and none gets through. Lenses made of quartz, though, have no particular hunger for ultra-violet and let practically all of it through.

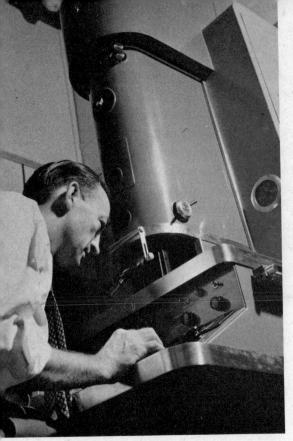

A researcher looking into the eyepiece of one of the first electron microscopes.

That's one complication less. Glass lenses are removed, and quartz ones are substituted. The other complication—how to "see ultra-violet light—is fairly simple. Take your eye away from the eyepiece and place a camera there instead. Photographic plates can be made sensitive to light outside the range of the human eye, at both ends of the spectrum.

The microscope now has become a completely different instrument. We place our imaginary mosquito wing under the quartz lens, turn on the ultraviolet light and take a picture on a huge, imaginary film. We can see every vein clearly, and the wing is twice as wide as before—about twelve feet.

What Is the Electron Microscope?

This is as far as we go with lenses and light. But the story of the microscope is not yet finished. In the last few years physicists have found that electrons—tiny bundles of negative electricity—act somewhat like light when they are in motion. Their wave length depends on the speed with which they travel, and they move in the same manner as light waves. From these scientific observations has come the marvelous electron microscope.

This instrument is one of the greatest scientific developments of modern times. Using electrons—infinitesimal bits of electricity—instead of rays of light, and magnetic electrostatic fields instead of glass lenses, it enables man's eye to peer deep into the submicroscopic world. Because it can magnify objects as much as 100,000 times, the electron microscope is from 50 to 100 times more powerful than the strongest optical microscope. With it science is exploring new microscopic worlds that were hidden before because of their smallness. For the first time human beings actually have seen molecules, for with the electron microscope it has been possible to take sharp, clear pictures of a molecule only three-fifths of a millionth of an inch in diameter and about twenty millionths of an inch long!

Who Discovered How to Focus Electrons?

The story of the electron microscope began very recently, and its development has been rapid. In 1926 Professor Hans Busch of Jena University in Germany made the discovery that electron paths and light rays are very similar. He asked the question, "Why not use electrons to see with?" Dr. Busch knew the limitations of the ordinary optical microscope, which uses light rays. To be visible to our eyes an object must be larger than one-half the wave length of the light used to illuminate it. The wave length of light is from .0004 to .0008 millimeters. Yet many objects, such as the virus of certain diseases, and molecules, are much smaller than this. Hence they cannot be seen at all with ordinary light waves because they are smaller than the waves themselves. On the other hand, the wave length of a 60 kilovolt electron beam is only 1/100,000th that of light.

Dr. Busch worked long and patiently and finally was able to prove that streams of electrons, passing through a coil of wire acting as a magnet, could actually be focussed to form a magnified image. This established the important fact that electron rays can be brought into focus, just as it is possible to focus light, although by different means.

Who Made the First Electron Microscopes?

Other scientists set to work to try to devise an electron microscope. By 1932 two German scientists, Max Knoll and Dr. Ernst Ruska, announced that they had created an electron microscope that worked. Though they called it a "super-microscope" it was a crude instrument. It could magnify images five times larger than any optical microscope, but the images on the view plates blurred

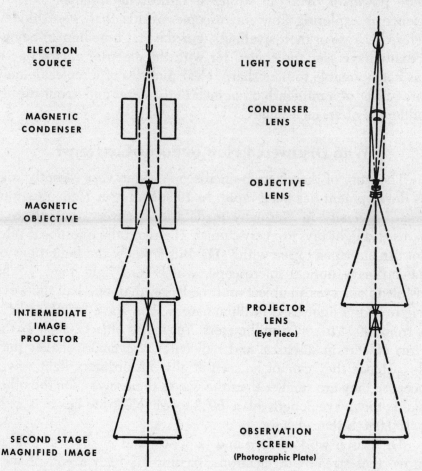

ELECTRON MICROSCOPE   LIGHT MICROSCOPE

ELECTRON SOURCE   LIGHT SOURCE

MAGNETIC CONDENSER   CONDENSER LENS

MAGNETIC OBJECTIVE   OBJECTIVE LENS

INTERMEDIATE IMAGE PROJECTOR   PROJECTOR LENS (Eye Piece)

SECOND STAGE MAGNIFIED IMAGE   OBSERVATION SCREEN (Photographic Plate)

These diagrams show the analogy between the electron microscope and the optical microscope.

and faded. They were fortunate if they succeeded in getting one good photograph in a thousand times. Their difficulty lay in controlling the high voltage current with the necessary degree of accuracy. If the current of a "magnetic lens" is not controlled with the greatest degree of fineness, the image breaks up in the same way that a reflection on still water breaks up before the wind.

In 1934 a scientist in Brussels, Dr. Ladislaus Marton, produced a similar microscope and made the first recorded effort to examine biological specimens with this type of microscope.

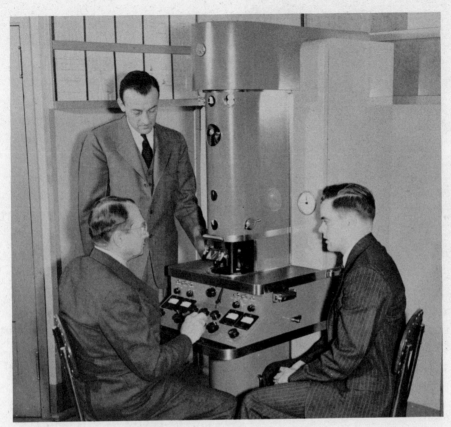

The young man at the right is James Hillier, pioneer of electron microscopy.

Who Perfected the Electron Microscope?

It remained for a young North American to take the final steps that made the electron microscope a marvelously useful tool of science. Although he was only in his early twenties when he undertook the work that made him famous, the name of James Hillier has a high place in the ranks of present-day scientists who have made great contributions to the advancement of human knowledge. The story of his work on the electron microscope is a fascinating one. When Professor E. F. Burton of the University of Toronto visited Europe in 1935 he saw the microscope created by the German scientists. The idea that a better one could be built took shape in his mind, and he came back to the university determined to make the attempt. He invited young James Hillier, a

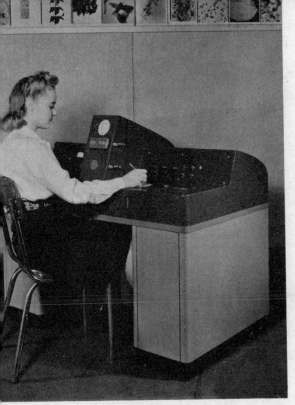

The modern electron microscope is now no larger than a desk.

brilliant physics student who had become an instructor at the university, to work with him.

Hillier and another young man, Albert Prebus, plunged into the work with complete enthusiasm. They knew that the task ahead was hard, and even at times dangerous. Working with the 30,000 volts of electricity necessary to produce the current used in the microscope is not too safe. Once Hillier was hurled the length of the room when his screwdriver touched an incorrectly wired connection. The young men faced many hardships, for there was little money provided for their work. They had to make practically a worldwide search for the special equipment they needed. Two condensers were found in Sweden, two more were borrowed from the University of Alberta. Discarded X-ray transformers came from the General Hospital in Toronto. Hillier and Prebus pieced together makeshift apparatus until at last they had made a microscope that they believed would work. It was a strange-looking contrivance, as tall as a room and festooned with wires, coils, and generators. To reach the eyepiece, Hillier had to climb a stepladder. After peering into the glowing slits for a few moments he was able to turn to his associates and proudly announce that the electron microscope worked. The images he saw were sharp and clear. Thus 1937 becomes the most important date in the development of the magic eye of science.

Meanwhile, Dr. Marton had been called to the United States to help the Radio Corporation of America in its efforts to create an electron microscope. Here he encountered the same difficulty that he had in Brussels. The images blurred and faded. Dr. Vladimir Zworykin, famed inventor of the iconoscope, the seeing-eye

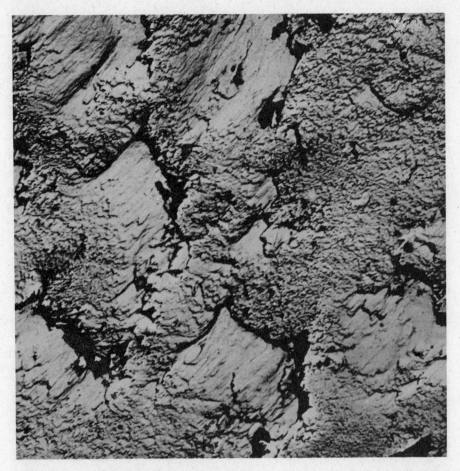

The enamel of a human tooth magnified 5,800 times. A toothbrush bristle magnified this much would be four feet in diameter.

of television, was in charge of the project. And when these difficulties threatened to stop the building of a successful electron microscope, he called on Hillier to come to the United States. Hillier accepted, and with all the resources of great modern laboratories at his disposal, he quickly created the most effective electron microscope yet developed. Not satisfied with his success, he went to work to reduce the vast bulk of the apparatus. The equipment required for a single electron microscope then filled an entire room. By reducing the number of magnetic lenses and making other changes, Hillier was able to reduce the height of the instrument from 6 feet to 16 inches! Present-day models are no larger

[67]

than a personal desk, yet they have all the magnifying power of the first clumsy model.

In principle, the electron microscope is very similar to the light microscope, but its physical appearance is very different. It is larger, of course, but a second difference is brought about by the fact that since electrons are almost completely scattered or absorbed by air, the entire electron optical path of the microscope must be maintained at a high vacuum. The microscope is provided with air locks for both the specimen and the photographic chambers. These locks are based on a principle similar to that used in the air locks of a submarine, and are arranged in such a way that the specimen or photographic plate can be moved into a small chamber which is then sealed off from the body of the microscope, and air admitted to the small chamber only. If air were present in the microscope tube, it would interfere with the motion of electrons, just as smoke or fog interfere with light.

What New Things Have Been Discovered by the Electron Microscope?

Already the electron microscope has contributed new knowledge in every branch of scientific research, such as particle size and shape, colloids, surface chemistry, thin film, plastics, textiles, fibers, and artificial rubber. In metallurgical research, a new technique has been developed for the study of bulk substances such as iron and its alloys, brasses and other materials, including heavy armor plate. An outstanding discovery in biological research has been the photographing of the influenza virus, made possible for the first time by the electron microscope in use at the University of Pennsylvania. Also, stereoscopic pictures, or micrographs, can be taken so that the specimen is viewed in three dimensions.

Modern science is advancing its frontiers swiftly with the aid of the magic eye, the electron microscope.

Reprinted in part, by permission, from Eyes for the Little Worlds, *by E. B. Ashcraft. Copyright, 1943, Westinghouse Electric Corporation.*

THE STORY OF ELECTRICAL POWER

Central power systems with their high tension lines, steam turbines, and generators supply most of our electricity.

THE world would be very different without the services of that modern genie, electrical power. Your home would have to find a dozen different substitutes. Instead of pressing a button to turn on the electric lights, you would have to touch a match to a gas jet or perhaps a kerosene lamp. Instead of a refrigerator that needs only to be "plugged in" and then regulates itself to preserve your food, you would have an ice box and would be dependent upon the regular visits of the ice dealer. To press clothes you would have to heat the irons upon a coal or wood stove, and you probably would not have a vacuum cleaner at all, merely an assortment of brooms and brushes powered by "elbow grease."

In industry, there would have to be many kinds of steam engines and coal furnaces to replace the electric motors and ovens that now do much of the heavy work.

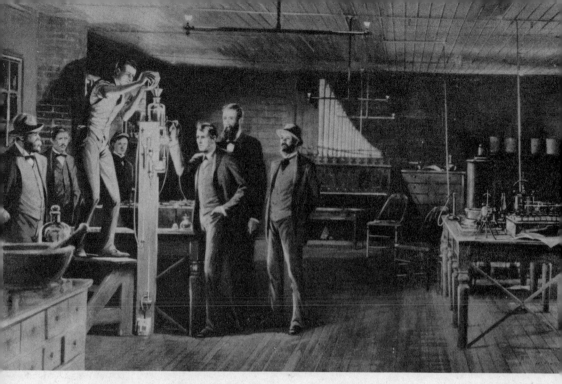

The historic moment in Edison's laboratory when the current was turned on and his electric lamp blazed with light.

Yet this world without electrical power is not so difficult to picture, for it is not long gone and many traces of it remain. It is less than a century since electricity first began to be generated and distributed on a scale that makes it available to homes and factories.

How Was Electricity Discovered?

Before there could be electric power plants, electricity itself had to be discovered. No one man discovered electricity. Many men found out a little about it, during the course of more than 2,000 years, and it was only by piecing together many little facts that the full meaning was discovered.

Electricity first began to be discovered when the first man watched, in fearful admiration, the sharp tongues of lightning lick across the sky.

Another part of the story began when someone—perhaps in China—found that certain dark and heavy stones have the power

[70]

of attracting, even of lifting, pieces of iron. And so these stones, by virtue of their strange property, were called loadstones.

About 2,500 years ago, on the shores of the Aegean Sea, a philosopher of Greece's golden age, Thales, absent-mindedly stroked a piece of polished amber. He found that it then drew to itself light objects, such as lint and chaff and feathers.

Centuries passed—the age of Aristotle in Greece, of Pliny in Rome, of Roger Bacon and the Middle Ages. The Renaissance swept across Europe. Science, which had all but stood still for a millennium, began to stir; men found courage to experiment.

Queen Elizabeth's physician, probing the mysteries of the loadstone, discovered in it most of the principles of what we

Edison's electric lamp had carbonized thread that glowed in a vacuum when the current was turned on.

today call magnetism. And this same man, William Gilbert, repeating the experiments of Thales, drew on the old Greek word for amber, elektron, to coin the now familiar word electricity.

In 1752, at Philadelphia, Benjamin Franklin flew a kite to draw down the lightning of the sky to prove it akin to the electricity made by rubbing amber.

In Italy, Professor Galvani watched frogs' legs twitch and kick when two unlike metals touched them. Another Italian, Alessandro Volta, applied this discovery; a disk of copper and a disk of zinc, with a piece of paper moistened with acid between them—thus he constructed the voltaic pile, the first electric battery, the first really new way of making electricity since Thales rubbed amber in 600 B. C. And with the development of the battery, electricity was at last freed from its static prison and, like an invisible fluid, could flow wherever wires would lead it. Men began to dream of transmitting power over long distances.

In Denmark, Hans Christian Oersted was experimenting with one of Volta's new batteries. He passed electricity through a wire. He then brought a magnetic compass near the wire, and the restless needle, forsaking its relentless search for north, was deflected. He reversed the direction of the elecric current, and again the needle was deflected, but this time in the opposite direction. And with this experiment the third original actor in the story of electricity fell into line. For lightning had been proved to be electricity, and now Oersted had shown that electricity in motion produces magnetism.

Who Invented the Generator?

Such was the state of knowledge about electricity when, in 1831, two scientists—Michael Faraday at the Royal Institution, in England, and Joseph Henry at the Albany Academy, in America—performed independently the experiment that showed that when a piece of metal is moved in the field of influence of a magnet, an electric current is produced in the metal. And this, the third method of making electricity, opened the way for most of the marvels which the mysterious force performs today. For these two men discovered the principle of the electric dynamo.

You can perform that pioneer experiment yourself if you wish. All you need is a length of copper wire and a toy magnet. First wind the wire into a cylindrical coil and fasten the ends together. Then shove the magnet into the coil. As you do it, a pulse of electricity will be created. Pull the magnet out. At that instant another pulse of electricity will be created, this time flowing in the opposite direction. Repeat the process at the fantastic speed of sixty times a second, and you will be generating sixty-cyle current —the same kind that comes to most of us over our power lines.

How much current? Ah, there's the rub! No matter how diligently you worked with your homemade generator, you couldn't make enough electricity to cause even the tiniest flashlight bulb to glow a dull red. For electricity is power, and it takes power to make power.

Coated inside with phosphors like those in fluorescent lamps, this glass globe lights when bombarded by the beam of a high-frequency radio.

A chemical coating on the inside of the glass tubes makes these modern lamps "fluoresce" when the current is turned on.

It is a far cry from Faraday's and Henry's coils and magnets to the great generators that make today's electricity. Just to collect the materials for them is an adventure in itself. Copper, iron, cotton, aluminum, mica, gums, and asphalt for varnish and insulation. Copper has to be drawn into wire and formed into coils. Iron has to be alloyed with a dozen other elements, cast into molds and machined into shape, forged into shafts, rolled into sheets, and punched into intricate patterns. And when the parts are made and dozens of skilled hands have fitted them to a compactness that shames a jigsaw puzzle and with an accuracy that rivals a watchmaker's art, the adventure has just begun.

For then the real miracle begins. Power is applied—from a water wheel or from a steam turbine. The giant rotor, weighing many tons, begins to turn. Slowly at first, then faster. A faint sound becomes audible—a hum, rising to a high-pitched whine. There is no smoke, no confusion, no spectacular shower of sparks. But something that did not exist before is being created. There, in the narrow gap that separates spinning rotor and the sullen, heavy stator coils, electricity is being made.

Who Built the First Central Power Plant?

It is to Thomas Alva Edison that we owe this modern miracle, for Edison organized and built the first central power system on which all electric generating systems are modeled today. By 1879 Edison had perfected the best electric lamp of the time. He had substituted a carbonized thread for the platinum wire of a previous lamp and enclosed the thread in a glass bulb after evacuating all the air from it. Having perfected his lamp, Edison found that it was necessary to devise a system for generating, metering, and distributing electricity to the users of his electric lamps.

There were at the time no really satisfactory dynamos, although many had been built both in Europe and America. There were no central power stations, no meters, no safety fuses, sockets, or electric light fixtures. Edison and his men devised all the complicated equipment necessary for distribution of power from a central station.

Where Was the First Central Power Plant?

The first central station for the commercial distribution of electricity was set going on the fourth of September, 1882, by Thomas Edison himself, at 257 Pearl Street, New York City. Newspapers of the following day had much to say. Wonder was expressed over the "blazing horseshoe that glowed within a pear-shaped globe." Another told of "the dim flicker of gas supplanted by a steady glare, bright and mellow." A third observed, "As soon as it is dark enough to need artificial light, you turn the thumbscrew and the light is there; no nauseous smell, no flicker, no glare."

An overhead view of a steam turbine-generator. The turbine is in the smaller cylinder.

Among the five or six buildings supplied with the new lighting were the Herald offices and the Drexel Building, at the time one of New York City's show places. The illumination of the latter was held to be a truly momentous achievement owing to its great size. The equipment, in other words, reached the grand total of 106 lamps. In comparison, it is interesting to mention the lighting equipment of the Municipal Building, in New York City, numbering something over 15,000 lamps.

This primitive central station in Pearl Street was a converted warehouse of brick construction, four stories high, and it was separated in two parts by a fire wall. One of these parts was used for the storing of underground supplies, while the other was occupied by the generating machinery,

Two turbines are hitched together for added power. Steam from one turbine passes through the U-shaped tube to the next one.

for the support of which a special foundation of steel and concrete was provided. The necessary steam boilers were accommodated in the basement, while the second floor was occupied by six generators of 125 horsepower each, nicknamed "Jumbos."

As simple as this original Edison equipment sounds, it nevertheless represented years of research and experimenting on the part of Edison and those associated with him.

When Was the Steam Engine First Linked to the Dynamo?

With the experience gained by an experimental system at Menlo Park, Edison began the construction of the first successful direct-connected steam dynamo in the spring of 1881, at the

Edison Machine Works, Goerck Street, New York City. The development of an adequate underground conduit proved also most serious. The district selected for lighting was the area—nearly a square mile in extent—included between Wall, Nassau, Spruce, and Ferry Streets, Peck Slip and the East River in New York City. In those days such electrical transmission as existed—this of course related largely to telegraphy—was accomplished by means of a veritable forest of poles and wires augmented by the distribution equipments of fire alarm, telephone, burglar alarm, and stock ticker companies. People had become so used to this sort of thing that even the most competent electrical authorities of the time doubted extremely whether Edison's scheme of an underground system could be made either a scientific or a commercial success, owing to the danger of great loss through leakage. However, the Edison conduits once in use, both the public and even the telephone, telegraph, and ticker companies

A small steam turbine-generator which produces 3,000 kilowatts. Steam turbines produce most of America's electrical energy.

A hydroelectric power generating station on the Susquehanna River. Driven by water under pressure, these water wheels turn generators which produce electricity.

acknowledged their feasibility. Such, in fact, was the success of the new method that the city compelled at length the removal of all telegraph poles.

How Were Electric Conduits Laid?

The systematic laying out of street mains in the first company district was begun in the summer of 1881. The method then used was to dig a trench, in which pipes measuring twenty feet in length were laid. Through these the conductors were drawn, two half-round copper wires kept in place first by heavy cardboard and afterwards by rope. The conductors having been drawn in, a preparation of asphalt and linseed oil was forced into the piping to serve as insulation. The spending of three and four arduous nights a week in these trenches by Edison and his associates suggests the rigor of the later European warfare. This work, together with that incident to the operation of the new station, often proved too much even for Edison's phenomenal endurance. At such times he slept on a cot close beside the running engines, while the rest of the crew crawled in on the lower row of field-magnet coils of the dynamos, a place warm enough, though a trifle bumpy. One of the inventor's early assistants tells of going to sleep standing up, leaning against a door frame—this, after forty-eight hours of uninterrupted work.

September 4 saw a full 400 lamps turned on from the Pearl Street station. From that day on, the station supplied current continuously until 1895, with but two brief interruptions. One of these happened in 1883 and lasted three hours. The other resulted from the serious fire of January 2, 1890, and lasted less than half a day. The record in the second case would appear astounding

One of the largest shafts ever assembled, this 150-ton giant is part of one of the Grand Coulee Dam's water wheel generators.

The upper part of this turbine's case has been removed, showing the rotor with its many "buckets" or vanes which turn under the pressure of steam directed at them through nozzles.

as no less a handicap occurred than the burning down of the station itself. The situation was saved, however, by the presence of an auxiliary plant that had already been opened on Liberty Street.

Who Was the Central Station Pioneer?

The average man, while appreciating the tremendous advance in generating machinery since the early eighties, is surprised to learn that the great Edison system of today is conducted upon principles that Edison developed and put into practice at that time. Edison's, in truth, was the master mind, the forming spirit of all the advances made in the seventies and eighties.

In the following manner Edison and his assistants became established in New York City. Current at first was supplied free

These two generators can produce momentary power torrents of 2 million kilowatts. They are used to test large protective switches called circuit breakers.

to customers for approximately five months, which speaks quite as much for Edison's Scotch "canniness" as for his inventive genius. Well before the period was over the new illuminant had justified itself, until today it shows itself an element indispensable in every phase of the country's activity.

Within two years from the opening of the station the demand for service had so increased that over 100 applications were filed in excess of what could be accepted, because the plant was taxed already to its utmost capacity. By 1887 not only a second but a third district had been mapped out, the whole extending from Eighteenth to Forty-fifth Street. All the underground system in the two new districts was laid according to Edison's new three-wire patent; and it was presently announced that customers would be supplied with power as well as with light.

Six months after the disastrous fire of 1890, in which the Pearl Street station was burned, the site was chosen for the Edison Duane Street building, on which operations were so hastened that machines were installed and current turned on by the first of May the following year.

For some time the need of a central generating plant had been apparent to all familiar with the company's facilities and prospects. Already during the summer of 1898 an engineering commission had visited all the chief electrical stations of Europe and consulted the best-known experts of the industry, and in 1902 the first waterside station in New York was opened upon a site bordering the East River. The operating room contained sixteen vertical engines from which current was generated by 3,500 kilowatt generators and sent out to the various distributing centers.

The noisy, clumsy steam engines that turned Edison's electric generators have disappeared from modern power houses. Today's generators are turned by high-speed steam turbines.

What Is a Turbine?

A turbine is something like a cross between a mammoth windmill and a giant spinning top. Its sails are vanes or buckets of polished steel. There are rows on rows of them, each set at its exact angle, each anchored fast to the mighty shaft. Against them blow tornadoes of steam— steam heated and superheated until the pipes that confine its rebellious pressure glow a surly red.

Angrily the steam charges against the beveled surface of the polished bucket. Under its force the bucket slips aside. The

Testing the complicated wiring of the revolving core or rotor of a great 18-ton electric generator.

Transformers installed in the face of the hydroelectric power house at Boulder Dam. Because of the many dams built on western rivers, much of the electricity used in the West comes from hydroelectric plants.

massive shaft is turned a little. Baffled, the steam moves on. Another bucket is encountered; under the charge of the steam it too sidesteps—turning the shaft a little more. On the steam goes, shouldering aside the rows on rows of vanes that impede its progress. As it moves, it loses its fury; and as it weakens, so the buckets grow larger. One by one, they tame and bleed the tornado of its power. And at the end, despoiled of its fiery energy, it emerges as drops of lukewarm water.

What happens to the energy that urges the steam onward? It is not lost, for at each of the buffetings the shaft is turned. And the forward drive of the steam is converted into the smooth, swift turning of the turbine.

This is no slow, drawn-out process. One instant a particle of coal is shot into the boiler. Less than a second later the energy of that coal, transformed into steam and then into electricity, is miles away, heating your electric iron, running your refrigerator, or lighting your reading lamp.

The turbine spins so quietly, so tirelessly, that it seems to turn almost without effort. Yet it bears a mighty load. For the turbine does not turn alone; it is merely the muscle that drives the great generator mounted on the same shaft. And the heavy tasks of half a city are shifted to its steel shoulders.

Some electric generators are turned by steam turbines, some by waterpower, a few by Diesel engines. What determines the choice of power? The answer is cost. And the fact that more than two-thirds of America's electricity is steam-produced is proof, if proof is needed, that in most places the steam turbine is the most efficient producer.

Sometimes, of course, water-power is cheaper. When a natural falls provides a ready-made dam and the water is flowing anyway, it is relatively easy to make it work as it travels downward to the waiting sea. But Niagaras are not found everywhere—seldom, indeed, near great centers of population—and a storage dam is a vastly expensive structure, even if the river is available. Moreover, times of drought do come, times when the flow of water thins from a surging flood to an anemic trickle. But however often rains fail, the flow of electricity must not fail. So even in the domain of waterpower, steam stands ready to pick up the bur-

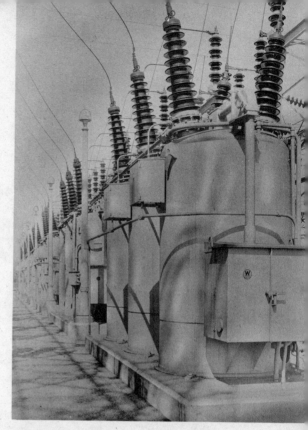

Typical of the automatic switches which protect power systems are these oil-insulated circuit breakers which guard high tension lines from short circuits.

den, ready, at a moment's notice, to take a pound of coal and convert it into a kilowatt hour of electric energy—enough to keep your reading lamp burning for more than two evenings.

It is more than sixty years now since the first crude electric generators began to sing their song. There were only a few at first, providing the power for one or two arc lamps here, a few of Edison's little incandescent lamps there. How their music has grown! Today, in more than twenty-seven million homes and countless factories and offices, there are wires attuned to their singing, wires that draw from the electric generators of the nation power equal to the plunging strength of sixty million horses. You reach out your hand and touch a switch; the power is there. And it is there, waiting, because back in the power house a coil of wire is making magic with a magnet.

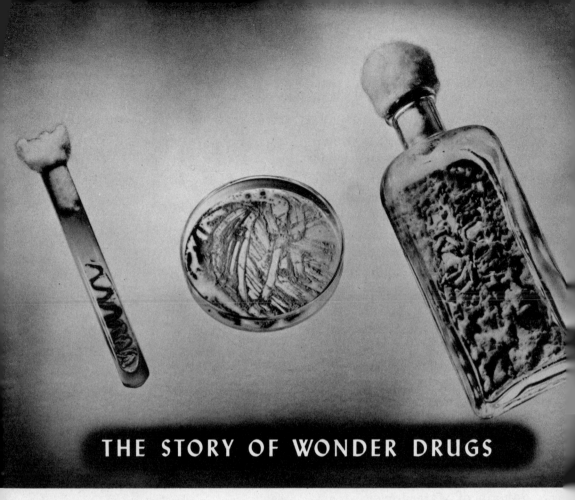

THE STORY OF WONDER DRUGS

Penicillin is derived from a common mold, penicillium notatum. *Here the mold is shown growing in a test tube, a Petri dish, and a culture bottle.*

ONLY in the past hundred years have doctors and scientists learned the real causes of disease. Although the "medicine man" has been an important and often powerful member of the community since earliest historical times, his drugs have worked on the symptoms rather than the causes of human ills. In the middle of the last century, the French scientist Louis Pasteur announced the theory that fermentation is caused by microscopic organisms called bacteria. After long controversy, the reality of bacteria was established, and various kinds of these one-celled creatures, which have both animal and vegetable characteristics, were found to be responsible not only for fermentation and decay but also for many of the more serious human and animal diseases.

What Is a Specific?

It has long been recognized that most drugs in common use do not attack the cause of disease directly, but improve the general condition of the body, or relieve immediate symptoms, thereby helping the body itself to fight the cause. Physicians have long searched for *specifics,* drugs that would directly attack the bacteria or viruses that cause disease. In the long history of medicine up to 1910, it may be said that only one such specific was discovered—quinine for the treatment of malarial fever.

The discovery of bacteria spurred renewed search for specifics. A new science called chemotherapy came into being—the treatment of disease with chemical compounds. The first success of this science was achieved by Dr. Paul Ehrlich in 1910. Iodine was known to be a specific against certain types of bacteria, and after trying 606 compounds of iodine Ehrlich discovered "salvarsan," also called "606," a compound that can be administered without injury to the patient. Salvarsan is a specific against sleeping sickness and other diseases.

Just before and during World War II, the spectacular advance of chemotherapy was marked by the release for general use of three new wonder drugs—the sulfonamides, penicillin, and streptomycin.

What Are the Sulfa Drugs?

The story of the sulfonamides, or sulfa drugs as they are called, started at just about the time Ehrlich made his discovery of formula 606. But it took nearly thirty years before sulfa was put to work. In 1909, a young student named Gelmo, at the Vienna Institute of Technology in Austria, discovered a white powder. He made it from coal-tar dyes, and it was exactly the formula which is used today for sulfanilamide, the best known of the sulfa drugs. But the therapeutic value of the powder was not realized.

In 1932, Dr. Gerhard Domagk, a German medical researcher, hit upon Gelmo's formula, and found that it produced amazing results in streptococcus infections in mice. Then, the following year, a strange thing happened, and it is still not clear what was the reason behind it. Two coworkers of Domagk, Dr. Fritz

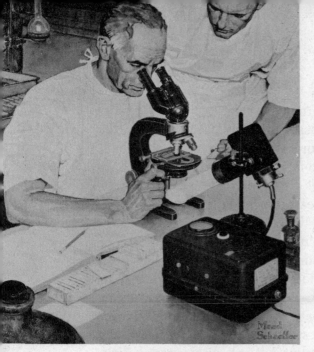

Thousands of substances are examined under the microscope in the search for life-saving specifics.

Mietzsch and Dr. Joseph Klarer patented a new drug, registering it for I. G. Farben Industrie, the great German dye company. They called it prontosil, and it was made up of Domagk's formula plus some complicated red dye. It was later suspected that "I. G." made the Domagk formula more complicated than necessary to prevent its being copied by others. Nevertheless, in 1935, when prontosil was first tried on humans, the drug produced amazing results in curing blood poisoning, rheumatism, childbed fever and other diseases for which no effective medicine was known.

In France, Ernest Fourneau, Constantin Lavaditi and M. and Mme. Jacques Trefouel learned of the new drug, and experimented with it. They discovered that it was the sulfanilamide which was the effective part of the drug. In 1936, two English doctors, Leonard Colebrook and Meave Kenny put prontosil to work in Queen Charlotte's Hospital in London. The wonders of sulfa were spreading.

It spread to the United States largely through the efforts of Drs. Perrin H. Long and Eleanor Bliss, who had heard of the success achieved in London. They had been working on similar cures of streptococcus infections. From this point on, the use of sulfa drugs developed rapidly. New types were developed. Sulfapyridine received a major test in 1939, when several English doctors used it on African natives to stem a spinal meningitis epidemic in the Anglo-Egyptian Sudan. Out of 2,000 sulfa compounds developed since 1935, about ten have proved to be of major use.

Sulfa drugs were widely used in World War II to fight battlefield infections. They are now used in ordinary small bandages to combat minor injuries. Their principal use, however, is against

[86]

pneumonia, meningitis, gas gangrene, and dysentery. Once sulfa drugs became known, they were tried against almost all disease and infections, and were "oversold" to the public. Against many diseases, they were not effective at all. In the first days of the use of sulfanilamide, a tragic development occurred. A Tennessee drug company offered an Elixir of Sulfanilamide for sale. The company had ignorantly mixed with the sulfa a dissolving ingredient called di-ethylene-glycol, which made the medicine poisonous. Before the harmful drugs were recalled, nearly one hundred victims had died.

But this is all part of sulfa's early history. Now, doctors and chemists know what it can and cannot do. Because it can be taken in pill form, or in drops, or as a powder, it is not only a potent but a simple medical wonder.

A colony of penicillium notatum *growing in a dish containing a substance it thrives on. Penicillium is the family name of a green mold that grows on cheese, bread and other foods. For the production of penicillin, the mold is started growing on a small scale, then transferred to a metal tank called a germinator, and finally to 10,000-gallon tanks where in two days it yields about one billion units of penicillin.*

[87]

What Does Penicillin Do?

Penicillin is another wonder drug, which attacks many of the diseases for which there was no previously known cure. Like the sulfa drugs, penicillin does not kill bacteria directly, but prevents their growth and development, and allows some of the cells in the human blood stream to handle the remaining bacteria themselves. Penicillin can be used in many cases where the sulfas are ineffective. New applications are being discovered every year.

Penicillin was discovered purely by accident. Dr. Alexander Fleming, a Scottish bacteriologist, made the lucky discovery in the fall of 1928. Working in his laboratory in St. Mary's Hospital in London, he noticed that one of his glass containers holding growing bacteria had been contaminated. This often happens in medical laboratories. A mold, a stray speck of plant life, had blown into the glass dish. Dr. Fleming was about to throw the contents of the dish away when he noticed something very strange. Instead of an ordinary mold growth, he noticed that his bacteria (staphylococci) were being destroyed by some mysterious juice coming from the mold.

What Fleming had noticed, and what had gone unnoticed by countless others before him, was that here was a potential disease killer. If the mold could destroy the staphylococci in the laboratory dish, perhaps it would kill germs within the human body.

Fleming spent the next ten years experimenting with the mold, which he called penicillin. In 1938, Dr. Harold W. Florey, an Australian, began to experiment with penicillin, hoping to improve it. He succeeded, and tested his improved product on mice. In 1941, penicillin was first used on a human patient. Because there was not enough of the new drug, the test was not completely successful. But it was encouraging. The patient had improved while the penicillin was used.

While laboratory experiments with penicillin continued, penicillin production did not keep up at the same pace. Producing penicillin is more of a growing job than a manufacturing one. In the midst of the German aerial bombings of 1940-41, Britain was no place for large-scale penicillin production. The job was therefore transferred to the United States. Scientists and govern-

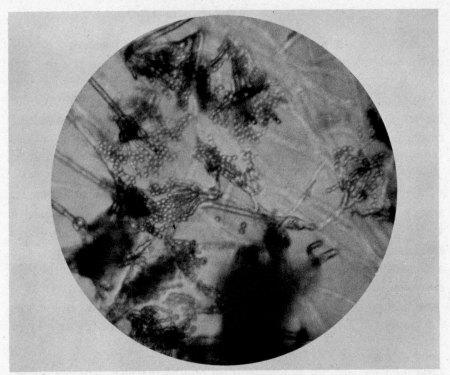

Microphotograph of penicillium notatum, *magnified 5,000 times. The mold develops a mass of filaments. From those of brushlike appearance develop the spores that give new growth.*

ment officials recognized the value of penicillin, not only in fighting ordinary diseases but as a battlefield medicine for soldiers. Penicillin production was given highest priorities. By 1945, it was available in sufficient quantities to treat half a million persons a month. American laboratories were producing 300 billion units, about 15 pounds, a month, in assembly-line fashion. The man in charge of American wartime penicillin production and experiment was Dr. Chester Keefer, director of the Evans Memorial Hospital in Boston, Mass., and chairman of the National Research Council's Committee on Chemotherapy.

Penicillin promises to be a far more effective cure of syphilis than Ehrlich's formula 606. It works wonders against pneumonia, meningitis, gonorrhea, boils, impetigo, burns. Unlike sulfa drugs, it must be injected in liquid form. But, like other new medicines, penicillin is only in the infancy of its use.

What Is Streptomycin?

Penicillin was discovered in a mold growth. Streptomycin, one of the newest of the wonder drugs, was discovered in the red soil of New Jersey. Penicillin's discovery was an accident; and it was developed by the ten-year experimentation of Dr. Fleming and others. Streptomycin's discovery was the result of painstaking research of Selman A. Waksman, Russian-born scientist, at the New Jersey Agricultural Experiment Station at Rutgers University. The story parallels Ehrlich's search for salvarsan.

In 1940, Waksman decided to investigate the family of microscopic organisms known as actinomycetes. He first developed a method for testing the germ-killing powers of actinomycetes, and soon learned that he was on the right trail. Thirty percent of the actinomycetes he tested showed a remarkable ability to destroy disease-producing bacteria.

The first drug he developed was called *actinomycin,* but it was too powerful. It destroyed animal bodies as well as germs. Then

From the huge tank, the penicillium is led through this filter press and concentrated into about one-half gallon of liquid.

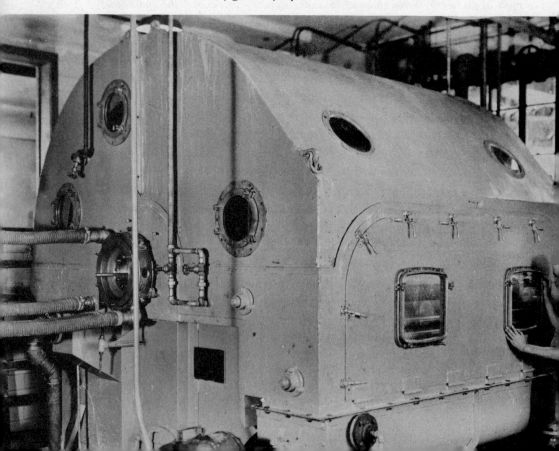

came *streptothricin*, which also was a failure. It seemed to work when first tested, but had a delayed harmful effect. Finally, in 1944, Waksman and his assistants hit upon *streptomycin*, extracted from decomposed fertilizer. It was as effective as streptothricin, but did not have its harmful aftereffects. Again, the drug was tested on animals before it was tried on human beings. It proved successful from its first test, and, most exciting of all, attacked diseases which penicillin and the sulfa drugs could not reach.

Streptomycin is especially effective against rabbit fever, certain types of blood poisoning, dysentery and bladder and kidney infections. Experiments now in progress may prove it to be the first real weapon against tuberculosis.

As with the development of other drugs, the spreading use

This electron tube condenses a half-gallon of the liquid derived from penicillium to about a cupful. This small quantity may contain as much as a billion units of penicillin.

of streptomycin was hindered at first by its low supply. For a year, it was too scarce even for adequate experimentation purposes. But in early 1946, one company was building a $3,500,000 plant for the production of streptomycin. In September, 1946, 1,600 general hospitals received limited quantities for distribution to other hospitals and to doctors in their areas.

The fight against disease will continue on new fronts and with new weapons. Within the limits of their time and patience, scientists will discover and develop still newer wonder drugs.

THE STORY OF RADAR

The "beach umbrella" antenna of a portable radar unit. The antenna is used as a transmitter to send out short-wave radio pulses, and as a receiver to catch the echoes reflected by the target. This United States Marine Corps radar unit has a range of eighty miles.

THE WORD RADAR is a contraction of "radio detecting and ranging." *Ra* stands for radio, *d* for detection, *a* for and, and *r* for ranging. Radar, an important milestone in the evolution of radio, has a long story, for it is not an overnight development. The basic principle is as old as radio itself, but it was not harnessed until, for self-preservation, warring nations sought a device that would counteract the military advantage of the warplane, the submarine and other weapons of modern warfare.

What Is the Basic Principle of Radar?

Heinrich Hertz demonstrated in 1888 that electromagnetic waves can be reflected. It remained for Nikola Tesla to recognize and point out the practical application of the radio "echo." Describing his 1889 method and transmission of wireless energy in "Century" (June 1900) Tesla said:

"That communication without wires to any point of the globe is practical with such apparatus would need no demonstration, but through a discovery which I made I obtained absolute certitude. Popularly explained, it is exactly this: When we raise the voice and hear an echo in reply, we know that the sound of the voice must have reached a distant wall or boundary, and must have been reflected from the same. Exactly as the sound, so an electrical wave is reflected, and the same evidence which is afforded by an echo is offered by an electrical phenomenon known as a 'stationary' wave—that is, a wave with fixed nodal and ventral regions.

"Stationary waves . . . mean something more than telegraphy without wires to any distance . . . For instance, by their use we may produce at will, *from a sending station*, an electrical effect in any particular region of the globe; *we may determine the relative position or course of a moving object, such as a vessel at sea, the distance traversed by the same, or its speed.*"

Marconi was another who envisaged the possibility of using the radio "echo" to locate ships and other objects during poor visibility conditions. The following is quoted from a paper he presented on June 20, 1922 before the Institute of Radio Engineers in New York:

"As was first shown by Hertz, electric waves can be completely reflected by conducting bodies. In some of my tests I have noticed the effects of reflection and deflection of these waves by metallic objects miles away.

"It seems to me that it should be possible to design apparatus by means of which a ship could radiate or project a divergent beam of these rays in any desired direction, which rays, if coming across a metallic object, such as another steamer or ship, would be reflected back to a receiver screened from the local transmitter on the sending ship, and thereby immediately reveal the presence and bearing of the other ship in fog or thick weather.

"One further great advantage of such an arrangement would be that it would be able to give warning of the presence and bearing of ships, even should these ships be unprovided with any kind of radio."

Yet years of exploration of the ether were to pass before pioneering made it possible to open up the ultra-short wave spectrum, aided by research and engineering in radio circuits, special electron tubes, and the application of electronic techniques.

When Was Distance First Measured by Reflected Waves?

Technical investigations that opened the way to radar development began in the 1920's when scientists, intent upon measuring the altitude of the "radio roof" or Kennelly-Heaviside surface, projected radio signals toward it and measured on a nearby receiver the time required by the radio wave to reach the reflecting layer and return. (Kennelly-Heaviside surface, named for its discoverers, Arthur E. Kennelly and Sir Oliver Heaviside, is a conducting layer of ionized air at high altitudes, which acts as a mirror, reflecting radio waves back to earth.) From the known speed of electromagnetic waves, the height of the ceiling was calculated to be 50 to 130 miles.

On What Devices Does Radar Depend?

The research men found that the shorter the wave, the easier it is to focus a radio beam. Measurement of short distances with directed beams, now known as radar, had to await the development of electronic devices which could develop power and receiver sensitivity at suitable radio frequencies, and other apparatus capable of measuring split-second time intervals. With the development of new radio tubes capable of generating ultra-short waves, the building of radar-beam apparatus became practical.

When Were the First Radar Devices Tested?

In 1934, microwave apparatus was used for a series of co-operative reflection tests with the U. S. Army Signal Corps on the beach near Sandy Hook on the New Jersey coast. Some distance away, small ships travelled through the channel into the harbor. It was possible, by listening in the radar receiving equipment for the tone of the reflected wave, to determine when one of these ships intercepted the stationary radio beam. These tests, carried out in secrecy, gave definite proof that even with equipment in the early stages of development, ships could be detected and located by means of microwaves.

At the time of these tests, the experimental equipment utilized a form of a modulated continuous wave which was found to be limited in its usefulness since it did not readily determine the distance of the reflecting object. Therefore work was started on an improved apparatus which utilized waves transmitted in trains of short pulses in order that distance, as well as direction, could be determined. Throughout this work the Army and Navy were kept constantly informed of progress.

By 1937, this equipment had been developed to the point where it could determine short distances with considerable accuracy and at the same time obtain reflections from more distant objects. Equipment was installed on the roof of an RCA building in Camden, New Jersey. By use of swinging antennas, images of radio-reflecting objects on the Philadelphia skyline and in the river between the two cities were obtained on a cathode-ray tube. The form of this equipment, using microwaves, pulse transmission, scanning antennas and a cathode-ray indicator, arranged to show distance and angle, was much the same as is now used in a large part of existing radar installations.

When Was Radar First Installed on Warships?

In 1938, experimental radar equipment was installed on the *U.S.S. Texas* and the *U.S.S. New York.* The tests proving satisfactory, the Navy decided to install additional radar sets. In October, 1939, because of RCA's pioneer radar work, it was awarded contracts for six sets of aircraft-detection equipment patterned after a model built at the Naval Research Laboratory, and as installed on the *U.S.S. New York.* This was the first Navy service radar equipment order. The apparatus built by RCA was installed on United States naval vessels beginning in 1940.

When Was Radar First Installed on Airplanes?

At the same time that this work was proceeding on equipment for the location of ships and aircraft from the ground, scientists were continuing research on radar equipment to be carried on aircraft. An ultra-short-wave pulse radar equipment was installed in an airplane in 1937 and soon proved its practicality. One beam pointing downward gave accurate altimeter readings; the second beam, which was quite sharp in direction, pointed straight ahead to detect objects in front of and also somewhat below the aircraft in flight. With these two beams working together, the pilot was able to get information concerning both the terrain ahead of him, by the traces appearing on the indicating screen, and his exact height above ground from the altimeter reading.

Darkness or fog had no effect on the signals. This is believed to have been the first airborne pulse radar set, which in principle was the prototype of much of the airborne radar which has followed. Extension of the test flights in 1938 and 1939 further showed the effectiveness of radar apparatus in warning of collision between aircraft or between planes and mountains or other fixed obstacles.

How Did Radar Save a Nation?

Radar became one of the greatest weapons of the United Nations during World War II. It is credited with saving England

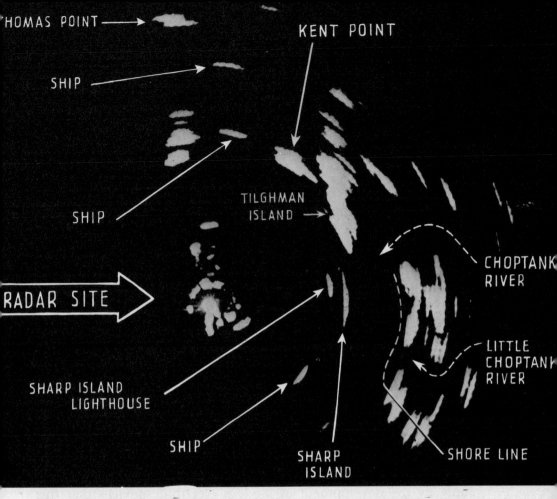

THOMAS POINT →

KENT POINT

SHIP

SHIP

TILGHMAN
ISLAND →

CHOPTANK
RIVER

RADAR SITE →

LITTLE
CHOPTANK
RIVER

SHARP ISLAND
LIGHTHOUSE

SHIP

SHARP
ISLAND

SHORE LINE

Radar equipment of the Naval Research Laboratory, Chesapeake Bay Annex, made this "search" of surrounding terrain. Written on the photograph of the PPI (Plan Position Indicator) are designations of points picked up by the radar pulse.

during the terrible air attacks of 1940 and 1941, for radar was able to warn the British of the approach of swarms of enemy planes, and to spot the enemy planes during night raids.

Because of the military importance of radar, it did not come to wide public attention until 1941. On the fateful morning of December 7, 1941, Private Joseph L. Lockhard was using the radar device at Pearl Harbor and detected planes approaching. He flashed the report to his superior officer, who, knowing that a number of American planes were due from the mainland, believed that the radar had spotted them, and therefore took no action. Radar as an electronic sentinel had done its duty. Although the warning went unheeded, its signal summoned America to the most tremendous undertaking in its national history. It was an undertaking that would bring into existence thousands of radar sets, and give radar a chance to prove itself as one of the greatest developments in the exciting history of radio.

How Does Radar Work?

How does radar work? How can it "see" a plane or planes above the clouds, detect a ship or a squadron of ships twenty five miles or more away, or supply the outline of terrain thousands of feet beneath a reconnaissance plane flying in fog?

The boy who yoo-hoos at a cliff and hears the echo is in effect illustrating the radar principle. The sound strikes an object and is reflected. Radio waves also are reflected. But, of course, radio waves travel much faster than sound; they travel at the speed of light, 186,000 miles a second. Knowing the velocity of the radio wave, and by recording the time required for the echo to come back, the distance to the object that reflected the signal can be determined. Thus, the essential contribution of radar resides in the possibility of measuring distance accurately by means of the radio echo.

The speed of the radio waves, however, is so great that it is only by the development of modern electronic devices that this measurement has been made possible. For instance, the time required for a radio wave to travel to an object fifty feet away and back again is only one ten-millionth of a second, yet radar can measure it.

What Are Essential Parts of a Radar Unit?

Radar assumes various forms, depending on the specific purpose to which it is assigned. In any form, it is highly technical and intricate but the operation may be described as follows:

Most radar units consist of four basic elements—a microwave transmitter, a sensitive receiver, a cathode-ray tube indicator and a directive antenna system—all working in exact synchronization. In the pulse system the transmitter generates a series of pulses of very short duration. These pulses of radio energy strike

HOW RADAR WORKS...

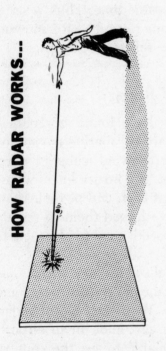

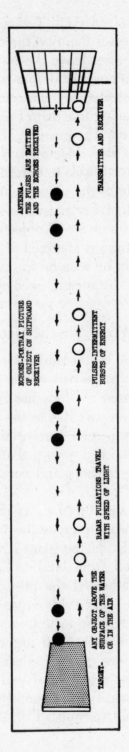

ANTENNA—
THE PULSES ARE EMITTED
AND THE ECHOES RECEIVED

TRANSMITTER AND RECEIVER

ECHOES—PORTRAY PICTURE
OF OBJECT ON SHIPBOARD
RECEIVER

PULSES—INTERMITTENT
BURSTS OF ENERGY

TARGET—
ANY OBJECT ABOVE THE
SURFACE OF THE WATER
OR IN THE AIR

RADAR PULSATIONS TRAVEL
WITH SPEED OF LIGHT

Schematic diagram of how radar works. Intermittent pulses of short-wave energy are sent out by the transmitter. These pulses are focused in a beam, just as light rays are focused in a search-light. If the beam encounters a solid target, it is reflected back to the radar antenna. The effect is analogous to throwing a rubber ball against a wall and catching it on the rebound. When a pulse is reflected back before the next pulse is sent out, the "echo" picked up by the antenna is transformed into a spot of light on the Plan Position Indicator. Through the focusing of the beam, each ray when reflected affects its own small area on the PPI, so that the whole assemblage of lighted areas on it is a literal plan of the relative positions of objects within the area covered by the beam. Some images on the screen show clearly the shapes of objects, such as ships at sea. Many other images can be interpreted by skilled observers.

[99]

an object and are reflected. The receiver picks up the returning signals and impresses them on the cathode-ray tube. At the same instant that the pulses leave the transmitter the cathode-ray tube starts to trace a horizontal line across the calibrated viewing chart. When a reflected ray is received, it can be used to produce a hump in the tracing line or to brighten the trace at the position where it is received. The position of the hump gives the exact distance or range of the object. From the fluctuation of the hump, the skilled operator is able to determine, to a remarkably accurate degree, the nature of the object which reflected the pulses.

When the antenna is rotated to a new position, thus obtaining reflections from a new set of objects, the position of the trace on the cathode-ray tube is changed at the same time. Thus, a series of bright spots can be seen on the cathode-ray tube face showing the direction and distance of each of the reflecting objects.

What Are the Uses of Radar?

The principles of the radio locator have found numberless peacetime uses. A large part of the hazards of marine navigation are being eliminated as ships use radar to avoid icebergs, derelicts or other vessels invisible to the pilot. Big luxury liners whose profits depend on a quick turn-around at each end of their route can now ignore the heavy fogs that have forced them to remain for hours outside harbors and can proceed at normal speed to their docks.

Nor does low visibility by day or night halt plane traffic. The air-borne radio beam pierces the fog, the murk, the dark, and reveals all obstacles in the plane's path. With the help of radar, planes can take off from landing fields and glide in to airports whatever the weather. If the pilot is unable to see the country beneath him at a glance, his radar screen will give him all the information he needs for accurate and safe navigation.

During bad weather or at night, the traffic control operator at an airport will see on his indicator the position of all aircraft in proximity to the airport and will be able to direct them to a landing almost as easily as in conditions of good visibility without the time-consuming circling which is now required.

But these uses, presently visualized for radar, are only a hint of the applications which the world will find for this device. Radar promises miracles in many fields of transportation and industry.

Even astronomers have found a use for radar. On January 10, 1946, the exciting news was broadcast to the world that radar signals had been sent to the moon, and had been reflected back. The signal from the Evans Signal Laboratories at Belmar, New Jersey, had pierced 238,000 miles of interplanetary space to reach the moon, and had come bouncing back to the earth in just 2.4 seconds. A tell tale "pip" on a blue-white cathode-ray tube followed every 2.4 seconds after pulses were sent from the radar transmitter. A loud speaker, tied into the system, picked up the echo from the moon in the form of a 180-cycle sound—somewhat higher than the hum heard on the home receiver when a station is not tuned properly. Other evidence of the returning radio waves was shown in the form of jagged saw-tooth lines on an oscilloscope.

The success of the radar-to-the-moon experiment proved what scientists had long believed, that radio waves could penetrate the electrically charged ionosphere which encircles our planet. It was a successful first step toward the greater achievement of studying the topography of planets millions of miles away. Radar may take its place with the telescope as an important means of enabling man to explore the secrets of the universe we live in.

What Is the Rainiest Place Known in the World?

The rainiest places on earth are said to be Mount Waialeale in the Hawaiian Islands, with an annual rainfall averaging 432 inches, and Cherra Punji, India, with its 450 inches of annual rainfall. At Colon in the Canal Zone the rainfall in the wet season averages 116 inches.

What Is the Hottest Place in the United States?

A narrow valley in California, called "Death Valley," between the Panamint and Funeral Mountains, is considered the dryest and hottest place in the United States. Its central part is three or four hundred feet below sea level and is covered with salt. Its temperature has reached the extreme of 122° Fahrenheit. It is called "Death Valley" because a party of emigrants perished there in 1849.

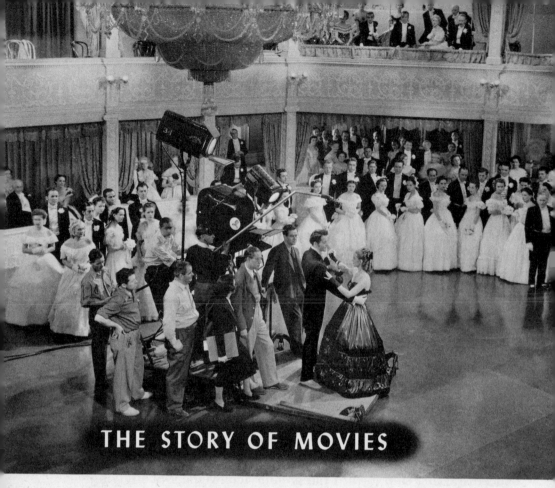

THE STORY OF MOVIES

The stage is set for shooting a close-up of the principals dancing. The dolly on which they stand will be pushed about the floor among the dancing couples. Directly behind the "hero" is the camera, flanked by two baby spotlights, while overhead is the crooked steel arm bearing the microphone. Clustered around the dolly are the camera and sound men. Note the script girl, carrying a large book.

So you want to see how a movie is made? Well, come with me; I have a couple of passes to "Sound Stage No. 7." From the outside, this vast concrete structure looks like a football stadium. On the inside, it looks like an armory drill shed. It seems as though thousands of people are walking around in aimless confusion; over a babel of conversation rises the sound of hammering; weird shadows leap about as long rows of overhead lights are switched on and off. Gradually we perceive the order in this seeming chaos, and realize that a dozen different crews are making last-minute preparations for "shooting" a scene.

[102]

How Are Movies Made?

At one end of the shed, the scenery men have already set up what is evidently the wall of a ballroom. Real wooden pillars support real mezzanine boxes, and behind the colorful drapery "practical" stairs give access to them. Property men swarming all over this set are taking elegant plush chairs to the boxes, fixing drapes, screwing make-believe gas jets in place, waxing and polishing a section of the floor. The lighting crew is experimenting with different batteries of overhead arcs, rigging metal reflectors around the sides of the set, and placing portable spotlights in position.

Over in a corner we see the principals, the "hero" and "heroine" of the story, talking animatedly. They are rehearsing their lines. Beside them is a girl carrying a large portfolio;

An elaborate outdoor scene simulated inside a sound stage. The camera is mounted on the end of a steel boom, which rests on a wheeled truck. The truck will be rolled along the tracks so that the camera can keep pace with the riders as they jog along the icy "road."

Even in bright sunlight, lighting is a problem. Note the overhead canopy, the reflectors in the background, and the man holding up a cheesecloth screen to diffuse the light. At right, a sound man is adjusting the long boom carrying the microphone.

she refers to the book and then directs the "heroine" to put on her gloves, the "hero" to remove the flower from his buttonhole. This is "the script girl." Her job is to check the continuity so that the costumes, make-up, "props" and so on in each scene will be consistent with those before and after.

Presently a horde of "extras" troop on the set, men and women in evening dress. These clothes have all been provided by the central wardrobe department of the movie studio. While the set was being readied, the extras were being outfitted by the expert modistes and tailors of the wardrobe department. An assistant director meets the extras and at once begins to instruct them where to stand, what to do. Meanwhile the stagehands

One of the first movie "studios"; the Lubin studio on a rooftop in Philadelphia (1900). In the pioneer days of movies, all scenes, even "interiors," had to be shot outdoors in full sunlight. Deep shadows often marred the scenes.

and property men have cleared off the floor, and the camera and sound men now invade it. A "dolly" is pushed forward, on which we can see the big "blimp" of the movie camera. This dolly is a low platform on rollers, with a space before the camera where the principals are to stand. But the stars do not yet come out of their corner. For the preliminaries, "stand-ins" take their place—a man and a woman of about the same height and weight as the stars. The stand-ins are directed to step on the dolly and embrace as though dancing. One man adjusts the camera until it focuses on them, while another measures their distance from it with a steel tape.

Now for the first time we become aware of the director, the boss of this entire assembly of people. He consults with the

A modern sound stage, during rehearsal of a United Nations pageant. Cameras are operating from two different levels of the tower in the right foreground. The elaborate "Spanish galleons" are being constructed for another picture.

cameramen, then directs the light crew to rig up a couple of "baby spots" on the dolly, which throw brilliant light on the faces of the stand-ins. Assistant directors scurry back and forth from the director to their several jobs, guiding the extras, instructing the lights crew, and so on. A couple of extra cameras are set up to shoot the ballroom from different angles.

In remarkably quick time the preliminaries are finished, the stand-ins depart, the stars take their places. A rehearsal gets under way. From somewhere comes the sound of a dance orchestra, playing a dreamy waltz. The extras move out on the polished floor in couples; the principals make slow gyrations on the very narrow confines of the dolly; four brawny stage-hands push the dolly around. We are amused to notice that the principals wear woolen socks and no shoes—the clatter of heels on the dolly would sound like machine-gun fire over the microphone.

From the lengthy preparations, you may have the impression that this scene is to be a lengthy one. In fact, the whole action takes less than a minute! The director puts the company through three rehearsals in less than five minutes. Then comes the order "Camera!"

A startling transformation occurs. The hum of conversation, the noises made by the service crews, went right on during the rehearsals. But now as red lights spring on all over the "drill shed," there is instant silence. The crews stop in their tracks and stand immobile. If we were outside the sound stage, we

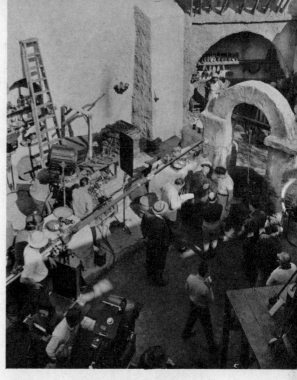

The actors' voices are picked up by a microphone, which must be placed very near to them. When the overhead boom cannot be used, microphones are concealed in the furniture or other "props" close to the action.

would see a red light go on over the door, warning that "shooting" is under way within, and prohibiting entrance until it is finished.

The dance begins again, but now the camera is clicking away in its soundproof blimp; the dialogue of the principals rises clear above the subdued music.

It may seem to you that the short scene was played without a hitch. Nevertheless, it is played over and "shot" six times. You think that a waste of film? Well, film is cheap. Just think of the

Principals rehearse their lines under the eye of the director. The script girl, holding the book, has the duty of checking that all details are in accordance with the written scenario.

Lavishness was the keynote of many early pictures. The peak was reached by this Babylonian set for D. W. Griffith's Intolerance, *filmed in 1916 at a cost of $300,000.*

The modern trend is away from lavishness toward realism. Here a rainstorm interrupting a political rally is simulated by real sprays. Note the camera crew riding on the end of the steel boom.

cost if the scene were shot only once and then had to be shot over again at a later time because some defect came to light in the one shot!

After each shot, a man holds a slate momentarily in front of the camera. On the slate are written cabalistic figures whereby the shot is identified out of the literal thousands that go into the making of a single picture.

What Does the Film Editor Do?

How is a single connected story made out of the thousands of repetitious and out-of-order shots? That is the job of the film editor or "cutter." Script in hand, he must pick out the most satisfactory shot of each scene and put the shots together in correct order. He must shorten scenes that seem too long when viewed as part of a story; he must cut out bits of a scene that are extraneous or faulty. Naturally, the responsibility of cutting is entrusted only to men of long experience and proved skill.

Immediately after a scene is shot, the film is developed and printed. The first prints, called "rushes," are given to the cutter for processing. Later they are viewed by the director to check that they accord with his ideas. Often they are viewed by the producer and by sound-track men also, in order to plan musical accompaniment and other sound effects to be "dubbed in." Before we go further, let us see just how movies move and talk.

How Do Pictures Move?

The moving picture projector flashes on the screen a rapid succession of still pictures—sixteen pictures per second. Now, your eyes tend to see a picture for about a tenth of a second after

Contrast this picture with that of the 1900 rooftop studio. Here, an outdoor winter setting is staged indoors — so that lighting and sound can be fully controlled. No detail is spared in making the scene authentic.

it is removed, so that through "persistence of vision" the series of stills blend into continuous sight. Small differences from one picture to the next appear to be motion.

Motion picture film is a continuous strip, on which still pictures are taken at the rate of sixteen per second. These pictures show successive stages in the action being photographed, and when the prints are run through a projector at the same rate they reproduce the action before your eyes.

In both the original photography and the projection on the screen, the film is not spun in uniform motion, but by jerks. The film must be at rest when the picture is photographed, and must stop (only for a tiny fraction of a second) on the screen. Each "frame" therefore comes to rest for an instant, and then sprocket wheels that engage perforations at the edge of the film jerk the next frame into position. Furthermore, the shutter of the camera or projector must be closed during the time the film is moving,

An assistant holds up a panel bearing the identification numbers and names for the scene just filmed.

Close-up of a movie camera. The film is unwound from a drum in one of the compartments at the top, passes before the lens aperture, and then is wound on a drum in the other compartment. Cameras were formerly cranked by hand, but now are operated by electric motors. The rectangular case at the left is the "blimp" that is placed over the camera, shutting in the sound of its operation so that it will not be heard in the microphone. This is a Technicolor camera, in which three separate films are run synchronously. The regular camera is smaller, but operates in the same way.

else in the one case the film would be blurred and in the other your eyes would see only a blur. The key device—whose invention made motion pictures practicable—is the rotary shutter. This is simply a spinning disc with two or three sectors cut away. It is synchronized with the sprockets so that the solid part masks the film while in motion and the holes pass before it when at rest.

A Technicolor camera in operation. Handwheels enable the operator to swing it up and down, left and right, with steady uniform motion.

How Do Pictures Talk?

Efforts to make pictures talk began with the very invention of motion picture devices (about 1894). Some of the early movie theaters had crews of sound effects men backstage, who supplied the noises supposed to occur in the pictures on the screen. There was some experiment with spoken dialogue, supplied by actors and actresses offstage. Later the phonograph was impressed into service, a record being made of the dialogue which was then run off in synchronization with the film.

Two major difficulties were: keeping the phonograph and film synchronized, and the "phoniness" of the early phonograph—which always sounded like a machine, never like a real voice.

[113]

A film editor at work. He is running strips of film through a "movieola," which magnifies the pictures as they pass under the eyepiece. He will select the best shot of each scene, and cut out imperfect or unwanted parts. In the background, an assistant is taking the "rushes" out of cans and hanging them on a rack in correct sequence.

Both difficulties were overcome, and modern "talkies" began, with the advent of the electronic tube. See "The Story of Electronics."

So-called "electric recording" brought new realism to the reproduction of the human voice and musical instruments. The tinny quality of the old mechanical phonograph was eliminated.

The cutter scrutinizes a length of film from which he must delete a portion.

The projection room of Radio City Music Hall, from which the movies are thrown upon the screen 190 feet away.

Complete synchronization was achieved by putting the sound right on the film, along with the picture!

On a modern film there is a "sound track," a narrow band near one edge. While the film is being shot, microphones pick up the dialogue and other sounds. An electronic tube converts the sounds into variations of light in a "glow tube." Focused on the

The "rushes" — first prints made after the film is developed — are stacked here in the sequence they should appear in the finished picture, awaiting the attention of the editor.

sound track of the film, the tube makes a light-record. In the film projector, the variations in light caused by the track fall on a photo-electric cell; an electronic tube reconverts light to sound.

In many instances, the sound effects are made separately from the action photographed. For example, the shot shows a troop of cavalry riding to the rescue of settlers besieged by Indians. From somewhere come the strains of the William Tell overture. The orchestra was not loaded in trucks racing at forty miles per hour with the troops.

Prints for distribution to movie houses are made in batches from the original film by this duplicating machine.

The sound track was made separately, by an orchestra in a studio, and was "dubbed in" the film. Dubbing is just a matter of synchronizing a separate sound track mechanically with a soundless film, and putting both on one print.

Here the sound track is synchronized with the action of a film.

Making the sound track for the performance of a piano concerto. The music is played to match the film, which is projected on a screen at the left. The piano and orchestra are set apart, each with its own microphones, so that the "mixer" seated at the right foreground can adjust the volume of each as the occasion requires.

How Are Color Movies Made?

As in still photography, many attempts were made to bring color into films, before satisfactory results were achieved. One of the earliest devices photographed alternate frames through red and green filters. The prints were of the ordinary black-and-white kind, but with variations of intensity between adjacent frames due to the filters. The projector had an added rotary shutter with red and green sectors which were brought alternately in front of the frames. Superposed by "persistence of vision," the red and green views of the same scene showed the resultants of the complementary colors. Obviously this method was far from nature: the intensities came from the film, but the actual hues came from the shutter.

One of the earliest applications of "orthochromatic" emulsions used two different emulsions on the two sides of the film, sensitive

[117]

Glimpses of the property rooms of a modern movie studio. An enormous amount of equipment must be kept on hand — chairs, tables, rugs, lamps, and other furniture sufficient to outfit a large apartment house; period costumes, military uniforms, modern clothing for literally thousands of persons; cars, boats, sleighs and other vehicles with all their accessories.

to two different complementary colors. Photography by white light affected the two sides differently, and projection of the prints by white light blended the two colors in the same values as the original scene. Besides mechanical difficulties, this system suffered the same defect as any two-color system—the range of hues reproduced with fidelity is rather narrow.

The modern technicolor system photographs the same scene through three separate filters, red, green and blue, upon three separate films, run through the camera synchronously. The three separate negatives are used to print a single positive, on which

Animators plan the key drawings for a comic cartoon film. This basic sketch of The Captain and the Kids *will be used as a guide by dozens of artists and scores of assistants.*

dyed relief images in all three colors are combined. The color being embodied in the print, the ordinary projector made for black-and-white films can be used—a fact of considerable importance in popularizing color films. And the use of three colors instead of two greatly enhances the fidelity of reproduction.

How Are Animated Cartoons Made?

The comic cartoon you saw the other night probably contained twelve thousand frames. Every one of them was drawn and colored by hand!

Animated cartoons are actually older than moving pictures, for the precursors of the movie were devices for passing hand-drawn pictures rapidly before the eye. But it is a far cry from these ten-second or one-minute peep shows to the modern half-hour animated fairy tale.

After the script of an animated cartoon is planned, the directing staff makes a series of drawings of all the characters, showing

[119]

essential details of faces, forms, clothing. Copies of these master guides are distributed to all the "animators," who are then assigned to various portions of the action. The animators make key drawings for the whole script. For example, if a deer is to be portrayed jumping over a log, the animator may make three key drawings. The first shows the deer at the start of the leap, with his legs still on the ground. The second shows him halfway over the log with legs spread in air. The third shows the landing with legs bent. The key drawings are turned over to a large corps of helpers or subanimators, who supply the intermediate frames, which may number from five to forty.

All these drawings are made on paper. After they have been approved by the directing staff, they are turned over to a still larger corps of skilled workers, who trace them on celluloid and paint in the colors. One by one the finished tracings are placed on

Hundreds of pictures have to be drawn and colored after they are outlined by the animators. All the pictures on these racks will pass before your eye in about ten seconds.

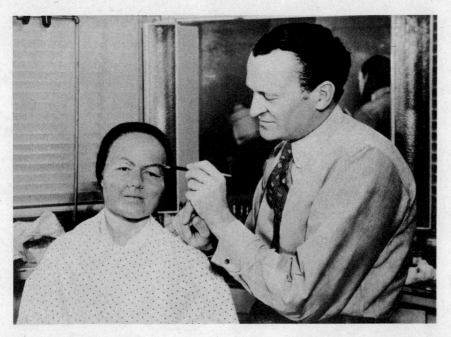

Heavy make-up, applied by experts, is necessary to offset the extremely strong light under which a movie is filmed.

a glass plate and photographed by transmitted light, to make the original negative.

Considerable labor is saved by building up each frame in sections, wherever possible. Thus, if action takes place against a fixed background, the background will be on a separate tracing which is combined with each of the variable tracings of the action. As many as four separate tracings are often combined to photograph one frame.

Music and sound effects are executed separately and recorded on a sound track, which is later added to the film.

You are probably most familiar with the animated cartoon as a comic feature. But it is becoming more and more important as a method of instruction. During World War II, many cartoons were made to show how to operate guns and other devices, how to dig trenches and build shelters, how to read maps, how to conduct scouting patrols, and so on. Pictures in many cases are clearer than written words, and the educational cartoon is being adopted by many schools as well as by our military forces.

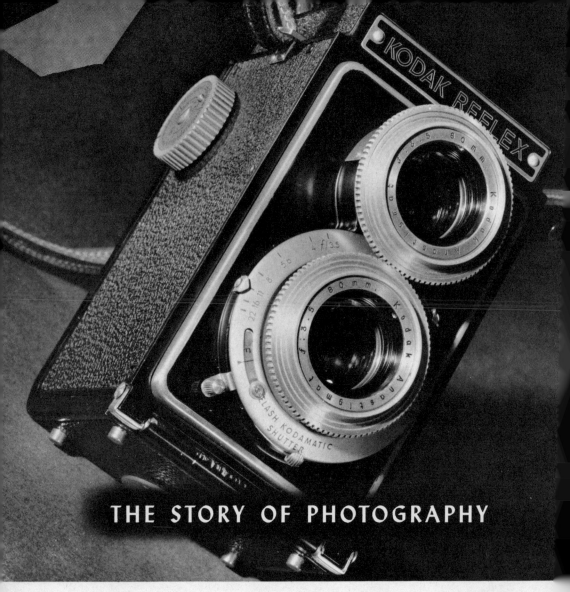

THE STORY OF PHOTOGRAPHY

A reflex camera. This type of camera has twin synchronized lenses. The image received by the upper lens is reflected by a slanting mirror behind it to a sheet of ground glass which acts as combined finder and viewer. The lower lens makes the picture.

PHOTOGRAPHY has become an enormously complex subject. The cumbersome but simple camera of early days has been supplanted by scores of specialized types, with a wide variety of "stops," shutter speeds, and so on. However, the basic principles on which the camera works are relatively simple. First, then, let us take a look, with "X-ray eyes," at a simple camera.

[122]

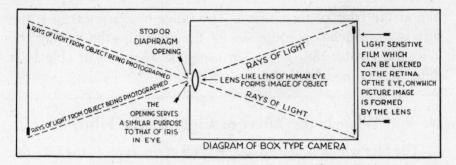

The camera is a mechanical counterpart of the human eye. In both, light is admitted to a dark chamber through an aperture covered by a lens. The diaphragm and the film of the camera correspond to the iris and the retina of the eye.

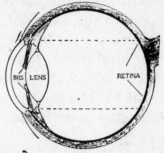

What Is a Camera?

A camera is essentially a box, made light tight, with a lens at one end and a means for supporting a light-sensitive film at the other. The bellows used on folding cameras takes the place of the light-tight box and permits the camera to fold up, thus helping toward compactness. It also provides a means for setting the lens at different distances on certain "focusing" cameras.

The purpose of the lens is to form a sharp image of the object and to project the picture image onto the sensitive film at the back of the camera. The simplest means we could use for a camera lens would be a very small hole, made with a needle. But it takes a long time for sufficient light to pass through such a small hole to record a picture on the sensitive film, so a larger hole covered by a glass lens is used.

The shutter is a mechanism for allowing light to pass through the lens for a definite period of time—seconds and split seconds. There is also an adjustment on most shutters to keep them open as long as desired for "time" exposures. There are different kinds of shutters, but they all perform the same service.

The diaphragm or stop opening in the shutter controls the volume of light admitted through the lens to the light-sensitive

[123]

film at the back of the camera. The range of sharpness in a picture is dependent upon the size of the opening—the smaller the hole, the greater the "depth" or range of sharpness of objects at different distances from the camera.

What Is the Effect of Light on the Film?

The film which is placed at the back of the camera to make the negative is coated on one side with a light-sensitive substance known as the "emulsion," and when an image is flashed on this sensitive coating by the light that is admitted through the lens, a chemical change takes place. No change, however, is noticeable to the eye should we examine the exposed film in the darkroom by the aid of a photographic *safelight*. Nevertheless, an invisible image has been formed and this invisible picture, or "latent" image as it is called, can be brought out by a further chemical change. This change is made by placing the film in a solution known as the "developer."

Early photographic equipment was no light load.

After the image has been made visible, the film must then be placed in another solution in order to make the negative image permanent. This solution is called the "fixing" bath.

The developed film is now called a "negative" because the dark objects appear light and the light objects dark. A second step is necessary to make a "positive," another process called "printing." A sensitized photographic paper is placed in contact with the negative and exposed to a light for a time. The paper then goes through solutions like those which were used to obtain the negative, and a print, or picture, results.

Who Developed the Chemical Basis of Photography?

In 1732, J. H. Schulze discovered that chloride of silver is darkened by light. Many men contributed to the invention of photography. The way was opened by chemists who discovered the properties of silver nitrate. In 1737, M. Hellot, of Paris, stumbled upon the fact that characters written with a pen which had been dipped in a solution of silver nitrate, would be invisible until exposed to light, when they would blacken and become perfectly legible. However it was not until early in the nineteenth century that these two discoveries were put to any practical use, as far as photography was concerned.

A fashionable method of making portraits was by what was called "silhouetting." The sitter was posed before a lamp that threw a profile of his face in sharp shadow against a white screen. The artist then either outlined the profile or cut it out from the screen.

Artotype copy of the earliest sunlight photograph taken of a human face. Miss Dorothy Catherine Draper, taken by her brother, Professor John W. Draper, in 1840. The exposure time was six minutes.

It occurred to a man by the name of Wedgwood that this profile might be printed on the screen by using paper treated with silver nitrate. As a first step, to get a sharp image, Wedgwood perfected what was then called the "camera obscura," the forerunner of the Kodak of today. The camera obscura consisted of a box with a lens at one end and a ground glass at the other, just like a modern camera. It was used by artists who found that by observing the picture on the ground glass they could draw it more easily.

Wedgwood tried to make pictures by substituting his prepared paper for the ground glass, but the paper was too insensitive to obtain any result. Sir Humphrey Davy, continuing Wedgwood's

Assembling automatic shutters for Kodaks. The shutter of a camera is a split-second timing instrument that requires all the skill of a watchmaker to assemble. Shutter speeds on some cameras range from 1 second to 1/1,000 of a second.

experiments, and using chloride of silver instead of nitrate, succeeded in making photographs through a microscope, by using sunlight. These were the first pictures made by means of a lens on a photographic material. But none of these pictures was permanent, and it was not until 1839 that Sir John Herschel found that "hypo," which he had himself discovered in 1819, would enable him to "fix" the picture and make it permanent. In France, J. N. Niepce for many years worked on a process that was perfected by L. J. M. Daguerre after Niepce's death. The French Government in 1939 gave recognition to the "daguerreotype." This process led to the popularization of portrait photography, and it survived many years, although it was slow and troublesome. The daguerreotype was made on a thin sheet of copper, silver-plated on one side, polished to a high degree of brilliancy, and made sensitive by exposing it to the fumes of iodine. The first daguerreotype made in America, that of Miss Catherine Draper, was exposed for six mintes in strong sunlight, with the face of the sitter thickly powdered, to facilitate the exposure. An exposure today with a modern camera, under similar conditions, could be made in 1/1000th of a second.

It was impossible, of course, to find many sitters as patient as Miss Draper—try keeping perfectly quiet for even a minute if you would know why Miss Draper should be ranked as a photographic martyr—and many experiments were made in an attempt to shorten the time of exposure. The only real solution, of course, was to find some method where the light had to do only a little of the work, leaving the production of the image largely to chemical action.

[126]

Who First Made Negatives?

The first great step in this direction was taken by Fox Talbot in 1841. He found that if he prepared a sheet of paper with silver iodide and exposed it in the camera, he got only a very faint image, but if, after exposure, he washed over the paper with a solution of silver nitrate and gallic acid, the faint image was built up into a strong picture. Not only was Fox Talbot the first to develop a faint or invisible image; he was also the first to make a negative and use it for printing.

How Was Amateur Photography Made Possible?

In spite of all these advances, photography was almost exclusively a professional undertaking until 1880 when experiments were begun which were to place photography within the reach of everyone. The bulk and weight of the old-time photographic outfit was extreme.

To supply the light-sensitive salts needed in photographic paper and film, bars of silver are dissolved in nitric acid. The resulting silver nitrate crystals are redissolved and evaporated many times until absolute purity is achieved.

These machines convert fluid "dope" into the familiar transparent, flexible film base. The finished film base is cut to desired lengths as it emerges from the machines.

How to lighten this burden, how to simplify the various photographic processes, were the problems that confronted the American inventor. It was film photography that relegated camera bulk to the scrap heap. The first step was a roll film made of coated paper to which a sensitive emulsion was applied, but the real goal was reached only when cellulose was substituted as a film base. This made practicable the present flexible, transparent film with its attendant convenience and dependability.

George Eastman (1854-1932) produced the first photographic roll film, and was the first to produce and market film in continuous strips or reels. In 1888 he invented the camera known as "Kodak," a hand camera that revolutionized the art of photography, and brought its use and enjoyment to the masses.

All sorts of hand cameras are now manufactured, to suit the most exacting demands: telephoto rifle cameras, stroboscopic cameras, miniature cameras (popularly called "minicam"), stereo-cameras, special police cameras, and the "candid camera." Any camera may be a candid camera, but the term is usually applied to a small camera used for taking more or less "intimate shots" of people who may be unaware they are being photographed.

How Was Color Brought to Film?

One of the greatest advances in photography has been the development of color film. There are two Eastman color processes, Kodachrome and Kodacolor. Kodachrome film has to be developed in the Rochester laboratory. Kodacolor can perhaps be developed by the photographer himself, but up to the present it is developed by Eastman.

Photographic paper is made from purified cellulose fibers, seen in this picture as they go through a "beater," preparatory to fabrication on great paper-making machines.

Both types are based on what is called the Monopak process. Each film has four coatings. Next to the film is a red-sensitive layer in which the image, after development, is converted into a blue-green dye. Then comes a green-sensitive layer giving a magenta dye. The third layer of emulsion is a yellow filter to keep blue light from reaching the lower layers. Fourth, on the front of the film, as the light strikes it, is a blue-sensitive layer in which the image is formed in a yellow dye.

Natural colors of pictures taken with Kodachrome film are brought out with chemicals called dye couplers. These couplers, combined with the developer, oxidized in the formation of the image, produce dyes of the proper colors in the respective coatings. In effect, the negative is dyed to make the positive.

Before photographic paper receives a light-sensitive emulsion, it is coated with baryta, a chalky white substance applied to control the degree of gloss. At the end of the drying tunnels illustrated here, the baryta-coated paper is rewound.

Each coating must be developed without disturbing the emulsion in the other two. That makes three developing jobs on each film for a skilled technician. When he is through he has a film transparency which is the size of the picture originally taken. To see an enlarged version you must use a projector, which throws the picture on a screen.

Kodacolor film, in contrast to Kodachrome, has the dye couplers incorporated in the three color sensitive coatings. Thus it can be developed in one operation, simply by setting the dye couplers and the oxidized developer free to combine. Getting the couplers in the emulsion was a difficult problem. Eastman solved it by suspending the couplers in microscopic globules of oil. When the oxidized developer dissolves in the oil, the dyes and couplers in each coating get together.

Huge rolls of photographic paper in storage in airconditioned rooms at the Kodak Park Works.

Kodacolor is unlike Kodachrome, too, in that the colors developed on the negative are not those of the objects photographed, but are complementary to them. Red objects come out "cyan," green ones magenta, blue ones yellow. Then when the film is printed on similarly coated color paper, the print returns to the original colors the photographer saw.

Another Eastman color process, called "wash-off relief" or "dye transfer," is of value to commercial photographers, but involves too much labor and skill for the average amateur. The process employs a film from which three separate negatives are made. Each of these negatives is used to make a positive. Each positive is dyed, to bring out objects of its color in the original picture. Then the positive is rolled onto a prepared piece of paper, so that its dye transfers onto the paper. When this has been done three times, if the register of the three positives on the print paper is microscopically exact, there appears a completed picture of unusual beauty and fidelity of shading.

What Is Aerial Photography?

Another outstanding development in photography has been the perfection of the aerial camera and its special films. Aërial photographs are amazingly detailed. In photographs taken from a height of 10,00 feet, small objects, such as rural mail boxes and their shadows, have been identified. They have been put to many uses in agriculture, mining, engineering, geology and biology, and have been useful in building such projects as reservoirs and dams, transmission lines, factories, highways and railroads. The peacetime uses of the aërial camera promise to increase steadily.

Aërial photography has been widely used by the United States Forest Service. Large areas of the National Forests have been mapped from aerial photographs. Aërial pictures are also useful for timber-type studies, range surveys, fire detection and suppression, transportation planning and other forest activities. In some cases photographs are made which, when viewed through a stereoscope, produce a tridimensional image in which ridges, mountain canyon valleys, streams, roads, trails, buildings, and other features stand out in relief just as they would appear to an observer flying over the country.

With its bellows and lens, the enlarger is very much like a camera. Inside the aluminum head there is a powerful lamp. After a negative has been inserted and the light turned on, an enlarged image of the negative will appear on the board below.

During the 1920's an aërial exploration of the huge Tongass National Forest in Alaska was made by the Navy in coöperation with the Forest Service, the Bureau of Public Roads, the Geological Survey, and the Bureau of Biological Survey. As early as 1926, the Northern Region of the Forest Service initiated an aërial mapping program.

The Forest Service has been making a nation-wide survey of forest resources. The task of covering and making a survey of 3/5 of a billion acres of forest land is a tremendous one, and aërial surveys have been employed to help secure needed information. During 1938 more that 13,000,000 acres were photographed from the air. By the end of 1939 Forest Service aërial surveys had covered over 96,000,000 acres.

Aërial photographs have been utilized in planting surveys. The air photos reveal the size, location and distribution of open areas needing reforestation and aid in planning tree-planting programs.

Range-survey work in the National Forests is carried on with the aid of aërial photographs. A range-management officer takes contact prints of vertical aërial photographs to the field. Upon these prints he outlines his grazing types and writes in the type designation and forage condition. He also notes all watering places, including springs and streams; classifies the roads and trails; locates fences, particularly fence corners, ranch buildings and all possible section corners. At the end of the field season the prints are brought in and the map detail shown on them is incorporated in the planimetric map. It has been found that the use of these aërial photographs over maps is of material help to a range-management officer.

An aërial camera made for the U. S. Army. Cameras of this type can be used in the freezing atmosphere encountered at 40,000 feet. Here it is ready to undergo low temperature tests in a climate testing room where the temperature drops from 45 to 70 degrees below zero.

Aërial photographs are equally important in erosion, flood control and watershed protection studies. Natural cover, which has a direct effect on the degree of runoff and erosion, is discernible on the photographs, so plans can readily be made from them. The air photograph also has its use in engineering and improvement projects in the forests, as in transportation-planning and bridge and dam location, and has been found very useful in making preliminary road locations.

How Is Aërial Photography Used in Modern Warfare?

The heroic figure that rides or runs far ahead of advancing armies, sprawls on his stomach to peer furtively from behind a tree, and then dashes wildly back to make his report to headquarters has become legendary. The scout has always been an important man in any army. He still is, but now he has taken to the skies, in the form of an aërial camera man. Airplanes, cameras, skilled pilots and technicians have replaced the romantic character, and they do a much better job. The modern scout not only sees, but also brings back a record of what he sees.

The aërial scout uses a variety of equipment and flies under a variety of conditions, sometimes roaring along above the tree tops, sometimes taking his pictures from a height of twenty thousand feet. He works in broad daylight, or in night blackness. His work is dangerous.

For low altitudes, the Air Force uses a strip camera, the photo-plane flying at a height of one hundred and fifty feet. The shutterless camera takes a continuous picture of the scene below and even if the plane flies at four hundred miles an hour, the resulting photograph is as perfect as if the plane had been standing still. This camera takes pictures in color, so that when the film is later developed, it reveals many important things that are not shown on ordinary black-and-white photographs. For instance, a gun may be hidden from the camera's eye on a black-and-white photograph because its shadow is approximately the same color as the shadow of the tree under which it is located. On a color photograph, the trained observer will be able to see a considerable difference in the colors of the two. Leaves used for camouflage

An air-view mosaic. At the top are the nine separate photographs taken simultaneously by a nine-lens camera. In the picture underneath the separate photographs have been assembled and made into a single composite print by a special photographic printer.

over guns soon wither—a fact which does not show on black-and-white photographs. On the color pictures, however, the color of the withered leaves is plainly visible. Targets in industrial areas can often be selected for bombing by the revelations of color. Raw materials in factory yards also possess typical colors.

High-flying photo reconnaissance is just as important as that carried out at low levels. Photographs are frequently taken from a height of 20,000 feet or more, yet so powerful are the cameras used that it is possible to count the ties in a railroad track in pictures taken by a telescopic-lens camera from a plane flying 300 miles an hour at 35,000 feet!

Since some targets must be photographed at night, the photographer uses giant flash bombs which are attached to parachutes and dropped to a point close to the earth before they are ignited by a delayed action fuse. The burst provides millions of candle power of light and lasts about a sixth of a second. The camera in the plane automatically comes into action at the moment the flash is brightest. The reconnaissance pilot must immediately dash for home, because in the brilliantly lighted skies he is a perfect target for antiaircraft and roving enemy fighters.

Another kind of camera that takes pictures in pitch blackness has been developed. It uses infra-red rays, and permits the pilot to fly over enemy territory protected by the darkness. The resultant photographs are as sharp and clear as those taken in broad daylight with the ordinary camera.

One of the greatest accomplishments of aërial photography is aërial mapping. Through the centuries, mapmaking has been slow, plodding work carried out by men afoot and on horseback, by patient observation and survey. The aërial camera has changed the whole science of mapmaking, and it will not be long until an aërial map of the entire world will be available.

The most valuable tool used in making aërial maps is the tri-metrogon camera. Tri-metrogon means simply "wide angle, horizon to horizon." With a tri-metrogon camera it is possible to cover eight times the area in a single flight that was possible with the old-style vertical camera. The photographs from a tri-metrogon camera cover two square miles for every thousand feet the plane is high; that is, if the plane is at 15,000 feet the picture covers a 30-mile area. One plane can photograph 8,000 square miles of terrain an hour. Normally a plane taking such pictures travels 200 m.p.h. with 40 seconds between each exposure. Actually, the tri-metrogon camera consists of three cameras, which operate simultaneously, as if they were one. Thus the aërial camera serves the needs of war and peace.

What Is a Thermostat?

A thermostat consists of two strips of metal riveted or welded together which have different coefficients of expansion. A change in temperature will cause the strips to bend and if one end of the combined strips is held firmly, this property can be used to operate temperature recording instruments and control heating apparatus.

When Were the Olympics First Held?

The Olympic Games are of so ancient an origin that they go back beyond the historical era of Greece. Ancient Grecian traditions attributed them to divine origin. The earliest record we have is that of the Olympiad at which Coroebus, the Elean, was victor. That was seven hundred and seventy-six years before the Christian era. This festival, which continued to be celebrated until A.D. 393, became the basis of the only universally accepted chronological system among the Greeks. They counted backward to the Olympics of 776 B.C.; but whether this was really the first Olympiad it is impossible to say. It was the Christian Roman emperor Theodosius, who issued the decree abolishing the games, condemning them as relics of heathenism.

In 1896 the Olympics were revived at Athens. The Second Olympiad was held at Paris, 1900; the Third at St. Louis, Mo., 1904 (with few contestants outside the U. S.); the Fourth at Athens, 1906 (special series); the Fifth at London, 1908; the Sixth at Stockholm, 1912; the Seventh at Antwerp, 1920; the Eighth at Paris, 1924; the Ninth at Amsterdam, 1928. The Tenth Olympiad was held at Los Angeles, Calif., in 1932; the Eleventh at Berlin in 1936; and the Twelfth in London in 1948.

Who Were the Seven Wise Men of Greece?

The Seven Sages, or Wise Men, of Greece were:
(1) Solon of Athens, whose motto was, "Know thyself."
(2) Chilo of Sparta: "Consider the end."
(3) Thales of Miletos: "Who hateth suretyship is sure."
(4) Bias of Priene: "Most men are bad."
(5) Cleobulos of Lindos: "The golden mean." "Avoid extremes."
(6) Pittacos of Mitylene: "Seize time by the forelock."
(7) Peiander of Corinth: "Nothing is impossible to industry."

THE STORY OF RADIO BROADCASTING

A radio program under way and going out over the air waves. The actors cluster around the microphone in the center. In the background may be seen a pianist and other musicians. At the right is a sound-effects man. At the extreme right is the window of the control room, from which the producer directs the performance.

WHEN you tune your radio to your favorite comedian, the show you hear is a product of the combined efforts of probably not less than fifty persons, perhaps twice as many. There are writers and editors concerned with creating the script, actors and actresses who present it, a producer and his assistants to direct the rehearsals and performance, an announcer and perhaps some assistants in giving commercials, engineers to supervise the radio machinery, adjust the volume controls, advise the producer, perhaps musicians and sound-effects men to highlight the action. The following pages tell in pictures the story of how a radio broadcast is made.

[138]

Through the window at the left of this studio may be seen the news room, where girls watch the news coming in over the teletype machines, which have direct wire connections with such agencies as Associated Press, United Press, and International News Service. The producer behind the window at the right is in a control room. During emergencies, all programs of a network are fed through this control room so that the newsroom can break into any program to read an important bulletin.

Broadcasting an interview. In the background, the producer standing in the control room raises his hand to cue the interviewer at the left of the microphone. The microphone is the starting point of all radio programs. Sound waves, set in motion by voices and musical instruments, are converted into radio waves by the microphone.

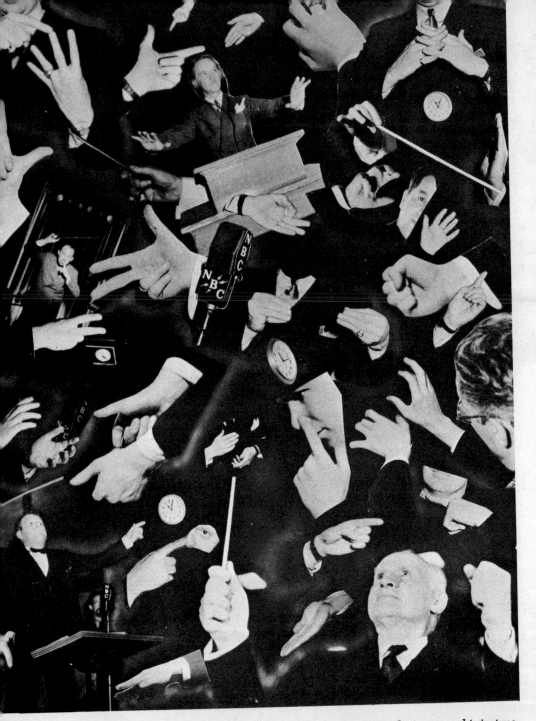

While a program is on the air, the producer uses hand signals to convey his instructions to the actors, sound men, music conductor, and other participants. Pictured here are a few of the standard hand signals. Some of the more important ones are detailed on the opposite page.

"Stand closer to the mike!"
Behind the glass panel of the sound-proof control room, the producer of a radio program signals his instructions to the actors.

"Play louder!"
A signal to the orchestra leader. Sitting beside the producer is the engineer, who adjusts the sound controls.

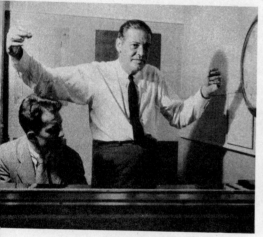

"Slow down!"
During rehearsals, every part of the program is timed to the second. If the performance goes too fast, the producer signals "Stretch it!"

"Play softer!"
The loud speaker in the control room lets the producer hear the program just as you hear it over your radio.

"On the nose!"
The program is running exactly on scheduled time. Commercial radio time is extremely expensive, and exact timing is essential.

"Okay!"
The signal the actors like best—it means that they are putting the program over.

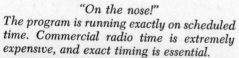

Sound effects are used to give realism to a radio story. The man in the right foreground is imitating the sound of marching men with a framework containing wooden pegs. Behind him, another man strikes a screen to simulate thunder. The man at the left is operating a wagon wheel and a telegraph key. In the left background, a man is playing a phonograph record that has certain recorded sound effects.

The sound technician at the left is creating the sound of a wagon rolling over a road of loose stones.

In the foreground is the engineer's monitoring board, inside the control room. Most programs use several microphones at different points on the stage, and the engineer must adjust the volume of each. His equipment includes indicating lights, talk-back microphone (through which the producer can talk to the actors during rehearsals), and a volume indicator dial which shows whether the program is too loud or too soft.

The master control room of a radio network. The control rooms of all stations in the network are connected by telephone to this control board. A station that wishes to broadcast a program originating elsewhere is hooked into the network for the duration of the program. The sound is piped over the telephone lines from the station of origin to this control board.

Each individual station has its own master control room, connected with each of its studios so that the engineer in the master room can switch each studio on and off the air at the proper time.

The transmitter of a New York City station. Radio stations are usually located in the heart of a city, while their transmitters are usually in open fields. If the transmitter is too close to a city, it drowns out all remote stations. Broadcasts are piped over telephone wires from the radio station to its transmitter.

[144]

One of the masts of a transmitter. The radio wave received from the microphone is passed through a series of amplifying tubes that carry 20,000 volts, superimposed on a carrier wave, and sent out in the air from the transmitting towers.

The transmitter of a New York City station, far away from the station on an island. Radio waves get a better start where there are no tall buildings, and the best possible start over open water. The transmitter has to "boost" the current, for the radio wave reaching it from the station is too weak to be heard over the great area served by the radio station.

[145]

Not all radio programs originate in a studio. Many come from places of action—an airplane, a baseball diamond, a city street. For such a so-called "remote pick-up," a mobile unit like the one carried in this car sends out radio waves from the spot. The waves are picked up by the parent station, amplified, and wired to the transmitter for broadcast.

A radio news reporter describes what is happening on the floor of a political convention. Attached to his microphone is a portable transmitter. From this unit the radio waves are usually picked up in a temporary control room set up in the same hall, and from there the sound is sent over direct wire to the local station. At the station, the sound is amplified and wired to the transmitter for local broadcast. If it is to go out also over a network, the sound is simultaneously wired by telephone lines to the master control board of the network, in another city. This board in turn relays it to the affiliated stations that have subscribed to the program.

THE STORY OF TELEVISION

The dome of the Capitol at Washington, D. C., as seen on a television screen in New York City.

THE WORD television means "to see at a distance." And for you to see at a distance by sitting in front of a receiving set in your home, engineers must combine the techniques of radio and motion pictures.

Only a few people witnessed the successful combination of these techniques in 1936, when the first regularly scheduled telecast (television broadcast) went over the air. Three years later the first commercial television receivers were sold to the public.

World War II developments in radar and other scientific near-miracles advanced the technique of television by leaps and bounds. By 1946, nine television stations—in New York, Philadelphia, Chicago, Los Angeles and Schenectady—were in operation.

How Does Television Work?

Radio sending equipment transforms sound waves into electrical energy so that it can pass through distant spaces to reach your receiving set and then be changed back to sound in your loud speaker. Similarly, the television transmitter transforms light energy into electrical energy so that it can be sent to your television receiver. The two important units in television are the *iconoscope,* the heart of the video (television) camera, and the *kinescope,* the heart of the video receiver.

Suppose we want to televise your face in action. The iconoscope, like an ordinary movie camera, takes a picture of your face. Instead of recording it on a strip of film, the iconoscope transfers your image to a metal plate composed of millions of separate electric eyes. Electric eyes are tiny electrical contacts which respond to light impulses. The plate is called a "mosaic." Every time your face moves, a new picture is taken by the iconoscope, and the arrangement of the mosaic changes.

A television program in action. An expert is demonstrating golf strokes while two televisors pick up the action from different angles.

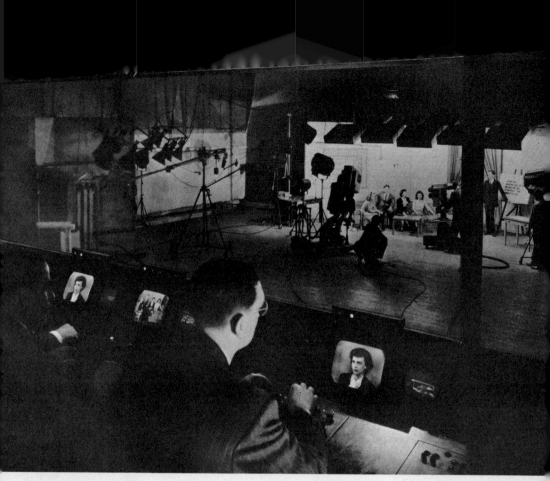

A television broadcast as seen from the control room. Note the three screens on the control panel. The center screen shows what is going out over the air. The side screens show a "close-up" that will be switched on the air after the group picture.

Now we have your face transferred onto the mosaic in the form of several million dots of light and shadow. Next into operation comes the cathode beam, a ray of electrons. Its job is to "scan" the ever-changing mosaic. It does this by sweeping back and forth across the different horizontal rows of electric eyes, continuing until it has seen the whole mosaic.

The scanning is done at incredibly high speed. For black-and-white television, the cathode beam travels over 525 different lines on the mosaic—30 times every second. During the scanning process, electrical impulses are created when the cathode beam meets the mosaic. It is these impulses, varying in strength according to the light or darkness of your face, which are transmitted over the air.

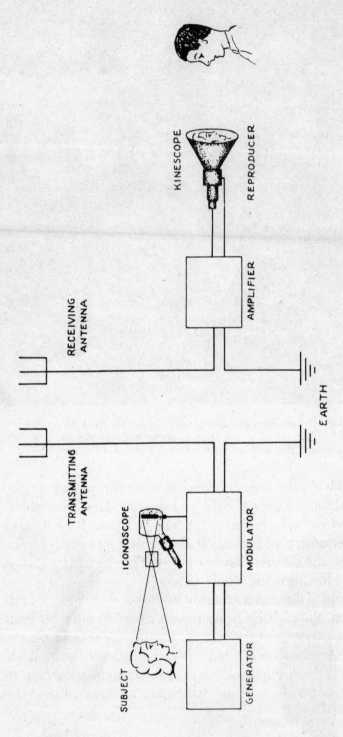

Diagram of how television works. The iconoscope picks up the image of the subject, and the intensity of light reflected by different parts of the picture affects the intensity of the current passing through the modulator from the generator. Sent out from the station's antenna, the radio waves are picked up by the receiving antenna, amplified, then changed back to light in the kinescope. The diagram on the opposite page shows the arrangement for simultaneous broadcast of sight and sound.

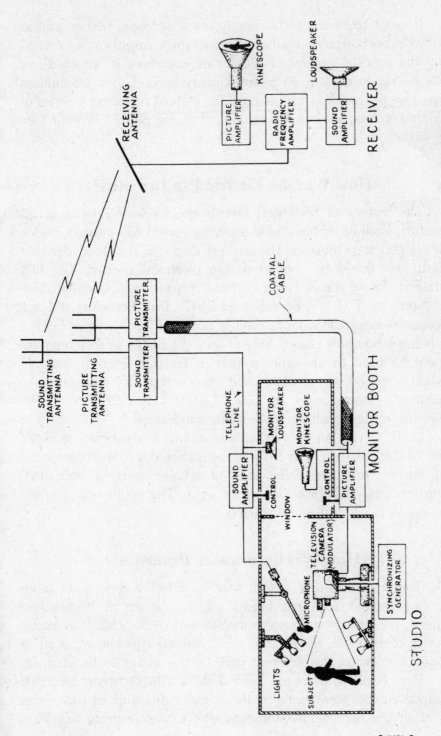

RECEIVER

RECEIVING ANTENNA

KINESCOPE

LOUDSPEAKER

PICTURE AMPLIFIER

RADIO FREQUENCY AMPLIFIER

SOUND AMPLIFIER

PICTURE TRANSMITTER

SOUND TRANSMITTER

COAXIAL CABLE

SOUND TRANSMITTING ANTENNA

PICTURE TRANSMITTING ANTENNA

TELEPHONE LINE

MONITOR LOUDSPEAKER

MONITOR KINESCOPE

SOUND AMPLIFIER

PICTURE AMPLIFIER

CONTROL

CONTROL

WINDOW

MONITOR BOOTH

TELEVISION CAMERA (MODULATOR)

MICROPHONE

SYNCHRONIZING GENERATOR

LIGHTS

SUBJECT

STUDIO

[151]

In your receiving set at home, the kinescope, with a similar cathode beam, stands ready to receive these impulses. By reversing the sending process, a picture of your face is "painted" on the television screen, 30 pictures every second. But the human eye does not work as fast as that. So, instead of seeing a series of single pictures, we see a continuous moving picture of your face in action.

How Was the Electric Eye Invented?

The history of television reveals the work of dozens of inventors, each of whom added something vital to a process which developed step by step. The earliest step was the discovery that light rays could be converted into electrical energy. The first material found which could perform this task was selenium, discovered by J. J. F. Berzelius in 1817. But Berzelius did not recognize selenium's photo-electric power. Fifty-six years later, a telegraph operator named May observed that the selenium equipment he used in his cable station in Ireland reacted strangely when exposed to sunlight. He discovered that the metallic element's resistance to the flow of electricity decreased as the intensity of light falling on its surface increased.

G. R. Carey, an American, was one of several men to make use of this discovery. In 1875, he constructed a mosaic composed of minute selenium cells, each of which operated individual shutters placed before a beam of light. The result was a crude image in black and white squares.

How Was the Scanner Developed?

The first scanning device was invented a few years later. Unlike today's scanning beams which operate at tremendous speed, these early units were mechanical disks. The disks had a series of holes in them, and, when turned quickly, exposed in rapid succession the different parts of the image to be scanned.

Paul Nipkow patented such a device in Germany in 1884. Improvements were made on the Nipkow disk and, in 1926, John L. Baird, a Scotch inventor, was able to demonstrate television in public. Instead of ordinary holes in the disk, a series of lenses were used by Baird. C. Francis Jenkins added another development in Washington, D. C., by use of his prism disk, a glass disk of varying thickness. Several others used mirrors with their scanning disks, but all of these mechanical disks were soon discarded for a much better device—the electrical scanner.

These electrical scanners were cathode-ray tubes. See "The Story of Electronics." They were developed simultaneously with mechanical disks, and were first put to use in 1925. Important men in their development were Vladimir K. Zworykin and Philo T. Farnsworth. All-electronic television was first demonstrated

A *high-frequency, full-color television receiver. The screen on which the picture appears is at the left, controls on the right.*

to the public in Los Angeles in 1933. The tube developed by Zworykin became the iconoscope we know today. A new type of television camera tube—the Image Orthocon developed by the Radio Corporation of America—now makes brilliant studio lighting conditions unnecessary.

Farnsworth's tube, operating in a different fashion, is known as an *image dissector*. In the iconoscope, the cathode beam sweeps across the mosaic. In the image dissector, something similar to the mosaic is made to move before a single stationary "eye." The result is the same—an electric image is translated into a sequence of electric impulses.

While improvements in the television camera follow one another rapidly, improvements in television receivers keep pace. Home receivers now can present television pictures with the same clarity as the motion picture. Although the screen is fairly small, ways will undoubtedly be found to enlarge the picture.

[153]

Why Has Television Transmission Been Limited?

Like any public service, television is subject to a certain amount of Government supervision. The Federal Communications Commission has set up broadcast "channels" for television stations throughout the country. As new stations begin operating, they will know in advance the transmission wave lengths they may use without interference.

Because of the high frequency of the radio waves used for television, the range of a television station is limited to the area within direct sight of the station's antenna—about 30 or 40 miles. However, television networks across the country are a long-range aim. As with our major radio chains, networks are the only way to get the same program to a nationwide audience.

Television brings sports events to millions of spectators. Here an Image Orthicon camera picks up the action in a national championship tennis match at Forest Hills, New York.

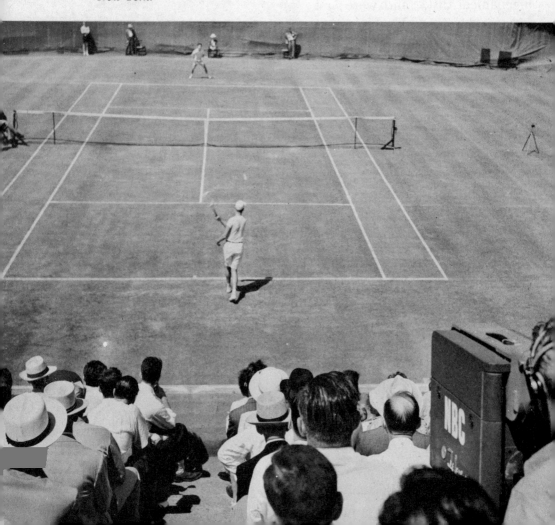

One way to tie in television stations is by using automatic relay towers, spaced about 40 miles apart. As these towers pick up a television broadcast, they reinforce its strength and pass it on to the next tower.

The most promising method of extending the range of television is by using coaxial cables. These are specially designed underground groups of wires, used to carry telephone as well as television signals. By mid-1946, about 1,500 miles of cable had been installed. Additional cables are constantly being installed to try to link all major cities.

Stratovision, sponsored by the Westinghouse Company, is the third and most dramatic proposal for a television network. With stratovision television signals are relayed between airplanes flying above centers of population across the country. From these aircraft, video signals can be beamed downward over a large area.

"Play ball!" Television cameras with multiple quick-change lenses broadcast to fans all over the country a "crucial" game between the Yankees and the Boston Red Sox at the Yankee Stadium, New York.

Is Color Television Possible?

Television in color was demonstrated before World War II, and was brought out again in October, 1945, by the Columbia Broadcasting System in a public demonstration. However, if the present color system is used, all video receivers in use or in production would have to be scrapped since color transmission takes place in the ultra-high frequencies, out of range of present receivers.

The FCC has permitted CBS to make experimental color broadcasts. But it is likely that all regular television broadcasting will be in black-and-white for at least several years. When the move "upstairs" to the higher frequencies finally comes, you may have to turn in your television receiver for a still newer model.

Why Is Television Broadcasting Costly?

The high cost of programs is one of television's major problems. Video programs are much more expensive to produce than similar programs over "blind" radio. Most television programs call for the use of visual materials, settings and costumes. Television actors must spend more time in rehearsal, since they cannot stand before the television camera with scripts in their hands.

A television studio looks like a combination of radio studio, movie set and a theater stage. The actors and announcers, supported by stage sets and make-up, are placed on a well-lighted stage. The many television cameras, used to take pictures of the scenes from different angles, are trained on the stage. From the glassed-in control room, engineers and directors control the cameras, music and speech, and blend them together before they are sent over the air.

Individual stations meet the high expenses of television production in several ways. The most obvious way is to limit the number of hours of telecast each day. For some time, you will be able to receive television only for a limited number of hours each day. And, of course, you will only get television at all if you are in range of a studio or a television relay point.

Another way which stations will attack the problem of high costs is to present many motion picture shorts instead of "live"

One of the military secrets released after World War II was an air-borne television iconoscope, which was used extensively in radio-guided pilotless bombers and crash-boats, in aërial bombs and gliders, and even in rockets.

Diagram of the operation of air-borne television, as arranged in the first public demonstration after World War II. Views picked up by the iconoscope in a plane can be transmitted to other points on the ground and to other planes.

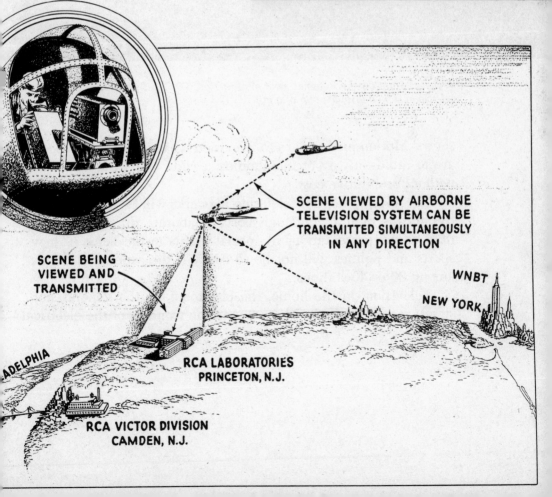

SCENE VIEWED BY AIRBORNE TELEVISION SYSTEM CAN BE TRANSMITTED SIMULTANEOUSLY IN ANY DIRECTION

SCENE BEING VIEWED AND TRANSMITTED

WNBT
NEW YORK

RCA LABORATORIES
PRINCETON, N.J.

ADELPHIA

RCA VICTOR DIVISION
CAMDEN, N.J.

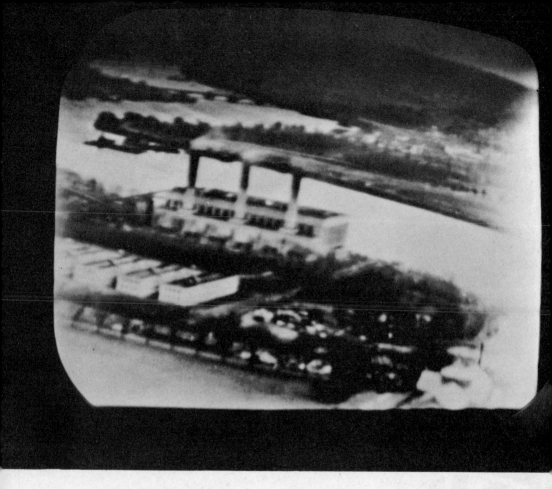

A power plant on the Potomac near Washington, D. C., as picked up by airborne television from a distance of half a mile.

shows. Motion pictures are to television what phonograph records are to radio—a way of maintaining a wide and varied repertory without prohibitive cost.

The development of television networks will be the most effective means of reducing high costs. Elaborate dramatic productions or the presentations of special events in the fields of news, sports and politics will not be so costly if the expense is divided among 30 or 40 stations.

Television, in the home, the classroom, or the general store, stands ready to take its place among the wonders of the electrical age.

THE STORY OF ROCKETS

Ironically called Tiny Tim, *this rocket was the most powerful in the world when it was tested at the Naval Proving Ground, Dahlgren, Virginia, in May, 1946.*

THE SUPER-SWIFT rocket, despite its speed and power, is one of the simplest of all machines. While we are just beginning to learn how useful they can be, rockets have been built and used for two thousand years.

You are probably familiar with the Fourth of July type of rocket which shoots into the sky and bursts forth in a beautiful spectacle of color. These harmless and brilliant rockets employ the same principle in their operation as the deadly bazooka guns and rocket shells used in World War II.

What Makes a Rocket Go?

The principle behind the rocket was clearly stated by Sir Isaac Newton in 1687. Newton formulated the three laws of motion. The third law is, "For every action, there is an equal and opposite reaction."

The bazooka of World War II was a long tube firing a rocket projectile, carried and handled by two men. The bazooka in this picture halted and destroyed an advancing enemy tank. (Luzon, 1945.)

What does this have to do with a rocket? You can see the connection if you will inflate a toy balloon, and hold its mouth closed. The balloon, filled with compressed air, will shoot off into the room if you release your fingers. The pressure of the air coming out of the mouth of the balloon creates an equal pressure in the opposite direction, and off shoots the ballon—until all the compressed air is out.

Regular rockets, of course, do not depend merely on a limited amount of air to send them through space. Your balloon will come to rest after it has traveled only a few feet. Inside rockets made today are engines that use a mixture of fuel and oxygen to create a powerful pressure stream out of one end of the rocket. The rocket will continue on its path so long as the fuel holds out.

A multiple rocket launcher mounted on a tank goes into action against retreating enemy forces. (France, 1945.)

Why Can Rockets Travel in a Vacuum?

Unlike airplanes, rockets do not depend on the surrounding air to go forward. The propeller blades of an airplane must have the pressure of air around them. Even propellerless planes (known as jet planes, and discussed in another article) require oxygen from the atmosphere. But rockets carry their own fuel, as well as the amount of oxygen they require. Operating on Newton's third principle, they can travel just as well in a vacuum or beyond the earth's atmosphere. That is why the rocket is the only known means for possible travel far into space beyond the stratosphere.

[161]

Batteries of volley-firing rocket launchers in action during World War II. (Germany, 1944.)

What Fuels Are Used in Rockets?

Most rockets today carry liquid fuel, usually liquid oxygen and gasoline or alcohol. Only small quantities are required to produce the expanding gases which send the rocket forward. Earlier types of rockets, and many of those of today, use a mixture of gunpowder as their fuel. Fourth of July rockets and distress rockets used by ships are driven by powder.

Atomic energy, still in the infancy of its use, may provide the perfect fuel for rockets. It provides collossal power packed into a small space, and also requires no help from the surrounding atmosphere.

[162]

Flaming rockets fired from United States landing ships were credited with a large share in consolidating the first phases of the assault upon Okinawa.

Who Made the First Rockets?

The Greeks, who had a word for everything, also had a machine for almost everything. One of the first known rockets was built by Hero of Alexandria in the second century B.C. His machine consisted of a boiling pot of water, which provided steam for a hollow sphere set above it. The sphere had two nozzles. As the steam forced itself out of the nozzles, the sphere, suspended by two supports, whirred around. Although Hero's machine was never more than a plaything, it employed the same principle used in today's steam engine, jet-propelled plane and rocket.

Terrific fire power was developed by launching rockets from airplanes in full flight, during World War II, when millions of rockets were used.

When Were Rockets Used in Warfare?

The ancient Chinese also developed their own forms of rocket, although the earliest record of their work concerns the "arrows of burning fire" used against the Tartars in 1232. These arrows probably carried a cylinder filled with burning gunpowder, with which the Chinese were already familiar.

In the fifteenth century, Joanes de Fontana, an Italian, designed some of the first battle rockets. His rockets, camouflaged as rabbits or fish, were equipped with rollers. Scooting over the ground, they were intended to strike terror in the enemy's heart,

The Gorgon, *one of the first of rocket-powered and radio-guided missiles. Developed by the United States Navy, this streamlined instrument of destruction hurtles through the air at 550 miles per hour.*

and to burn his fortifications at the same time. But the early military experts believed cannons were superior to rockets as battle weapons.

The first rockets intended to carry passengers were developed by a Frenchman, Claude Ruggieri, in 1830, who designed a vehicle to carry a ram into the air. When a young boy volunteered to take the ram's place, alarmed police officials stepped in and the whole experiment was called off.

Rockets were not used as military weapons during the sixteenth and seventeenth centuries. The next century saw a great revival, however. In distant India, Hyder Ali, Prince of Mysore, had an entire rocket corps in his army in 1780. His 1,200 men

Body of a V-1 bomb, ready for assembly of elevator and wings. This was one of hundreds of bombs found in a huge plant near Dannenberg, Germany, that was captured by American troops.

effectively used their rockets, weighing six to twelve pounds, against surprised and confused British forces.

The use of rockets in India influenced the work of William Congreve, an Englishman, who began to experiment with rockets in 1801. Congreve developed a wide number of new types of powder rockets, which his country's army and navy were able to use in the war against the United States. When the British attacked Copenhagen in 1807, they used 25,000 rockets, and almost completely destroyed the city. Our own national anthem gives proof of the use of rockets in the War of 1812 against Britain. Francis Scott Key, imprisoned on a British ship besieging Baltimore, wrote about the "rockets' red glare" which lit up the

A German rocket bomb in flight. The V-bombs unloosed upon Britain in the last year of World War II proved an even more dangerous threat than the airplane assault of the first year.

night to show him "our flag was still there." The British weapons, brilliant and fiery as they were, did not win the day for them.

Congreve's rockets were limited in their efficiency because they were not accurate and had only a limited range. The discovery of high explosives, such as nitroglycerin, made bombs and guns far more deadly and accurate, and put rockets into the background for a long period.

How Were Rockets Used in World War II?

Rockets were a neglected weapon in the First World War, but played an important part in World War II. Many of the "secret" weapons of the war were actually some form of rockets.

Most widely used of the new rocket weapons was the American "bazooka" gun, so named because of its resemblance to a radio comedian's famous stovepipe musical instrument. The bazooka is usually operated by two men, though it is light enough for one man to handle. It consists of a hollow metal tube about four feet long. Into the tube is inserted a rocket, twenty inches long, which is fired through it. It must be fired at short range, but its high explosive power made it very effective against the largest tanks or pillboxes. Light enough to be carried by paratroopers, simple

[167]

A V-2 rocket raised to position for firing, in tests conducted by the United States Ordnance Department. (New Mexico, 1946.)

enough for the most rugged mountain or desert fighting, the bazooka was a potent addition to our offensive weapons. Germany, Britain and Russia all used variations of the bazooka.

When England was under siege by German bombing planes during World War II, the British army found rockets to be a

The V-2 bomb taking off on its 200-mile flight.

powerful weapon against the attackers. Fired almost directly upward from launching platforms which were merely metal rods, the rockets sped skyward much swifter than any regular anti-aircraft shells.

The rocket moved from defense to the offense when rocket bombs were attached to the wings of fighter planes. Shot singly or in series from planes such as the British Typhoon and the American Thunderbolts, rocket bombs were death to many enemy submarines and locomotives.

Near the end of the war the Germans unleashed the most deadly rocket weapon of all, the V-2, or Vengeance weapon number two. These 13-ton, 46-foot rockets shot into the stratosphere and found their marks in England, killing dozens of people and destroying whole blocks of buildings at one time. In the summer of 1946, U. S. Army experts tested captured V-2's at the White Sands Proving Grounds in New Mexico. Some of them went as high as 100 miles, far outdistancing flights by previous rockets. The V-2's carry eight tons of fuel, and attain a maximum speed of 3,000 miles an hour. The largest rocket produced by the U. S. Army, called the *Wac Corporal*, weighs only 700 pounds and travels at a maximum speed of 800 miles an hour.

How Can We Use Rockets in the Future?

Up to now, rockets have found their main usefulness in war. Rockets as ship signals and fireworks are only minor. But men have dreamed for centuries of the rockets which have no connection with war—rockets which would take them far into space, perhaps on visits to the moon or our planetary neighbors. During the 1920's and 1930's, hundreds of experimental rockets were tried out. Already, rockets go high enough to record valuable data for our weather experts, who want to know more about the upper regions of the air.

Before we can take off in a rocket trip to the moon, we must know more about what will happen when we get out of range of the earth's gravitational pull. How to get safely back to earth

A United States Army rocket, the WAC Corporal.

is another problem to be investigated, too.

Small rockets, such as the bazooka, employ powder as their fuel. Larger rockets, and the ones which may be used for interplanetary travel, carry liquid fuel. As our knowledge of chemistry and engineering progresses, new types of liquid fuel are being discovered constantly.

Over the centuries, men have tried to use rockets to drive land vehicles. Five hundred years ago, a Chinese inventor, Wan-Hoo, attached forty-seven rockets to a wheeled chair. At a signal, the rockets were ignited. But instead of sending Wan-Hoo across the plains of China, the entire apparatus blew up—Wan-Hoo with

A captured German V-2 rocket set up for test firing at the White Sands Proving Grounds, New Mexico.

it. But rocket-driven vehicles may be more successful than this, and are fresh in the imaginations of our rocket experts today.

A test of the liquid fuel used in rockets of the Gorgon *type. This compact engine delivers a thrust of 350 pounds for a period of about two minutes.*

THE STORY OF JET PROPULSION

A hydroplane rises from the water like a bird under the powerful kick of JATO (jet-assisted take-off).

ONE OF THE great scientific advances made during World War II was the perfection of the jet propulsion engine. The idea of this engine was not new—indeed, it traces its lineage back through centuries to the first rocket. See "The Story of Rockets." But only under the lash of war emergency were the technical problems solved that had long impeded the construction of practical jet propulsion engines.

Aerial warfare placed a premium on speed. The limit of propellor-driven craft was reached at about 400 miles per hour, by the famous P-38 Lightning planes—and the airmen asked for still more speed. It was supplied to them—by jet propulsion. Applications of this principle also aided conventional planes in take-off,

A plane catapulted from the deck of an aircraft carrier by JATO, one of the first applications of jet propulsion.

created "buzz" bombs and a whole new series of projectiles, and was actually on the point of revolutionizing warfare when the conflict came to an end. But the development of jet propulsion for peacetime purposes continues, at such a rapid pace that what is written today may be obsolete tomorrow.

What Is Jet Propulsion?

Many people confuse *jet propulsion* with *rocket propulsion*, and with entire justification, for the terms do not properly indicate the difference between them. They are actually the same thing as concerns the *operation* of the driving force, the gases released by

The Shooting Star, *one of the first propellerless planes built to test jet propulsion. Note the intake port at the side of the fuselage.*

combustion of a fuel. These gases escape through a vent in the rear of the machine or projectile, and drive it forward by reaction. In neither case does the propulsion depend upon pressure against air, as is the case with a rotating propeller. The propulsion is explained by Newton's third law of dynamics—"To every action there is an equal and opposite reaction."

The burning of fuel to supply power to jet or rocket motors requires oxygen. The terms *rocket* and *jet* have acquired conventional meanings to differentiate the two ways in which this oxygen can be supplied. In the *rocket,* the fuel contains it own oxygen (as in nitroglycerin), or the oxygen (usually liquid) is stored in the rocket along with the fuel. Thus the rocket can operate in a vacuum, and is the only type of motor that can power ships intended to go outside the earth's atmosphere. In the *jet* motor, oxygen is drawn from the surrounding air, so that while the blast of exhaust gases would still have force in a vacuum, the fuel will not burn unless it is supplied with huge quantities of air.

What Is the Advantage of Jet Over Rocket Propulsion?

The advantage of the rocket over the jet motor is obvious—since it will run in a vacuum, it would fly us to the moon, if we could fly to the moon. But the rocket pays a heavy price for this advantage, in a literal sense. The major part of the weight of a rocket is its initial fuel load, and of the fuel load the oxygen is the largest part, in ratio of not less than three to one, in some cases as high as eight to one. Thus the "pay load"—the additional weight that a rocket can carry for each pound of its fuel—is relatively small. In fact, it has been computed that to lift one pound of pay load into outer space, away from the earth's gravitation, would require hundreds of thousands of tons of ordinary combustion fuel.

Rear view of the Phantom, *the United States Navy's first jet-powered plane. In its first tests, the* Phantom *flew at a speed of more than 500 miles per hour.*

The jet motor, by drawing on the atmosphere for its oxygen, saves greatly in weight and so has a much higher pay load. That is why, during World War II, rocket propulsion was applied only to relatively small projectiles, while jet propulsion was invoked to carry the huge loads in "buzz" bombs and V-bombs.

What Is the Turbo-Supercharger?

The story of jet propulsion, as distinct from rocket propulsion, really begins with the story of a device called the turbo-supercharger.

The efficiency of a fuel is proportional to the *pressure* at which it is burned: the greater the pressure, the higher the efficiency. One way in which combustion engines have been constantly improved is to step up the pressure in the combustion chamber.

A gas turbine built by Westinghouse for use in Navy combat aircraft. The end of the tube nearer the floor is the rear, through which emerges the jet that has a propulsive force of a piston engine about four times the size of this gas turbine.

See "The Story of the Diesel Engine." Different kinds of *super-chargers* have been tried with gas engines. A supercharger is a device for compressing the vaporized fuel, beyond the ordinary compression of the piston.

In 1918, a test was made on top of Pikes Peak of a "turbo-supercharger" designed by Dr. Sanford A. Moss. In effect this was a small turbine run by exhaust gases, operating a fuel compressor. The locale of the test was chosen because the immediate problem to be solved was to find a way to get air into a gas engine fast enough so that it would operate effectively at high altitudes. Without the supercharger, the Liberty engine developed 230 horsepower, but with it, 356 horsepower was reached. In September, 1919, Major R. W. Schroeder took a plane up to 18,000 feet with help of the turbo-supercharger, and six months later he reached 36,160 feet above sea level.

Looking into the forward end of the gas turbine. Visible are the blades of the compressor, which packs air into the combustion chamber at the rate of 600 miles per hour.

What Did Metallurgy Contribute?

Despite these striking feats of the turbo-supercharger, the device was far from perfect. The device tended to break down under the terrific heat of the exhaust gases, and both of Major Schroeder's record flights ended in near-disaster and forced landings. Before further progress could be made, it was necessary to develop new alloys that would stand up to the extreme conditions.

Metallurgists made a long search, and the problem was finally considered to be solved in 1922 with the introduction of a chrome-nickel-molybdenum alloy capable of withstanding high stresses at temperatures over 1,100° Fahrenheit. The vanes of a modern gas turbine in a jet motor hold their form and strength although white hot!

What Is the Duct Engine?

Before discussing the gas turbine, let us look at the simplest type of jet propulsion engine. This is a cylindrical duct, with air flowing into the forward end; the air vaporizes fuel released and burned in the interior; the exhaust gases shoot out the rear and propel the cylinder forward. A device of this kind, burning gasoline, was developed in England under the name "athodyd" (from aëro-thermodynamic duct). The possibilities of this simple duct engine have not been fully explored, since its invention by a Frenchman, Lorin, in 1913. But it enters our story because the modern gas turbine is essentially an athodyd to which a turbosupercharger has been added.

What Is a Gas Turbine?

Jet propulsion during World War II was principally a story of the gas turbine, and that device with due modifications is considered to be the "engine of the future," for commercial transportation as well as for instruments of war.

The "axial flow" gas turbine takes in air at its forward end, flowing at about 300 miles per hour. Expanding through a ring of stationary blades arranged radially inside the tube, the air jumps

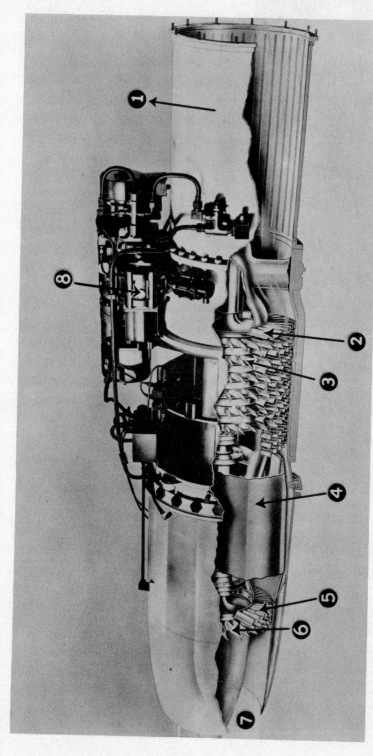

Operation of the gas turbine. Air enters through the inlet duct (1), passes through stationary blades (2) into the air compressor. Six rows of whirling blades (3) pass it into the combustion chamber (4), where it is mixed with fuel and burned. The expanding gases pass through stationary blades (5) that direct them into the turbine wheel (6). The shaft to which this wheel is fixed drives the air compressor and also the engine auxiliaries (8). Before emerging from the jet orifice (7), the gases jump in speed from 600 miles per hour to over 1,200. They exert a propulsive force of 1,400 pounds.

up to about 600 miles per hour. Then it passes through several rows of compressor blades, rotating at 18,000 revolutions per minute. These blades pack air at the rate of 50 tons per hour into a combustion chamber, where it is mixed with fuel and burned. The exhaust gases fire backwards through stationary blades that direct them against the "buckets" of a turbine wheel. This turbine is the motor driving the compressor unit, to which it is connected by a shaft. Relatively little of the power in the expanding gases is so diverted to run the turbine. After passing through the turbine, the gases jump in speed from 600 to 1,200 miles per hour and emerge through a nozzle at the rear, exerting a thrust of 1,400 pounds.

The tips of the blades of this air compressor whirl at the rifle bullet speed of 1,100 feet per second. The compressor packs a wallop that would be enough to hurl a 10-pound weight 15 miles into the sky.

Who Perfected the Gas Turbine?

The gas turbine was made practicable by an Englishman, Frank Whittle, and began to be applied to airplanes in the spring of 1941. The British authorities immediately communicated the results of the tests and plans of the Whittle engine to American engineers, and a group was set up under 83-year-old Dr. W. F. Durand, the leading American authority on jet reaction engines, to direct American research and production. Many small improvements in design were made in the Whittle engine, while airplane manufacturers designed frames to carry this new superpower plant.

At a small-scale test in California on October 1, 1942, the first American gas turbine plane flew to a height of 100 feet and reached the speed of propellor planes. In June, 1944, a jet motor built in a Lockheed P-80 flew it over 500 miles per hour. At the end of the war, large-scale production had just begun on fighter planes equipped solely with gas turbine engines.

What Is the Future of Jet Propulsion?

One application of jet propulsion is a "here and now" reality. This is jet-assisted take-off, or "Jato" as it is called. Auxiliary jet engines were attached to all types of planes during World War II, to provide the initial high acceleration necessary to get planes into the air from short runways and restricted spaces. Jato will certainly be utilized in all heavy transports to avoid the take-off accidents frequent in the past history of aviation.

The aëronautical engineers almost with one voice say that the gas turbine will eventually replace the gas engine as the prime mover in most planes. Before that day comes, however, there are serious problems to be solved. Jet engines operate most efficiently at high speeds beyond those of present commercial transport. A general increase in air speed will require larger landing fields, or special deceleration devices, or both. While it is believed that the human body can sustain even supersonic speeds (beyond 765 miles per hour), there are sharp limits to what it can stand in acceleration and deceleration.

The extreme simplicity of the jet engine makes an appeal in itself. As was said by an Army mechanic, "Here I've spent all my life learning how to take care of airplane engines. Now these squirts come along and some pink-cheeked baby with a monkey wrench and a bucket of stove oil can keep it flying just as well

This small gas turbine, weighing only 145 pounds, has been used to power "buzz-less" buzz bombs, radio-controlled pilot-less planes, and can be adapted to propeller-driven planes and helicopters.

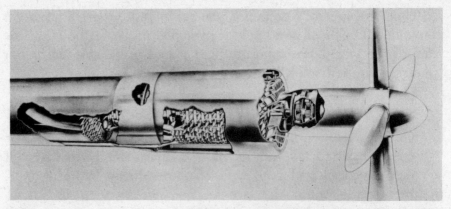

Schematic view of a gas turbine adapted to propeller propulsion. The jet drives the rearmost turbine wheel, which is fixed to a central shaft extending forward to the nose, where gears reduce the speed for transmission to the propeller.

as I can." The jet engine has no ignition system, cooling system, crankshaft, gear boxes, carburetor, or timer to worry about. Quite possibly the jet engine will be generally substituted for the gas engine in propeller-driven craft. Experiments to this end are already under way. If the shaft of a gas turbine is extended forward and a propeller mounted on it, the turbine then absorbs most of the power of the exhaust gas, leaving it only a low thrust force as it shoots from the tail. Reduction gears step down the turbine speed (18,000 revolutions per minute) to feasible propeller speed (around 2,000 r.p.m.). Thus the gas turbine can be used to fly planes at present-day speeds.

Another role for the jet engine has been foreshadowed—powering of helicopters. The jet could be directed up the hollow shaft of the rotor, emerging through vents in the tips of the rotor blades. If such a machine is ever built, it will complete the cycle of history, for the first "reaction engine" of which we have record is Hero of Alexandria's "aelopile," a vessel revolving through the thrust of steam spurting from nozzles!

THE STORY OF THE TELEPHONE

Telephone men and women who build and operate the plant go "all out" in event of ice storms, floods, fires, hurricanes, or earthquakes to furnish emergency service and restore damaged lines.

BEFORE our earliest ancestors could communicate their thoughts and ideas they had to learn to talk. Spoken sounds came to be words and language began. In time men learned to write and, much later, to print. When man could write, his words could be preserved. No longer was it necessary to be within sound of man's voice to get his words. Written messages could be sent from one man to another. But written messages take time to write, and to send, and to be read.

What man needed was some method of communication that would enable his actual speech to be heard miles away and only by the particular person addressed. For thousands of years this was so impracticable that it was not even a dream.

[183]

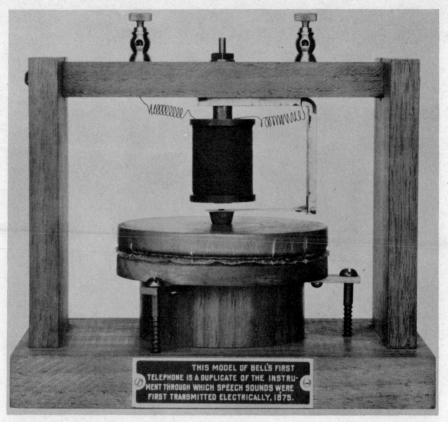

THIS MODEL OF BELL'S FIRST TELEPHONE IS A DUPLICATE OF THE INSTRU- MENT THROUGH WHICH SPEECH SOUNDS WERE FIRST TRANSMITTED ELECTRICALLY, 1875.

A duplicate of Bell's first telephone. The modern telephone has a very different outward appearance, but is the same in principle.

After the discovery of electricity, men learned how to make batteries send currents of electricity through long wires. They learned about electromagnets that could be operated by a current of electricity. When the current flowed, the electromagnet would attract a little piece of iron, pulling it up sharply until it struck with a click.

The electromagnet and the battery could be far apart, with only wires to connect them. With this idea the telegraph was born, and for years it has permitted communication between persons who are widely separated. Of course, there has to be some agreement as to how the clicks shall stand for letters; and each word of a message has to be spelled out in dots and dashes according to a code.

This famous photograph shows Alexander Graham Bell, inventor of the telephone, at the New York end of the first telephone connection to Chicago.

Who Invented the Telephone?

Alexander Graham Bell, a teacher of elocution and a student of electricity, had the vision of a new machine that would carry not dots and dashes but the human voice. In the ear the tiny disk of the eardrum responds to a spoken word. Could he make a disk of iron to catch the sound and send it electrically to another disk that would give it out again? In 1875, working with strips

A central telephone exchange in 1879, as visualized by a motion picture on telephone history. Girl operators have long since replaced the boy operators.

of clock spring, Bell built a transmitter which could send the feeble twang of a vibrating reed and a receiver which could reproduce sound.

This he called the "harmonic telegraph," and by its use he hoped to send several telegraph messages simultaneously over the same wire. While experimenting with this apparatus he discovered the way to make the speaking telephone, but it required nearly ten months of further experimenting to make his instrument transmit an intelligible sentence.

"Mr. Watson, come here, I want you," he called into the instrument, and his assistant, listening intently at the other end of the line, dropped the receiver and rushed to Bell in the adjoining room shouting: "I hear you. I can hear the words."

Bell's historic words were repeated thirty-nine years later under circumstances that gave them double significance. At the official opening of the Transcontinental Line, in January, 1915, Dr. Bell took part in the exercises at New York, while Watson was at San Francisco. Over a circuit 3,400 miles long, Dr. Bell repeated to the man who had been his assistant the first sentence ever spoken over a wire, and Watson laughingly replied that this time it would take him a week to come.

At first the invention seemed too wonderful for belief. Judges at the Centennial Exposition in Philadelphia almost passed it by. Perhaps they would have, had it not been for Don Pedro, the emperor of Brazil, who had met Bell as a teacher of speech to deaf mutes. He recognized him and spoke. Then Bell went to the other end of the wire and spoke into his transmitter while Don Pedro listened at the receiver and the judges watched. "My God—it talks," cried the emperor.

Lower Broadway in New York City during the 1880's. As more and more people began to use the phone, overhead phone lines increased until they seemed almost to darken the sky. Today more than 65% of telephone wire mileage is in underground cable.

How Can Sound Be Sent Over a Wire?

What is the telephone? It is a marvelous device that catches a spoken word and turns it like magic into something we cannot see or hear which speeds along the wires to another telephone; and there the magic is undone, and the hidden word comes forth.

What is the spoken word? It is a motion of the tiny particles or molecules which compose the air about us. But it is a particular

[187]

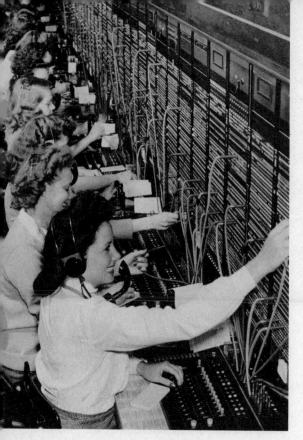

kind of motion that our ears can receive and our brains can appreciate. It is started by the voice of the person who is speaking. His breath and tongue and lip positions control it. As he changes these, he changes the kind of motion in the air molecules so that they produce different effects on the delicate drum of the ear, of the bones and fibers within, and hence different sounds to the listener.

The motion which one gives to the molecules of air when he speaks is not like that of the wind, where a multiude of air molecules sweeps along. In a spoken word, or in any musical sound, the molecules dance back and forth. First they advance, pushing against the eardrum, and then they retire and the membrane of the ear flies back. Over and over again this happens, hundreds and even thousands of times every second. The higher pitched the voice of the speaker, the more rapid is the dance. And yet it is a dainty dance, for the weight of a snip of human hair only about one-thousandth of an inch in length would press as heavily upon the sensitive eardrum.

Long-distance operators at a modern switchboard in a big telephone exchange.

How Does the Transmitter Work?

The transmitter is an electrical ear that receives the shock of the dancing molecules, just as does the membrane of the human ear. Within the human ear these motions are taken up by the tiny bones and sent on to the brain by the nerves. We do not know how, for we know less about transmission along nerves than we know about transmission over wires.

[188]

The transmitter has its eardrum, the diaphragm, which is set vibrating by the dance of the air molecules. Back of the diaphragm is a small chamber partly filled with grains of carbon—grains of roasted coal, in fact. Through this carbon chamber and the connecting wires a battery sends an electric current. From grain to grain of carbon and through the wires and battery, there is a steady procession of billions of tiny specks of electricity called electrons. They are a multitude of little gnomes residing in the wires and carbon grains, and all the marvels of electricity are due to their activities. The battery causes the procession and, under its steady urge, billions of electrons march each second around the circuit formed by the wires and the closely packed carbon grains.

When the diaphragm is moved back and forth ever so slightly by the dancing molecules of air, the carbon grains behind it are first packed more closely and then less closely. Over and over this happens, as often as the diaphragm vibrates back and forth. Imagine a vast army of men crossing a lake on floating blocks of ice while the wind freshens and dies alternately. When the blocks are blown close together, crossing is easier, and then more men get over than when the irregularly spaced blocks are loosely packed and only occasionally close enough together. This, on an enormous scale, is a picture of what happens when electrons cross from grain to grain in the carbon of the transmitter. Men can move only slowly, but the tiny electrons move with an enormous speed of thousands of miles a second.

How Does the Receiver Work?

The receiver is an electric mouth which can utter human sounds. There is a thin diaphragm of iron and a coil of wire wound on a magnet. The magnet attracts the iron diaphragm, bowing it slightly toward itself. The stronger the magnet pulls, the more the iron bows toward it, but if the pull decreases, the iron flies back, like the bottom of a pan bent with the fingers.

When the electrons follow through the turns of wire which form the coils about the magnet, they increase the pull upon the iron diaphragm. When a great crowd of electrons is marching, the

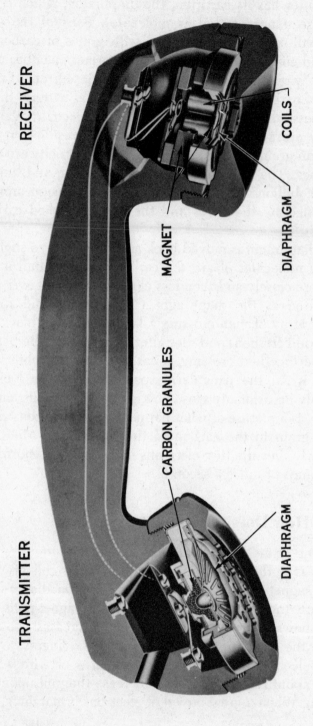

RECEIVER

TRANSMITTER

COILS

DIAPHRAGM

MAGNET

CARBON GRANULES

DIAPHRAGM

Cross-section of a hand phone. The telephone transmitter is a sensitive electric ear. Fastened to the back of its eardrum (diaphragm) is a chamber filled with an exactly measured quantity of carbon granules—grains of roasted coal. A battery sends an electric current through this carbon chamber and the connecting wires. As the diaphragm is moved back and forth ever so slightly by the dancing molecules of air, the carbon grains behind it are packed more closely and then less closely. The current varies according to the compression of the carbon, and in turn causes vibrations in the diaphragm of the receiver.

magnet pulls harder; but when only stragglers come, the bent diaphragm springs back.

The motion of the diaphragm of the receiver is just the same as that of the diaphragm of the distant transmitter. And the air molecules near the receiver are set into the same kind of motion as those which danced against the transmitter diaphragm. That is why the receiver speaks, undoing the magic which turned a spoken word into an irregular procession of electrons.

To make a receiver diaphragm vibrate it is not necessary, however, to vary the procession of electrons. Electrons moving uniformly in the coils will produce the same effect. It is very easy for the electrons to change into a to-and-fro dance from a procession which is alternately larger and smaller. All that is needed are two separate coils side by side or wound on the same iron core. If through one coil marches an irregular procession, then in the other the electrons will dance, moving in one direction when the procession increases and in the opposite direction when it decreases.

Two separate coils wound around the same core form what is known as a "transformer." A transformer is used on light and power lines to step the dangerous high voltage down to the safer low voltage used in household lighting; but in that case there are more turns in the coil connected to the power line than in that connected to the household lighting wire.

What Happens at the Central Office?

In your telephone the procession of electrons through the transmitter is changed into a dance by a transformer at the telephone central office to which your line connects. Each subscriber's line has its own transformer, but all lines are supplied by a common battery. Because it makes for quieter telephone lines, the winding on your side of the line is divided into two parts and the battery is connected between them. The use of the transformer confines the battery current to the part of the circuit between your telephone and the central office. There is no current from the battery and there is no motion of electrons except when you are talking.

[191]

When you telephone to someone whose line connects to a different central office, your line must be connected at your central office to a trunk line which leads to the other central office. There the connection can be made to the wires which go direct to the other person's telephone.

The trunk lines are our national highways of speech. Along these speech highways each central office is a telephone city with a few score or perhaps several thousand telephones. The line of a telephone subscriber is like a hallway leading from the house, or office, where he has his telephone instrument, to the central office of his telephone city. There he has a door opening into all the national highways of speech. Through this telephone door and along the hallway, formed by the wires which connect his instrument to the central office, conversation can take place with anyone else who also has a door on the national highway.

For every conversation two telephone doors must be opened, yours and that of the person whom you are calling. If the call starts from a dial telephone, the doors are opened, that is, the connections are made, by ingeniously designed electrical equipment. Otherwise they are opened by girl operators.

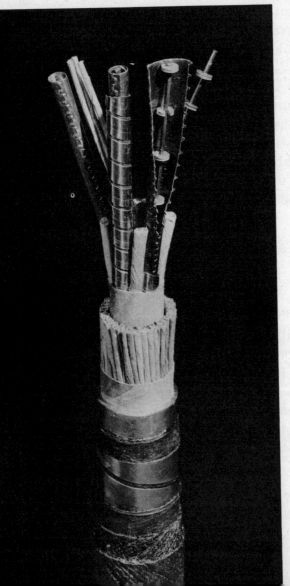

Newest method of providing additional communications channels in large quantities is the coaxial cable shown here in fanned out view. It consists of a copper tube a little larger than a lead pencil, through the center of which runs a single wire held in place by insulating disks. As many as eight of these tubes may be contained in a single lead sheath. Two coaxials can transmit several hundred telephone messages simultaneously or provide two one-way television transmission channels.

At the central office your hallway is closed by a number of doors, all alike. There are enough of these so that any operator may reach you without delay or inconvenience. For the telephone calls which you make there is a door directly in front of the operator who gives you telephone service. Beside it is a small electric lamp; this lights and attracts her attention when you take your receiver off the hook. In front of her are several short lengths of paired wire—cords, they are called. Each is a flexible hallway with which she can connect you to a speech highway or directly to the hallway of anyone who is in your telephone city.

How Does the Dial Telephone Work?

Similar operations must be performed by electrical equipment if your call starts from a dial telephone. This equipment is very

The workman in the pit is using a specially developed exploring amplifier to locate a pair of wires in the cable he is splicing. Cables may contain as many as 2,121 pair of wires.

A single operation buries this coaxial cable, which provides facilities for hundreds of telephone messages and may be equipped to transmit television. Here heavy "caterpillars" haul the plow and cable reel trailer through a quagmire.

complex; that is, it has a great many parts. The parts themselves are simple mechanisms; and the complexity is due to the way in which they are arranged to work together. The most important part is the electromagnet. This gives a pull on its armature when a current passes through its winding. The pull can be used for almost any purpose. It can close a switch so as to send current into other electromagnets and so make them work. It can make contacts between circuits, or move some other piece of equipment, sliding it along a little way, or giving it part of a turn if it is something that rotates.

In dial-switching equipment the complexity comes from the large number of telephone lines which the equipment must be able to handle, and from the wide variety of operations which it must perform. In the first place, the equipment must find your telephone line when you lift your receiver off its hook, picking out your line from the thousands which end in the same office.

You remember how the operator does this when the switchboard is manual instead of mechanical in its operation. She is guided to your line by a lamp which lights as your receiver is raised. The electrical mechanism, having no eyes, would not be aided by a lamp. It must hunt in the dark, and it does so by feeling electrically. When your receiver is raised, the switch in your telephone set is closed, and current flows along your line from a large battery at the central office. A switching mechanism is put into operation by this sudden flow of current. The apparatus starts hunting over the terminals of a small group of lines, among which is yours. It stops when it feels a line with current in it, and is then ready to do what you want; in that regard it acts like an operator on a manual board.

Control boards of overseas radiotelephone at the Long Lines headquarters of American Telephone and Telegraph Co. in New York. There are similar control boards at San Francisco, Miami, and Seattle.

The girl operator would ask you "Number, please." The mechanism cannot hear, so you dial the number. As the dial swings back there is a click for each unit of the digit you dialed. With each click a pulse of current passes through an electromagnet in the mechanism at the central office. That mechanism then proceeds to put the call through for you. Each of its actions is simple, but taken all together they are very complicated, and a very large amount of equipment is needed.

How Does the Long-Distance Telephone Work?

From New York to San Francisco, a word can fly by telephone in a twelfth of a second. That is almost as fast as light travels.

A modern radiotelephone installed in an automobile. Telephones on automobiles, trucks, boats, and other mobile units are connected with the general telephone system so that calls can be placed and received to and from any phone connected with the system.

Communications history in the making. Telephone and United States Army engineers testing two-way radio telephone communication with an airplane in 1917.

Compare that speed with the speed of sound traveling in air. If you have ever watched a baseball game from quite a distance away, or perhaps even from the centerfield bleachers of a large baseball field, you know the relative speeds of light (which is an electromagnetic phenomenon) and of sound in air (which is mechanical). You have seen the batter hit, drop his bat, and start for first before the crack of the bat reached your ears. A telephone line can carry a spoken sound from Minneapolis to New Orleans in one-fifth the time it would take for a word to pass from catcher to second baseman across a diamond.

Between cities telephone "repeaters" are installed, the devices that make telephoning over long distances practical.

Along the wires of a speech highway, the electrons pick up the step one from another, first those in the coil of the transformer and then those farther and farther away. Just an instant and all along the line the dance is on. Back and forth they go, once for every vibration of the transmitter diaphragm.

It is work to get electrons dancing even though they are so very tiny. Those nearer the beginning of the line must do the work of starting others farther away. The ability to do this work is used up along the line until there are fewer and fewer electrons engaged in the dance. If the line is very long, there may be so few dancing at the distant end that the receiver diaphragm will reproduce the speech too feebly to be understood.

Somewhere along the line, therefore, the electrons must be given more ability to do their work, more energy, as it is said. And that must be done without changing the step of the dance, because the speech is hidden in it and would lose naturalness or even sense. The device that supplies this energy is called a repeater, for it starts electrons dancing anew but repeating old figures. It is connected at a repeater station to the end of one section of the speech highway and to the beginning of the next.

Will Radio Supplant the Telephone?

You may wonder why the telephone highways are maintained, with their millions of miles of wire, when it is now possible to communicate over long distances by radio. The day may come when radio will supplant the telephone, but it will first have to overcome two great obstacles.

The first obstacle is that radio communication is not private. Anyone with a receiving set can listen in. People do not want to broadcast their personal affairs and business secrets. The other obstacle is the limitation of the air "channels." There are only so many frequencies available for radio communication, and even with careful government allotment and supervision they are already crowded. Endless as seems the air, and huge the range of possible wave frequencies, there is no present prospect of finding a way to make room for the daily millions of messages that are now carried by the telephone highways.

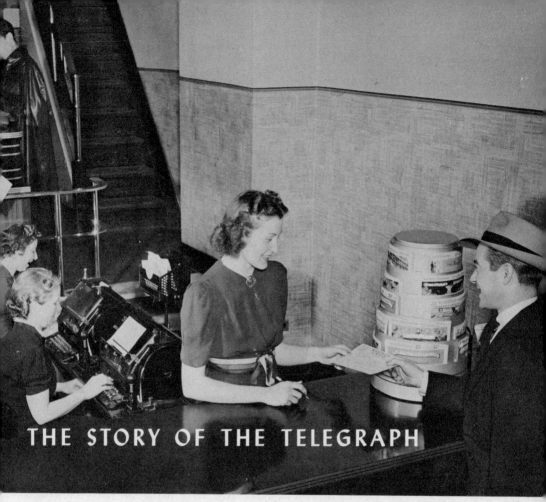

Many telegrams are handed over the counter at branch telegraph offices like this one.

THE STORY OF THE TELEGRAPH

THE cities and countries and continents of the earth are connected by thousands of miles of wire and cable, along which messages are sent with nearly the speed of light. This vast communication network depends upon the electric telegraph, a device first made practical by an American inventor. But, like most inventions, the practical telegraph was made possible by a long history of experimentation and discovery. Let us first take note of some of the pioneers in this field.

Who Were the Pioneers in Telegraphy?

The first man to direct thought to the use of electricity for communications was Roger Bacon, in 1267, and as his reward he

The girl at the left is a telegraph operator. She is writing a telegram on the typewriterlike keyboard of a Teleprinter which sends the message over a wire or over a radio beam. The girl on the right is receiving a message printed on tape. She pastes the tape on a telegraph blank, and then it is ready for delivery to you. These Teleprinters are in branch telegraph offices and the offices of large companies and are used to send and receive telegrams to and from the nearest main telegraph office.

was put in jail for twenty years for dealing in black magic. The burgomaster of Magdeburg, Germany, Otto Von Guericks, made the first electricity-producing machine in 1650. It was a sulphur ball that he charged by rubbing his hands on it, just as we can charge our bodies by rubbing our feet on a thick rug. An Englishman, Wood, found in 1726 that electricity could be conveyed by a metal conductor, and a few years later Gray and Wheeler sent electricity through 800 feet of wire. Thus the basic principle of telegraphy was known more than 200 years ago.

After that time, literally hundreds of men carried the knowledge of electricity forward, each adding something that helped in the invention of the telegraph. Oersted showed that current exerts a force which will deflect a magnet; Laplace advanced the idea that a magnetic needle might be deflected to receive messages at a great distance; and Ampere put magnetic needles at the ends of 26 wires, so that deflections would signal the letters of the alphabet. In 1820 Baron Schilling, a gay captain of Hussars in the Russian Army, produced a telegraph which he operated by the use of five magnetic needles.

Harrison Gray Dyar operated a telegraph line at a Long Island, N.Y., race track in 1826. Joseph Henry, a school teacher at the Albany (N.Y.) Academy, operated an electromagnetic telegraph in his room in 1830 and '31. He also built a line which he operated between two buildings at Princeton University in 1836.

Gauss and Weber devised a simple magnetic telegraph in 1833 at the University of Gottingen, and Karl August Steinheil improved on their system in 1836. In the following year, Sir Charles Wheatstone and Sir William Cooke obtained a patent for a telegraph, the first in England.

Who Invented the First Practical Telegraph?

The man who invented the first really practical telegraph system, however, was an American—Samuel Finley Breese Morse. Morse was not a scientist but one of America's great artists. He was founder of the National Academy of Design.

You can dictate your telegram by telephone. These Western Union recording operators are writing telegrams phoned in by the public.

Returning from a trip to Europe on board the packet ship *Sully* in 1832, Morse received the inspiration which led to his invention. He realized that, if he could transmit intelligence and record it at a distance, he would revolutionize communications. He thought of signs which could be transmitted over a wire, and realized that the dot, dash and space were three signs which could be sent. Morse was appointed professor of the Literature of the Arts of Design of New York University in 1835. This gave him a small salary, and provided the rooms in Washington Square where he built his first telegraph instrument, a crude affair, built on a picture frame with an ordinary lead pencil suspended by a pendulum to make the dots and dashes.

Morse demonstrated this first apparatus before a group of friends in his rooms at New York University on September 2, 1837. One of those present was Alfred Vail, son of Judge Stephen Vail, of the Speedwell Iron Works at Morristown, N. J. Young

The girl second from the left is sending a telegram by the Multiplex system. Four telegrams are sent in each direction at the same time over a single wire. The operator on the left, who has just received a telegram, is gumming the message on the face of a telegraph blank. Most telegrams are sent between distant cities by this system.

Vail became Morse's partner, providing money and building new and better instruments. These instruments were shown before an audience in the Geological Cabinet of New York University, January 24, 1838. General Thomas S. Cummings was present, and when Morse asked for a message to be sent, a friend of Cummings wrote a facetious military command "Attention, the Universe! By Kingdoms, Right Wheel!"

Morse exhibited the telegraph before President Van Buren and his Cabinet at Washington, D. C., but members of Congress called it a crazy scheme. Morse tried for years to get Congress to appropriate money for an experimental line, and finally his bill was passed on March 3, 1843. News of the bill's passage was brought to him by Annie Ellsworth, daughter of the Commissioner of Patents, and he gave Annie the honor of preparing the first telegram. The first telegraph line, built between Washington, D. C., and Baltimore, was opened before a distinguished group in the Supreme Court Chambers on May 24, 1844. The first telegram, handed to Morse by Annie Ellsworth, was "WHAT HATH GOD WROUGHT!"

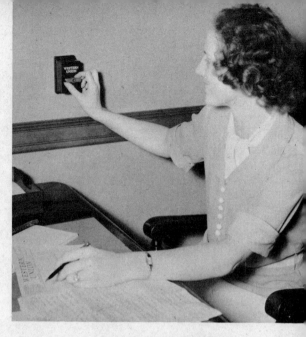

The call box is used in many business offices to summon a telegraph messenger, who carries the telegram to the nearest Western Union office.

How Was the First Telegraph Company Organized?

The experimental line was exhibited for a year, but government officials decided the telegraph was an interesting toy that never would earn enough money to support itself. Morse then persuaded a skeptical public to buy stock and finance the telegraph as a private enterprise. The telegraph industry has been a private enterprise ever since, far outgrowing and outprospering the subsidized, government-operated telegraph systems of foreign countries. More than a third of the world's telegraph mileage is located in the United States, and Americans send more telegrams than all the principal countries of Europe combined.

Morse and his associates extended the Washington-Baltimore telegraph line to New York City in 1846. Others obtained licenses from Morse and built lines between New York and Buffalo, New York and Boston, and other Eastern cities. The first telegraph line was along the Baltimore and Ohio Railroad, and since that time the telegraph had developed along the rights of way of the railroads. Most of the 2,279,843 miles of telegraph wire in the nation are along the railroads.

To speed up telegraph service, telegrams are relayed automatically through key cities by means of the reperforator switching system. Each message that arrives in one of these receiving offices can be switched from one telegraph line to another by simply pressing a button, and go on to its destination in a distant city.

Over fifty telegraph companies were in operation in 1851 when Hiram Sibley, Ezra Cornell and others organized the New York and Mississippi Valley Printing Telegraph Company. Thirteen other companies were operating in the five states north of the Ohio River. They were giving slow and unreliable service and were in poor financial condition. The new company bought them out and in 1856 was named the Western Union Telegraph Company, indicating the union of the Western lines in one system. The name Western Union was insisted upon by Ezra Cornell, pioneer telegraph builder, who used part of his telegraph fortune to found Cornell University.

What Was the Pony Express?

In the 1840's and '50's a tide of horse, mule and ox-drawn covered wagons carried hundreds of thousands of Easterners to

Telegrams from New York City are sent from this main operating room to their destinations in distant cities.

the Pacific Coast. By 1859 a half million emigrants from the East were scattered along the Pacific Coast, anxious to maintain contact with friends and relatives back home in the Eastern states.

Transcontinental mail in 1860 was handled principally by way of the Isthmus of Panama, requiring about a month. The overland stage mail was less certain, but a little faster. Ben Holladay, a mail contractor, and the overland freight firm of Russell, Waddell and Majors, joined forces to operate the Pony Express. They established 200 stations, bought 500 fast American horses and recruited eighty of the most daring riders, each to ride three mounts successively, taking fresh horses at stations from fifteen to twenty-five miles apart.

Thus on April 3, 1860 was established the eight-day Pony Express, to carry telegrams 1,400 miles between St. Joseph, Mo., and Sacramento, Calif. "Buffalo Bill" Cody, and "Wild Bill" Hickok, "Pony Bob" Haslam and other fearless Pony Express riders made history by "getting through" when Indians murdered riders and station attendants, and every hill bore Indian signal fires.

The Pony Express passed out of existence sixteen months later when the first transcontinental telegraph line was completed by Western Union as one of the epic achievements of American enterprise. In 1861 the nation was divided in Civil War, and it was imperative that California and the rest of the West be placed in close communication with the Washington Government, which needed Western gold and silver to finance the war. Hiram Sibley, president of Western Union, decided to build the line, although Abraham Lincoln believed it could not be done because of hostile Indians and the lack of poles on the vast treeless plains. Edward Creighton, whose fortune was used to found Creighton University at Omaha, was in charge of construction westward to

Salt Lake City, while James Gamble led the forces building eastward from California. The lines were built at top speed and were joined at Salt Lake City on October 24, 1861.

Gradually, through purchase, lease or stock ownership of 540 telegraph and cable companies, and by the construction of lines, Western Union built up a unified national telegraph system, serv-

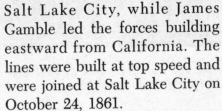

Reflectors, like the pair shown above, with radio antenna at their center, are used to relay telegrams from one radio beam telegraph tower to another.

ing practically every community. The latest step in the development took place on October 7, 1943, when Western Union purchased Postal Telegraph, Inc. This merger fulfilled the principle on which Western Union was founded: namely, that a proper telegraph service calls for a system reaching all important points, under a single management, with a fixed tariff and uniform standards of efficiency. The wire mileage of the company is about 2,279,843 miles now, which is more than enough for eight telegraph lines to the moon. The company has 31,299 telegraph offices and agencies.

How Are Telegrams Sent?

The Morse key and sounder and dots and dashes played a major role in early telegraph days. Before 1910, that method was used to handle about 90 per cent of the telegraph traffic. Now 95 per cent of all telegrams are

Western Union's radio beam telegraph towers, spaced from 15 to 55 miles apart, are used instead of wires to relay telegrams. Messages, traveling over "microwaves," or very short radio waves, flash from tower to tower until they arrive at their destination.

handled by automatic printing telegraph methods, such as the Multiplex system and the Teleprinter. All important cities are connected by direct trunk circuits operated by the Multiplex, introduced in 1915. The Multiplex system permits the transmission of as many as eight messages simultaneously over one wire, four in each direction. The operators type on keyboards similar to those of typewriters. The messages are printed in English at the receiving end on tape, which is then gummed to yellow blanks for delivery.

The Teleprinter, however, was developed for use on short circuits. Operated by a keyboard similar to that of a typewriter, it sends signals direct over the telegraph wire to a similar printer at the other end of the line. Thousands of these teleprinters are in business offices. The teleprinter is used to send and receive telegrams to and from the nearest main telegraph office, making deliveries between the two points practically instantaneous. Also, thousands of branch telegraph offices are operated in the same way. Business offices without teleprinters have call boxes, so you may twist a handle to call a messenger.

Another method of sending telegrams is by "Telefax." To send a telegram by the "Telefax," you drop your telegram into a slot, just as you would drop a letter into a mailbox. The machine automatically wraps the telegram around a revolving cylinder in

From this control room of a telegraph carrier system, as many as 288 telegrams can be sent simultaneously over a pair of wires, or 1,024 messages over a radio beam.

the Telefax cabinet. An electric eye rapidly scans the handwritten message, blue-print or maze of figures, and the Telefax transmits it over the wire to a receiving machine, where it arrives as an exact copy of the sender's message.

In the downtown areas of large cities, many telegrams are not sent by wire, but in small cylindrical containers that are shot through pneumatic tubes under the city streets.

Will Wires Be Replaced by Radio?

Already telegrams between major cities are sent by radio beam instead of by wire. Plans are underway to utilize radio to the fullest extent. Radio relay towers will replace thousands of miles of the familiar trunk pole lines and hundreds of thousands of miles of wire. Since the super-high frequency waves to be used travel in straight lines through the air, intermediate towers will be necessary to overcome the curvature of the earth. From 60 to 120 feet in height, the towers will be located on hills and mountains as far as 50 miles apart. The beam in each direction can be equipped to provide 270 multiplex printing telegraph circuits so that 1,800 operators can transmit telegrams simultaneously over it.

This system will improve the quality, dependability and speed of telegraph service. It will reduce interruptions due to ice and wind storms, falling trees, and electrical disturbances. Also, the cost over a period of seven years will be less than would have been required for maintenance and construction of the pole lines to be replaced.

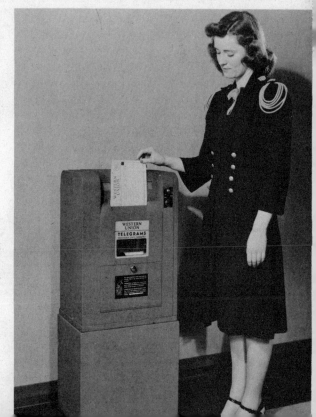

You can send your own telegram by dropping it into the slot of a Telefax *machine. This machine sends the message automatically so that it arrives at the other end of the wire as a picture of what you sent, even reproducing your own handwriting.*

THE STORY OF AIRLINES

The ticket counter at a modern airlines terminal building in New York City, where thousands of passengers check in each day before their trip to the airport.

After getting their tickets, passengers go to the rear of the terminal to wait for limousine cars which will take them to the airport in the suburbs of the city.

At the airport the passenger agent on duty checks on the arrival of all passengers. He also checks the arrival and departure of all the airline's planes at the airport.

At each passenger gate at the airport there is a huge blackboard which lists the times of departure and arrival of all flights that day. A passenger agent takes down this information.

The pilot taxis his plane out of the hangar to the concrete "apron" where mechanics make last-minute adjustments and prepare the plane for pre-flight servicing.

The captain (left) and his first officer ready the plane for servicing. Airline pilots receive very intensive training to fit them for their duties.

Just before departure a special gasoline truck carrying high-test aviation gas drives up to the plane. A hose is connected to the plane's tanks and the fuel is pumped in.

A stewardess welcomes passengers as they come aboard the big airliner. Because the plane's tricycle landing gear keeps the fuselage high off the ground, special wheeled stairways are provided for the passengers.

[213]

After permission for take-off is granted, the plane takes to the air. This type of plane carries fifty-five passengers and a crew of four, including a captain, first officer and two stewardesses.

The control tower above the administration building has a perfect view of the airport. From this room planes get their instructions for landing and take-off.

High in the air the passengers enjoy a meal served by the stewardess. Food is kept warm in a special electric cabinet in the little galley at the rear of the plane.

Every airline has a weather service. Here a balloon is about to be released. Through a telescopic theodolite the balloon's flight will be observed to check air movements at higher levels.

All weather information is recorded on a special chart prepared by the airlines' meteorological department. All flight captains are informed of weather on their route

The radio room of a big airline. Operators keep in constant, direct communication with planes aloft. They send a steady flow of information on airport and weather conditions.

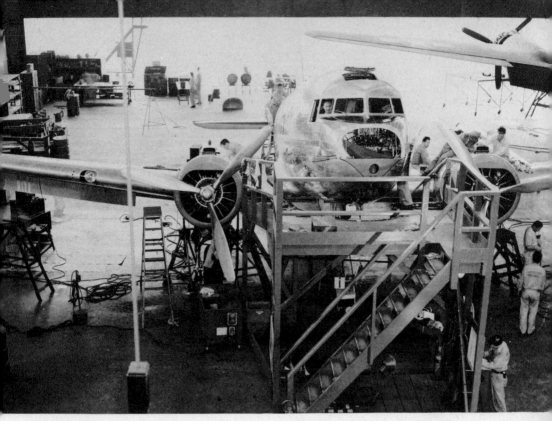

Maintenance is unromantic but vitally important to safety. All planes are constantly being serviced, checked and repaired. At certain intervals each plane gets a nine-day major overhaul.

This sketch shows how airliners follow radio paths through the air. Separated vertically by 1,000 feet, the planes fly at even altitudes westbound and odd altitudes eastbound. In all cases the planes use the directional radio beam as a guide to their course. The vertical beams in the sketch illustrate "cones of silence" directly over the radio range stations.

THE STORY OF THE HELICOPTER

Trying out an experimental helicopter as a crop duster. Helicopters are ideal for crop dusting because of their maneuverability and the fact that they can land in any cleared area large enough to accommodate the rotor blades. The downwash created by the rotor blades swirls the chemicals upward, thus spraying even the underside of the leaves.

THE helicopter, the amazing rotary wing aircraft that can fly straight up, stand still in the air, fly sideways or backwards, is a very recent invention, but the idea behind it is many centuries old. Some of the oldest toys and devices known to man —including the Chinese top, the Australian bushman's boomerang, and the familiar carnival plaything that consists of a little tin propeller which one pushes off a twisted rod—embody the basic principle. One might even describe the hummingbird, which can hover in one place and fly backwards, as Mother Nature's helicopter!

What Is the Origin of the Helicopter?

As far back as the sixteenth century, Leonardo da Vinci, the great Venetian artist-scientist who anticipated so many twentieth-century marvels, had worked out the fundamental idea of the helicopter. His imaginative mind had conceived of an air screw or flying windmill revolving in a horizontal plane, and there is proof in his notebooks that he built some successful small-scale models. The big stumbling block, of course, was the absence of an efficient power plant. That was the fault of sixteenth-century technology, not of Da Vinci. The principle was there.

Down the centuries since Da Vinci, many air-minded experimenters, fired by the idea of winged flight, pursued the tantalizing will-o-the-wisp that finally led to the helicopter. During the eighteenth century, a Frenchman named Paucton built a craft with two lift screws to be powered by muscle; another named Launoy tried a spring device as a source of power. At the turn of the next century, an Englishman, Sir George Cayley, perfected a spring-driven model, which rose ninety feet, and also planned a steam-powered one.

During the nineteenth century, many inventors tried putting steam to work, with varying degrees of success. An American scientist, Mortimer Nelson, in 1861, produced an astonishingly feasible idea. His craft, which carried two four-blade rotors mounted on outriggers and coaxial nose propellers to achieve forward movement, actually was to be equipped with a huge fabric-covered frame overhead to act as a parachute when the engine failed! Nelson must have had an aëronautical crystal ball, to have peered so far into the future!

Thomas Edison, always inquisitive, displayed a keen interest in developing electrical power plants for the helicopter. Twenty years before the Wright Brothers took off from Kitty Hawk, he was experimenting with rotors and air screws powered electrically, and for years after the fixed-wing plane came into its own, he continued to argue for the helicopter.

In the opening years of this century, Maurice Leger in Monaco rigged up a two-screw helicopter whose twenty-foot rotors were turned by motors that remained on the ground. In 1907 the Frenchman Breguet attained an altitude of fifteen feet and flew a distance of 64 feet in a 1,000-pound rectangular helicopter that was lifted by 4 rotors. Hundreds of other machines, most of them of little practical value but experimentally important, were built and tried out in Europe and America. The common fund of knowledge about these tricky ships grew slowly but steadily, both before and after World War I.

A two-place helicopter hovers in the air just above the grounds of the Bell Aircraft Corporation near Niagara Falls, N. Y.

In Russia, a young man not yet twenty, Igor Sikorsky, began to dream of building a helicopter. In 1908 he persuaded his father to let him go to Paris to study aëronautical science. Returning to Russia after his continental jaunt, Sikorsky built one helicopter that never left the ground. His second ship did manage to take off, but only without a pilot. After his initial setbacks, Sikorsky concluded that the helicopter was still an elusive vision of the future, and turned his attention to fixed-wing planes. By the time of the Revolution of 1917, although only twenty-eight, he was famed throughout his native land as an aëronautical engineer.

In 1918, abandoning a considerable personal fortune, he left Russia, and a year later landed in New York, broke and without friends, but bursting with ideas. Some White Russian émigres, including the pianist Serge Rachmaninoff, raised enough capital to set him up in business in Stratford, Connecticut. Before long, Sikorsky had a thriving plant in which he manufactured S-29's and, later on, the four-engine *Flying Clippers* with which Pan American Airways inaugurated the first regular passenger service across the Pacific and the Atlantic.

Although he built other types of aircraft, Sikorsky never gave up his boyhood dream of a helicopter that would really fly. During all the years when he was designing successful big airplanes, he was studying the problems of the helicopter. The worst problem was the twisting effect created by the big rotor, which would tend to turn the entire aircraft. For this difficulty Sikorsky at length found an ingenious solution. On the tail of his first successful helicopter, Sikorsky attached another propeller which would rotate in the opposite direction from the main rotor. This proved to be enough to counteract the turning effect of the main rotor. Other inventors following after Sikorsky found other ways to solve the problem of turning, one of them being to use two main rotors, one above the other, rotating in opposite directions.

Young men have played an important role in the development of the helicopter. Stanley Hiller, before he reached the age of twenty, had designed his remarkable "Hiller-Copter" and Arthur Young was still in high school when he began experiments that led to the successful Bell helicopter.

What Is a Helicopter?

There are two basic types of aircraft: fixed-wing and rotary-wing. The rotary-wing craft in turn are of two types: autogiros and helicopters.

The autogiro has a regular propeller on its nose, but instead of carrying fixed wings it has an overhead rotor. When the craft is pulled along by its propeller, the air stream causes the rotor above to revolve. This whirling movement is called auto-rotation, since it is not brought about by the machine's power plant.

In the helicopter, on the other hand, the rotor is turned by an engine geared to its shaft. There is no nose propeller at all. Move-

With capacity for five people and baggage, this Bell helicopter can readily be converted for rescue work or commercial purposes. The vertical propeller in the rear serves as a stabilizer.

ment of the helicopter stems from the action of the horizontal rotor, without any help from a propeller. When the lifting blades of the overhead rotor are forced to revolve faster, the ship goes up. Tilting of the rotor's blades causes movements backwards, left, or right.

These are the basic types, but there are intermediate types also. For instance, a clutch may be added to the autogiro to spin the main rotor before taking off. This is an important modification, since it cuts down the take-off run. Such an autogiro has some of the characteristics of the helicopter. And, when a helicopter's engine fails and it floats to ground safely through auto-rotation of its overhead rotor, it works in that period like an autogiro.

[222]

Most helicopters require a vertical tail propeller for stability. In this model the tail propeller has been eliminated. Instead of a single four-bladed rotor, it has two widely spaced double-bladed rotors.

Basically, the helicopter is an ordinary airplane with its stationary wings stripped off and its nose propeller shifted overhead, where it turns about a vertical axis. The propeller blades, of course, are considerably longer than those of fixed-wing planes, because they must now do the work of wings in addition to their regular propulsion job.

How Does a Helicopter Maneuver?

Helicopter control is achieved through the principle of cyclic and total pitch. "Pitch" refers to the angle a tilted blade makes with the horizontal plane, or the angle at which it bites through the air. In piloting a helicopter, you can change this pitch at will—both the total or constant pitch at which all the blades make their complete revolution, and the cyclic pitch, or the tilt of each blade, which can be varied in different phases of the revolution. Changes in the total pitch cause movement up or down. If you want to move forward, you make each blade take a bigger bite of air in the back half of its 360° turn. If you want to turn left, you change the tilt of each blade so that the blades bite deepest in the right-hand phase of the revolution. Backward movement is accomplished by giving the blades their sharpest tilt in the forward half of their rotation. The controls are set up so that when the blades enter the side on which movement is desired, they feather; that is, their tilt is decreased to make their bite shallow. This adjustment lessens to the desired movement.

What Are the Uses of the Helicopter?

Helicopters are becoming commonplace as they find more and more tasks for which they are ideally suited. They are used in forest fire control, pipe line control, Coast Guard rescue work, geological surveys, crop dusting, rooftop to airport taxi service, and in many other ways. The helicopter is a perfect aërial vehicle for work requiring observation of the ground. At 100 feet above the ground, or less, the helicopter can travel at any speed, or hover over the ground motionless. It can make a tight turn at 10 miles an hour, where as even the smaller light planes must turn

With its long canvas-covered floats, this type of helicopter can settle on water without difficulty. It can be used for rescue work at sea or for fishing and other sports.

in wide sweeps at a speed of more than 40 miles per hour. Thus, if something on the ground attracts the attention of the pilot of a helicopter all that has to be done for a second look is to turn sharply and retrace the area, or to stop perfectly still as would an automobile when the brakes are suddenly applied. The view from the helicopter is almost entirely unobstructed. Most of the cockpit is made of clear plastic and there is no engine in front or wings beneath to hinder the view.

The most exciting work of the helicopter has been in performing rescues. With it men have been rescued from breaking ice on lakes, doctors have been flown into snow-blocked communities, medicines have been carried through dense fog to ships at sea, pilots of crashed planes have been picked up from jungles where they might otherwise have lost their lives. Although it may be a long time before helicopters are widely used as private passenger craft, they are already proving their value in many useful activities.

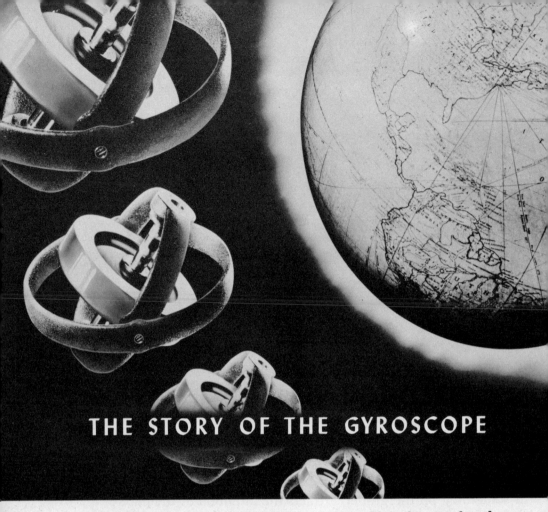

THE STORY OF THE GYROSCOPE

Gyroscopes are an aid to navigation all over the world, in the air and on the sea. No matter how the ship or plane turns, the gyroscope keeps its spinning axle pointing along a north-south axis like the meridian lines on a globe.

A GYROSCOPE is a kind of spinning top, a heavy flywheel mounted in a frame. The faster the wheel spins, the more strongly it resists any change in the original direction of its axis. The effect is familiar to all of us in the conical toy top, which spins on its point in apparent defiance of gravity, and topples on its side only when it has sufficiently slowed down.

This strange property of the gyroscope, its resistance to a change of direction, is utilized for two very important purposes. First, it allows the gyroscope to be used for a compass and so does away with the troubles of magnetic compasses—the frequent deflection of the needle by nearby iron structures and iron deposits. Second, it allows the gyroscope to be used as a stabilizer in airplanes and seaships, lessening or eliminating the jolts from air and sea waves.

How Old Is the Gyroscope?

The gyroscope may be said to be the oldest mechanism in the universe. It existed before any living thing could be found on the earth's surface, for the earth is itself a gyroscope. It spins around its axis at a very high speed for such an enormous body; any point at its equator travels at over 1,000 miles per hour. (The peripheral speed of the gyroscope in a gyrocompass is 214 miles per hour.) The earth may be said to be celestially mounted freely in space and within the knowledge of man it has kept its axis pointing constantly in one direction—namely, within one degree of the North Star or Polaris.

The direction is not absolutely fixed, for the axis of the earth, like that of a spinning top, wobbles slowly, causing the phenomenon called the "precession of the equinoxes."

A gyroscope in its simplest form consists of two steel rings attached to each other at right angles. The inner ring supports the end of the axle which runs through the center of the little flywheel. Notice what happens when the supporting frame is tipped forward. The axle of the gyroscope's flywheel continues to point in its original direction. As long as the little wheel continues to spin, its axle will point in the same direction regardless of how the supporting frame is moved.

Who Discovered the Laws of the Gyroscope?

In the seventeenth century, Kepler, Galileo and Isaac Newton discovered the laws which govern the movements of the earth. They showed that these laws apply to the other planets, and we have since learned that they apply equally to the sun itself and to most of the stars. Newton did not call the earth a gyroscope because the name had not been invented in his time, but the rules by which gyroscopic instruments are designed today are based on the laws explained by Isaac Newton.

Who Made the First Artificial Gyroscopes?

The first artificial gyroscopes were probably made by the Chinese and are what we call nowadays spinning tops. The

This cut-away drawing shows the Sperry Gyro-Compass removed from its protective binnacle. The Gyro-Compass always points to the true north and is not affected by magnetic disturbance.

friction trouble was overcome to some extent by giving the top a sharp, hard point which could rest on a flat, hard table and this allowed the top to spin for a long time. The spinning top shows all the peculiarities of the natural gyroscope. It keeps its axis pointing in a constant vertical direction, unless it is leaning out of the vertical, in which case it describes a cone just as the earth does, but with a much quicker motion. This precession is again caused by a coupling of two forces, the force of gravity pulling the top downward and the pressure of the table upward on the point. If the top leans, the two forces are not in line.

The gyropilot, often called "Iron Mike," steers a ship automatically and frees the helmsman for other duties.

How Was the Gyroscope First Used for a Scientific Purpose?

Spinning tops and hoops are made primarily for amusement. So far as we know, the first person to use such an instrument for a scientific purpose was Léon Foucault. Although Foucault lived one hundred years ago, there was at that time no completely satisfying demonstration of the theory that the earth was a rotating body. Some people still clung to the idea that the earth stood still and that the sun, moon and stars moved around it. Foucault wanted to demonstrate the earth's rotation by something on the earth itself and after he had made one demonstration by his celebrated pendulum experiment he decided to corroborate it by the gyroscope. He mounted a wheel in a frame on very delicate bearings so that the wheel could maintain its spinning axis in a fixed direction, and thus he was able to show the earth did turn relative to that direction. It was Foucault who first gave

[229]

Working by short-wave radio in conjunction with shore stations, LORAN (Long Range Navigation) is a new system for determining a ship's position without any other navigation instruments. A gyrocompass is still needed to keep the ship on course.

the apparatus the name of gyroscope, which means "to view the revolution of the earth." He gave it this name because his new instrument made the rotation of the earth visible.

Many years elapsed after Foucault's time before anyone else found any further use for a gyroscope as a scientific instrument. In a practical application, the gyro wheel had to be capable of sustained spinning for hours, days or even weeks, but friction at the points made this impossible. Further development had to wait for the invention of the electric motor and also for the development of ball bearings which could support, without quickly wearing out, a heavy gyroscope running at high speed.

Long before the era of steel ships, Foucault predicted that the gyro would one day be used as a compass. He determined the behavior of the gyro on a fixed platform, but the problem of determining its behavior on a rolling and pitching ship remained for later scientists to solve.

Who Made the Spinning Top a Useful Machine?

The gyroscope might have remained just a toy if a certain Dr. Elmer A. Sperry hadn't purchased one of the devices for his children. What happened then changed the history of transportation. For that is the moment when the brilliant career of the gyroscope had its real beginning.

Dr. Sperry saw something in that remarkable toy that spun around its own center of gravity. He didn't know just *what* he saw, but the thing fascinated him. He spun it again and again.

It was such a simple device—merely two steel rings that crossed each other at right angles, with a vertical axle that ran through the center of a weighted flywheel. As long as the little flywheel kept spinning, the axle would remain upright, and the little gyroscope could be poised on the point of a pencil, or even stand on a taut string. No matter how you moved the pencil or string, the gyroscope would remain with its little axle in a vertical position. Here was a device that maintained its position in space despite various movements of the structure on which it rested. But what could it be used for?

The marine world was then searching for a nonmagnetic compass. It was a pressing need. Ordinary compasses were affected by the magnetism of the vessel itself, its cargo or mag-

The officer at the left is watching the dial of the marine radar, which shows any obstacle or ship 100 yards to 40 miles away. By hooking the radar to the gyrocompass, the radar image can be seen in relation to its compass position.

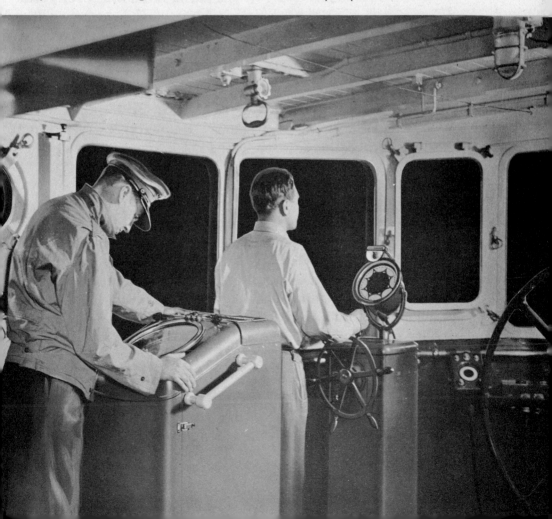

The controls of an aërial gyropilot. Rates of turn, climb or descent are automatically maintained, regardless of rough air, by a touch of the pilot's finger. With this instrument control of the ship is smoother than the pilot himself could manage.

netic conditions in the atmosphere. Dr. Sperry knew that the gyroscope tends to maintain its axis in a fixed position in space. That means that it can be pointed toward the North Star, and it will continue to point that way. Why not a gyrocompass? Its constancy would always give a true north reading.

But the experts thought differently. You couldn't make a compass like that, said the engineers. It was "mechanically impossible." With this decision handed down by the people who should have known, Sperry was unable to find investors willing to sink their money in the device. He was advised to forget the whole thing. But he was a persevering man who believed implicitly that his invention would work, whatever the experts might say. He mortgaged every thing he owned, risked his last cent, started his own company.

How Is the Gyroscope Used Today?

History records that the compass *did* work. It further records that, in the course of time, the gyrocompass became today's "Iron Mike," the device that skilfully pilots ships and planes alike. Iron Mike's career on the sea is well known. Giant gyroscopic devices weighing as much as 110 tons have brought new stability and safety to sea travel. By letting Iron Mike's steady motion counteract the effect of wave motions, new stability came to seagoing ships.

Iron Mike's new domain, the air, promises a brilliant future. If you were to ask any air-line pilot about Iron Mike, in all

The aircraft radio direction finder gives the pilot a continuous automatic bearing indication on a horizontal dial. Navigation scales are provided so that magnetic or gyro-compass bearings can be read without mental calculations or reference to tables.

probability, he would speak in warmly affectionate terms about this invisible pilot that rides with him. Sperry gyropilots are now being used by most of the world's leading airlines. They are helping to bind North and South America in closer alliance, to bring Europe, Asia, Africa and the Far East nearer together, to span the Alps, to bridge the Mediterranean and cross the jungles of Africa on regular scheduled flights. They also helped to blaze the trail for the airways of the Pacific and the Atlantic.

The Directional Gyro (left) is a stablized indicator of direction for steering straight courses and making precise turns, but is not a compass. The Gyro-Horizon (right) tells the pilot whether his plane is flying level; it is used at night or in bad weather when the natural horizon cannot be seen.

It's an odd fact, but Iron Mike began to grow his wings back in 1909. After successful application to vessels, it didn't take Dr. Sperry long to see that it would work for airplanes too. "As a result of the use of the gyroscope," says a news story of the time, "the most powerful wind gusts could not tip a beach monoplane suddenly in flight." But the coming of the World War stopped development. Not until the twenties did experimentation begin again in earnest. When it did, things happened fast. By 1933 the gyroscope had reached a high stage of perfection. It did most of the flying for Wiley Post on his solo dash around the world.

How Is the Stabilizer of an Airplane Operated?

Watch Iron Mike in action. Operating the device is simple enough. As soon as the aircraft is clear of the airport, and on its

The air-driven Attitude Gyro shows the pilot whether he is climbing or diving, moving left or right and whether the plane's wings are perfectly level. Seen in operation, the ball seems to be moving, but actually this gyro shows the position or attitude of the plane in relation to the marks on the ball, which always stands still.

course, the human pilot rotates the adjusting knobs on the gyro-pilot control unit. The "follow up" indicators must watch the gyro indications for direction, bank and climb. Then with a deft gesture the pilot moves the engaging level to "on," and takes his hands and feet from the controls. The climb knob is adjusted to obtain the desired rate of climb. It's as simple as that. Once this knob is set, the aircraft continues climbing steadily until the cruising altitude is reached. Then another slight turn of the climb knob puts the plane in level flight. In the air, quick adjustments of the proper knob permit banking or adjustment to the course indicated by the radio beam.

[235]

Modern high-flying planes start coming down a long way from the landing field, perhaps as much as a hundred miles away. Iron Mike has a job there too. A slight turn of the knob for glide is all that is necessary. The plane will then maintain a steady rate of descent. When he's ready to land, the human pilot disengages the gyropilot by taking over the controls and moving the engaging lever to "off."

When a sky liner blasts suddenly into a storm, when rough air fights at the plane, the gyropilot is on the job. Perhaps a great transport flies into a storm. Terrific bolts of lightning blind the pilots. In earlier days, that might have meant disaster, but Iron Mike rides through, steadying the controls. There are hundreds of such episodes in the career of this metal marvel.

What Was the First Aircraft to Cross the Atlantic?

Here are a few "firsts" in the history of transatlantic flying:

The first aircraft to cross the Atlantic was a seaplane, the *NC-4*, commanded by Lieut. Comm. A. C. Read. It flew from Newfoundland to the Azores, and then to Lisbon, Portugal: May 16–27, 1919.

The first aircraft to make a non-stop flight from America to Europe was a British biplane, carrying Captain (later Sir) John Alcock and Lieut. (later Sir) Arthur W. Brown. It flew from Newfoundland to Ireland in a little over sixteen hours: June 14, 1919.

The first dirigible to cross the Atlantic and the first to make a round-trip flight from Europe to America and back was the British *R-34*, commanded by Major G. H. Scott. It flew from Scotland to Long Island, New York, in 108 hours, and made the return flight in 75 hours: July, 1919.

The first solo flight across the Atlantic, and the first flight from New York to Paris without stop, was made by Captain (later Colonel) Charles A. Lindbergh in the *Spirit of St. Louis*. The long flight of 3600 miles was made in thirty-three and a half hours: May 20–21, 1927.

How Did the Dollar Sign Originate?

Many people imagine that the dollar sign, $, was derived by imposing the letters *U* and *S* (for United States) on each other. But this is a mistake. The dollar sign was used before America was settled. It is believed to date from the time of the pillar dollar in Spain. This coin is better known as the "piece of eight," from the fact that its value was eight *reals*. The *S* of the dollar sign is a partial representation of the figure 8, and the vertical stroke represent the Pillars of Hercules that were part of the design stamped on the coin.

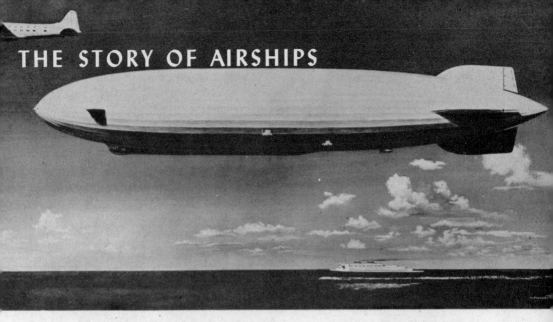

THE STORY OF AIRSHIPS

An artist's conception of the modern world transportation system which will employ fast airplanes, steamships and passenger airships. Although slower than airplanes, the long range of the airship makes it desirable for nonstop journeys.

THERE are two kinds of flying machines: those that are heavier than air and those that are lighter than air. We call the first kind *airplanes* and the second kind *airships*. Probably most of us have seen many airplanes and few airships, so that we tend to regard the latter as unimportant curiosities. But practical airships were flying the skies long before the airplane came into being, and they continue to be vital for certain purposes, such as transportation of heavy and bulky materials, hovering over a small area for observation, mapping and similar duties.

What Was the First Flying Machine That Worked?

The idea of flying in space has fascinated man from earliest times. The legend of Icarus, who made wings of wax and flew too near the sun, inspired many attempts in ancient days to construct artificial wings. In the Middle Ages, many inventors drew elaborate plans of machines that were intended to fly, but somehow they worked only on paper. It was not until the invention of the balloon that man got into the air and stayed there for any length of time.

Madame Jean Pierre Blanchard's husband made the first air voyage in America in 1793 from the yard of the Walnut Street Prison in Philadelphia. He ascended in a hydrogen-filled balloon, reaching a maximum altitude of 5,813 feet.

Captains Renard and Krebs flew the "La France," a French dirigible, at a speed of 15 miles an hour using a 9 horsepower electric motor. It was the first dirigible to make a successful flight.

At Annonay, France, in 1783, two brothers named Montgolfier watched smoke rising from a bonfire and wondered whether enough warm air could be enclosed in a light container to lift it off the ground. They built a 35-foot balloon of waxed paper, suspended a brazier of coal below it, and their question was answered—the balloon did indeed rise into the air. It was not long before large balloons were built, capable of lifting one or two men into the air.

What Is a Dirigible?

The next hundred years saw a great deal of experiment in what is called "free ballooning," with many balloonists performing feats of great courage and skill. But it was recognized that the balloon could never be made a practical mode of travel or transportation until a way was found to make it *dirigible*, capable of being steered. In free ballooning, the balloonist can go only where the wind chances to drive him. For steering purposes, a balloon would have to be equipped with some kind of engine, to drive a propeller, but the steam engines of the day were far too heavy to be lifted in balloons.

[239]

Santos Dumont, a Brazilian, made the first of a series of successful airship flights at Paris on September 20, 1898, using a gasoline engine. He built ten airships in the next several years.

The invention of the internal combustion (or "gas") engine, which made the automobile possible, also solved the problem of making balloons dirigible. The weight of a gas engine, relative to its horsepower, is low enough for this purpose. From 1906 to 1910, Santos Dumont, a wealthy Brazilian living in Paris, built successful dirigible balloons, and inspired similar efforts by others in England, Italy and the United States. It was seriously questioned whether the airplane, then in its infancy, could ever become a serious competitor to the airship, particularly since the introduction of rigid skeletons into balloons had greatly increased the load that a lighter-than-air ship could lift.

What Are the Different Types of Airships?

Three types of airships emerged from this experimental period—rigid, semirigid and nonrigid. The nonrigid is merely a balloon, shaped to lessen air resistance, with rudders and stabilizers attached at the back and a control car slung underneath to carry the engine and propellers. The bag has no metal framework; it keeps its shape entirely by the pressure of the lifting gas inside. When deflated it becomes merely a mass of fabric on the ground. The British referred to the nonrigids as "limp" airships, and Type B-limp, widely used in World War I, was contracted to "blimp" —a name which struck the public fancy and finally came into official use by the United States Navy in World War II.

In the meantime, Count Ferdinand Zeppelin (1840-1917) a retired German Army officer, had been working along on a different line. He wanted a dirigible big enough to carry larger loads and travel long distances, perhaps across the ocean. He first thought of fastening a number of balloons together, one behind the other, but concluded they would be hard to maneuver in rough weather. Then he conceived the idea of building a complete metal framework and stowing the gas cells inside it. This was the progenitor of the *Graf Zeppelin* and *Hindenburg,* and the American *Los Angeles, Akron* and *Macon.* They were called rigid airships, since they maintained their shape whether the gas cells were full or empty. The Italian and French devised a third type, the semirigid, which has a stiff metal keel running the length of the bag. The control car is attached to this keel.

What Gases Are Used in the Airships?

Hot air did not long remain as a lifting medium in lighter-than-air craft, for hot air cools off. In the second balloon built, the French physicist, Charles, turned to hydrogen, lightest of all gases and inexpensive to make. The one defect of hydrogen is that it is inflammable, and when mixed with a certain percentage of air, explosive.

In building their Zeppelins, the Germans sought to reduce the fire hazard. They bonded the metal framework so perfectly that if a ship were struck by lightning the charge would be dissipated harmlessly into the air around the ship. But the hazard of fire still existed. After years of successful flight, the greatest of the Zeppelins, the *Hindenburg*, burned with great loss of life as it was about to land at Lakehurst, N. J. The cause of the fire was believed to be static electricity.

An epochal event in the history of lighter-than-air flight was the discovery, in several western states of the United States, in 1907, of helium, a natural gas almost as light as hydrogen but noninflammable. This gas has been used in all American airships since 1925. It is still virtually an exclusive American resource— though small amounts have been found in Western Canada and Russia's Ural mountains—and is found in almost inexhaustible quantities. Helium may be exported only under strict government regulations, and the refusal of the United States to permit Germany to use it after the *Hindenburg* burned brought Zeppelin commercial operations to a standstill, after 168 successful ocean crossings and a four-stop trip around the world.

Training balloons ready for take-off at Wingfoot Lake during World War I. Navy airship pilots were trained here. Some of these pilots were still in the service in 1942. Balloons were used for artillery observation during World War I.

Airships that have no internal metal framework are called nonrigids or blimps. Here a U.S. Navy blimp practices maneuvers before going to sea for coastal patrol. Many blimps were used for antisubmarine and convoy duty during both World Wars.

What Are the Advantages and Disadvantages of the Airship?

The fact that the airship depends on a lifting gas to keep it aloft, as contrasted with the airplane, which can remain in the air only while it flys at high speed, brings problems different from those of the airplane. There is an important advantage in economy. Since the airship uses its power plant and fuel only to

[243]

drive it forward, it can get along with one-fifth of the fuel required by airplanes to carry the same load.

Any gas contracts or expands with changes in temperature and altitude, so that its lifting power is constantly subject to change. This is no great problem to the rigid airship. Hydrogen is cheap, and ships that used it let excess hydrogen pour out through the escape valves, when pressure was built up, without worrying about any resulting lack of lift, since the ships grew lighter as fuel was consumed. American ships, unwilling to discharge helium, since it is a natural resource and cannot be manufactured, met the situation in a different way. They would start off on a long trip with the gas cells only 90% full, knowing that they would not fly in any altitude great enough to let the helium completely fill the cells and overflow.

The nonrigid blimps, being smaller, meet the problem in a different way. Inside the balloon section are two or more smaller balloons called ballonets, which are filled with air, and may take up as much as one-fourth of the space. Consequently, as the gas expands, it forces air out, and as it contracts, more air is forced into the ballonets from the slip stream of the propeller. In this way, no helium is wasted.

The pilot watches the pressure gauge on the control board in front of him. One and one-half inches, which is equivalent to seven or eight pounds air pressure to the square foot, is ample to keep the bag taut, as contrasted to the average automobile tire, which has 28 pounds to the square inch.

As the pressure builds up, the pilot pulls a toggle, releasing air, as it goes down, he pulls another toggle, which opens a sort of damper in the intake tubes, which look like stovepipes and are located back of its engines. The pressure is kept up, when the ship is not flying, by a blower in the control car.

While the pilot generally keeps his ship at equilibrium, he can gain lift by pointing the nose slightly upward, getting the same dynamic lift on which the airplane relies. He can also start on a long cruise heavily overloaded with gasoline, taxi across the field and get flying speed in that way. Conversely if the ship is light, he can fly it at a slightly down angle and remain at the desired elevation.

[244]

Helium has one other advantage over hydrogen in that, as air seeps in and the purity of the gas goes down, the helium can be taken out, purified, and returned. Additional gas may be added from time to time because of seepage, but one filling of helium should last a ship a year, and with the lighter, tighter-woven new fabric recently introduced, which uses synthetic rubber neoprene, leakage is still less.

Blimps have been frequently shot at by thoughtless hunters, but that does not force them to land. The rubberized fabric of the bags tends to be self-sealing. In any event, the loss of lift is not serious. A routine part of morning inspection is to look into the interior of the bag, through a sealed window back of the control car, and in the gloom of the interior, even a pinhole of light is immediately discovered, and a small patch can be installed, even in the open. Because of the great size, even of the nonrigid

A "K" type Navy airship moored to a portable mooring mast. Although giant hangars are available at permanent Navy bases, airships can be moored wherever a mooring mast can be set up. Many of these masts are light portable structures.

Rigid airships have a light but strongly braced internal framework usually made of some aluminum alloy. The giant U. S. Navy dirigible, Los Angeles, *is shown here fastened to her mooring mast.*

blimp, the loss of lift is all but negligible, if the damage is discovered promptly. On a rigid ship, the metal framework makes the gas cells easily accessible for inspection and maintenance.

How Is an Airship Navigated?

Like the airplane, the airship has two sets of controls, one for altitude, and one for direction. The pilot can operate both controls in a blimp by a vertical wheel alongside of him and foot pedals on the floor. The nonrigid ships use two men, while modern rigid airships carry navigators, radio men, flight engineers, helmsmen and a crew of 30 or 40 men. A smaller crew can fly the ship, but since its journeys usually cover several days, it has a complete second crew aboard. The crew stands watches, as on a surface ship.

Early ships were landed by a ground crew and had a hangar at hand. The development of mooring masts, however, made the airship largely independent of cover, since it lands to the mast, and can remain there indefinitely. In World War II, hangars were built for Navy blimps at strategic locations along the American coast, but their antisubmarine work carried them into the Caribbean and along the coast of South America, where no hangars existed, and they used mooring masts as operating bases for months at a time.

What Future Has the Airship?

Both the Army and Navy used nonrigid airships in the first World War and afterward developed rigid and semirigid ships. The blimps were assigned to the Army, and the rigid ships were

The USS Akron under construction. Massive rings and longitudinal girders make up the metal framework of the dirigible. Ballonets, gas bags inflated with helium, are carried inside the framework to provide lift.

assigned to the Navy. In 1937, however, the Army turned its airships over to the Navy, which had three rigid ships built, the *Shenandoah, Akron* and *Macon.* A fourth, the *Los Angeles,* was acquired as reparations from Germany, after the first World War.

The only commercial airships in this country were those of the Goodyear Tire & Rubber Company in Akron, which had built most of the American airships, and operated a fleet of six blimps of its own, from 1928 until the second World War. A commercial airship line using the big ships was being projected in this country to parallel that of Germany when the loss of the *Akron, Macon* and the *Hindenburg* set back the program, and it was just being revived when the second World War broke out.

With the end of the war, airship men are again talking of commercial liners to be used in long, overwater routes carrying large cargoes, supplementing the work of the airplane and steam-

The framework of the Akron with its weather-proofed outer fabric laced into position. When completed the Akron went out on maneuvers with the U.S. Navy and proved her worth as a scouting ship.

ship. The modern cargo airship would be built to a size of ten million cubic feet, which is nearly half again as large as the *Hindenburg*. They would have a speed of upwards of 100 miles an hour.

As no rigid ships were at hand at the outbreak of World War II, the Navy turned to blimps, set up a procurement and training program, instituted a patrol jointly with airplanes and surface craft, which extended from Nova Scotia to Rio de Janeiro, and drove the undersea boats out of the coastal waters. Tankers and supply ships were being sunk faster than new ones could be built during the first year of the war. Sinkings fell off sharply, however, once the patrol was organized. Ship losses along the Atlantic fell off from 454 in 1942 to only eight in 1944, two years later. The blimps were also used extensively for convoying transport and supply ships. They were able to repeat the accomplishment of

A giant dirigible hangar. At a permanent base hangars are used as well as mooring masts. During high winds the dirigible is moored to a mast. If the weather is favorable, the dirigible is guided into the great hangar.

those in the first World War, namely, that no convoy escorted by blimps was ever successfully attacked by submarines.

The usefulness of the blimp in this field came from its ability to fly low and slowly in areas of extremely limited visibility, and to see deep under the water. Though the vulnerability of the rigid airship was debated in Naval circles, its advocates pointed to its usefulness in reconnaissance and as a high speed airplane carrier, able to run away from attack if enemy planes broke through its own air screen.

The projected passenger airship would have an operating range of 6000 miles, could carry a 90-ton pay load over the 2,500 mile route from San Francisco to Honolulu. Such a ship could carry nearly 300 passengers with

The value of the dirigible as an air scout was demonstrated many times during navy maneuvers before World War II. Carrying a number of airplanes with special landing hooks, the dirigible can act as a high-speed flying aircraft carrier.

accommodations comparable to a bus, or something over 100 passengers with full comforts of separate staterooms, promenade decks, dining rooms and recreation facilities.

The case for the commercial airship is based on its economy in long journeys, and comfort comparable to that of a passenger liner, except that there is no seasickness aboard an airship. Its huge bulk levels out rough air, which tosses other aircraft about and make rough travel for steamship passengers.

THE STORY OF AIRWAYS

Airway control officers regulate airway traffic just as a policeman regulates traffic at busy street intersections. As airliners arrive in the vicinity of the airport, the pilots keep in constant contact with the tower operators who advise them of other air traffic, barometric pressure, wind velocity and direction on the ground and the runway to be used for landing. The operator then gives the plane clearance to land. Planes are also cleared by the operator to take off.

EVERY year, millions of passengers are transported about the country in great air liners. At many fields, hundreds of planes land and take off every day. Already the traffic in the air above our land is huge, and it continues to grow. How is this traffic to be managed so as to avoid collisions, keep airplanes out of storm areas, find landing space for all the ships in air when sudden bad weather breaks, keep pilots on their courses, guide them at night or when daylight visibility is poor, and otherwise provide for the safety and convenience of air travelers?

There must be uniform traffic laws for the air as well as for the sea and for our streets. The task of making and administering the rules and safeguards of air traffic is given to a government body, the Civil Aëronautics Administration, known as the CAA.

What Are Airways?

The CAA has established and maintains a vast network of airways, composed of many different kinds of units and manned by many different kinds of experts. Growing rapidly, this great network by 1947 had come to include 300 range stations, 500 position markers, 2,000 beacons, 400 communication stations, 23 large airway traffic control centers. The whole system is knit together by 75,000 miles of teletype and telephone lines.

How Does the Control System Operate?

An airplane moving swiftly through the skies is constantly "watched" from the ground. At any moment, men of the CAA's Air Traffic Control system know exactly where the plane is, how high it is flying, how fast. At various intervals along the Federal airways are the twenty-three control centers where men known as "airways directors" completely guide the traffic of the airplanes.

A control center is a busy and exciting place, although the men in it do not actually see any planes in the course of their work. The airway director is in charge of all the airplanes flying along the section of the airway to which he has been assigned. This is usually 20 minutes of airplane flying time; that is, as an airplane enters his section, the director has 20 minutes to determine what information or orders he should give the plane. During those 20 minutes he is busy interpreting the information received by radio from each plane flying in his section. This information tells him the name of the airplane, the time it passes a certain point, known as a "fix," the height at which it is flying at that point. All this information is written on cards, which are posted on a big flight-progress board. If the director sees that two planes are too close to each other, he relays the information to the radio operators of the airlines to which the airplanes belong. The radio operators then contact the pilot.

Engineers and air traffic experts have figured out a way to improve this system, and, in the future, marvelous mechanical brains will perform much of the work now done by the airways directors and their assistants. The flight-progress boards will be

To guide pilots who have lost their way the Civil Aeronautics Administration has devised a standard system of airmarking that is clearly visible from above.

set up with rows of rotating drums, around the edges of which are lighted numbers and symbols. One horizontal line of these drums will serve the same purpose as the paper strips that are posted on the flight-progress boards. The flashing lights that appear on the big 15-foot boards will convey the necessary information to the flight directors.

What Are Ground Units?

The airways are made up of many ground units: emergency landing fields, flashing beacons, weather stations, and, of course, the radio stations which provide the faithful beam. Building

these ground facilities for the airways was an epochal accomplishment. Nature had set up staggering obstacles in the form of swamps, deserts, and mountains. If the location of the beacons and landing fields could have been fitted to the most convenient terrain, the job would not have been so difficult. But an air line has to be the short line, laid out "as the crow flies." Whatever may be the natural obstacles along such a line, the construction crews must find ways to conquer them.

Typical was the situation that confronted the engineers when they tackled Thanksgiving Peak in Arizona. A crude trail went part way up the rugged face of this extremely steep mountain. But then the trail disappeared, leaving only high cliffs. It was a hard task for a man to climb to the summit, and harder for a man burdened with equipment. The engineers solved the problem by rigging up a cable line operated by an automobile far below. On other slopes not so steep, the equipment was carried up by sure-footed burros.

Beacon by beacon, the airline markers were put in place. Emergency fields were laid out. But even when the ground installations are completed, the work has to go on. Someone has to take care of this complicated 20,000-mile system of airways. Every 15 miles there are revolving

Intermediate or emergency landing fields are designated and licensed by the CAA. At such fields there is usually a blinker beacon that flashes on and off continually at fixed intervals. Note the wind sock hanging from the tower. This device shows the pilot the direction of the wind.

beacons, all of which need servicing. Some of the mechanics assigned to this work cover a 200-mile stretch. They make daily trips to check all equipment and replace burned-out light bulbs. Other lights in isolated sections are cared for by men who live there and tend the single light.

One of the most isolated of all is the lonely beacon at Little Pass, Nevada. It is perched on a high rock, 6,860 feet above sea level. It might be said that the nearest neighbor is 18 miles away, because that is the distance to the beacon at Silver Zone. During the winter, when snow blankets the mountain passes, the keeper of the Little Pass Light communicates by means of flashing mirrors. No lighthouse keeper on a rock-bound seacoast ever had a more solitary job.

The men who take care of the unmanned beacons do not have any easy life. In all kinds of weather they must make their appointed rounds. Part of their

A radiosonde instrument ready for release. The balloon, inflated to about five feet in diameter, will carry the instrument up to about 12 to 14 miles. From that height the device sends out an automatic radio signal giving the temperature, humidity, and the altitude attained by the instrument. The balloon breaks at the top of the flight and descends by means of a red silk parachute.

traveling may be done by automobile, but sometimes they have to take to horseback or even snowshoes. Two mechanics found an odd use for their own beacon. In Great Salt Lake there is a revolving beacon on Antelope Island. The water had receded to such an extent that it was possible to haul the acetylene tanks and new bulbs across the lake bed in a wagon. Of course, there were shallow pools and nasty stink holes. It was night by the time the men were ready to start back. On the salt-encrusted lake bed of this inland sea there are no landmarks, just dead flatness. Getting lost might be serious, but they did not have to worry. On the mainland was the steadily winking beacon of their own home station to guide them back across the salt wastes.

The men at the emergency fields have plenty of work to do. They have numerous weather instruments to consult, and each hour they teletype reports of the readings. At intervals the mechanic releases helium-filled balloons. By following their course he is able to determine wind conditions at high altitudes. When air-line weathermen combine all the reports from stations on the route, they have an accurate picture of just what is happening along the line of flight to pass on to those most concerned.

Another job is to keep an eye on the automatic signal apparatus. The steady "beep-beep" of radio signals from this special broadcasting equipment is absolutely relied upon by modern air liners to keep them on their correct route. Each station has its own code letter, which is repeated again and again. It tells the pilot exactly where he is at any given time.

How Are Airplanes Guided?

In normal air-line operation, all pilots are required to make "position reports" at twenty-minute or half-hourly intervals during their entire flight. These are transmitted over the two-way radio telephone that is standard equipment on all the air lines of the United States. Radio ground stations of the line "stand by" constantly to receive such calls, repeating them, for the sake of accuracy, to the plane, which then acknowledges or corrects them. Ordinarily, the pilot reports only to ground stations at terminal or division points on the route over which he is flying, but all intermediate stations listen in and relay his messages if static or other conditions make transmission difficult.

The two-way radio telephone equipment carried by air transport planes is a separate communications system from the radio beacon weather-reporting service maintained along the airways by the Department of Commerce. It operates on entirely different frequencies, or wave lengths, and normally calls for the use of

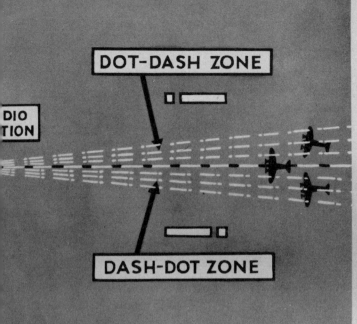

DOT-DASH ZONE

DIO
TION

DASH-DOT ZONE

All airliners that fly regularly scheduled trips are equipped with special "homing" apparatus. When the plane is on its correct course the pilot hears a constant hum in his earphones. If the plane deviates from the true course and goes off the beam on one side the pilot hears a dot-dash signal in his phones. If he goes off on the other side of the beam, he hears a dash-dot signal.

independent receiving sets aboard the airplane. This is not because it is difficult to tune to either frequency with the same receiver, but in order to provide, for safety's sake, duplicate communication channels from the ground in the event that one receiver should break down. Furthermore, most air-line operators in this country provide their ships with an emergency receiver of their own, in addition to the regular transmitting and receiving apparatus and the beacon receiver, so that, in all, there are three radio-receiving sets aboard.

The routine function of the government-operated radio beacons is to send out directional signals, enabling the pilot to follow the airway of his choice, even if a cloud blanket should blot out all sight of the earth and landmarks with which he is familiar. At regular intervals, these signals are interrupted by brief broadcasts of weather conditions prevailing along the airway—information that may be of vital concern to those aloft.

In emergencies, when the air lines are unable to "raise" their planes over their own two-way radio, (or when it is imperative to get a message to a ship equipped with a beacon receiver only),

[257]

Department of Commerce airways radio operators are authorized to break in on the regular beacon and weather sequence with the necessary special broadcast. Likewise, if a pilot is trying to get a definite "fix" of his position by means of the "cone of silence" immediately above a radio beacon, he may, by turning to his two-way radio, ask his company dispatcher to request uninterrupted beacon service for a short period, so that he will not fly over the beacon at the moment of a weather broadcast.

What Is a Radio Beacon?

In operation, the radio beacon projects a narrow band or "beam" of directional signals, which blend into a series of long dashes so long as the receiving airplane is flying down the exact middle of this zone. This is effected by using the dot-dash Morse A for one off-course signal and the dash-dot N for the other. If the pilot veers from the course, the blended signal gives way to a monotonously insistent A or N in his earphones, and he knows that he must alter the plane's magnetic heading enough to bring it back to the mid-course zone of dashes.

The nature of the beacon causes the A and N signal zones to become reversed when the plane passes over the beam transmitter, so that, if the A zone has been the right-hand side of the course, it now becomes the left—a circumstance that is highly confusing and may even be disastrous if a pilot, waiting for the "cone of silence" above a beacon, happens to pass over it when a weather broadcast is in progress and therefore does not know that it is no longer ahead of him. This, of course, is the reason that uninterrupted beacon service is rendered to pilots seeking a definite "fix" of their position.

In addition to the A and N directional signals, each beacon has an identifying code letter, which is transmitted at regular intervals between the signals upon which the airplane depends for guidance. Pilots are provided with charts showing all the radio beacons along the airway on which they are operating, together with their distinctive code letters. Thus the pilot is able to "ride the beam" from beacon to beacon, and, if neccessary, to locate emergency landing fields through localized "marker

[258]

Modern high-speed transport planes are never out of touch with the ground—thanks to the magic of radio. Two-way radio-telephone is maintained between planes and ground stations. Above is a scene in the communications center of a big air line. Radio operators keep in touch with planes in flight and make typewritten records of their conversations with pilots.

beacons" whose signals intersect those of the regular airway.

Such a "radio map" looks nothing like the maps seen in geographies or those used by auto tourists. But then, an airline pilot flying through the "soup," as flyers sometimes speak of fog, sees nothing that looks even remotely like the familiar countryside.

He does not need to see, for he can depend on the amazing invisible airways.

A plane picks up a sack of mail without stopping and landing.

THE AIR pick-up system is used where no airports are available. By this method, towns and villages without airport facilities are nevertheless able to receive air mail and air express service.

The system has three units: the mechanism in the plane, the ground station, and containers to transfer cargo.

The plane equipment comprises a compact, electrically powered reel, an elastic cable and a hook, a fifteen-foot retractable arm which swings below the fuselage, and a delivery release.

The ground station is simply two fifteen-foot sectional poles, the bottom section of steel and the top section wood or bamboo.

The container is designed to ride the air smoothly and withstand ground impact on delivery. Attached to a ring in its nose is a sixty-foot loop of elastic rope.

[260]

The ground attendant brings mail and express to the pick-up station.

Outgoing mail is loaded into the container, especially designed of reinforced fiber and rubber to withstand hard usage.

First step in erecting a pick-up station is assembling two poles. The doweled end of the wooden pole fits snugly into the steel butt.

The rope attached to the container is strung between the tops of the poles.

Anchoring the second pole, with the transfer loop in position.

The container is drawn back to the length of the loop, midway between the poles, and finally sealed.

[263]

Plane approaches the station with its pick-up arm down and incoming container trailing behind it.

Just before the pick-up, the pilot trips delivery release mechanism and inbound container drops to the ground.

The hook at the end of the transfer arm engages the transfer rope between station poles.

The container, cushioned against shock by the rope's elasticity and the pick-up mechanism, on its way as pilot begins to climb.

Inside the plane, the pick-up rope is attached to a drum. The flight mechanic flicks a switch and the container is reeled into the plane in a few seconds.

Pilot's-eye view of a typical air pick-up station.

Head-on view of a pick-up plane at the moment its pick-up hook engages the loop attached to outgoing container.

A fleet of air pick-up planes at the Pittsburgh Airport ready to start on their daily schedules.

Postal employee sorts mail for air pick-up routes. These mail pouches are specially designed for the purpose.

A flight mechanic loads a plane with air express and mail.

By means of air pick-up, a pilot lost at sea or lost in some inaccessible place on land where a plane cannot land can safely be picked up by a low-flying plane.

Man in position for aërial pick-up. His body harness is attached to a transfer loop suspended between two ground poles.

Plane lifts the man off the ground, just like a glide or container of mail. He feels no sudden shock or discomfort as the towline is paid out.

Inside the plane the automatic reeling device is started and man is drawn up. It is not necessary for him to do any hand-over-hand climbing.

Man grasps the pick-up arm after being reeled up to the door of the cabin. Crew members are ready to assist him aboard.

Journey's end! None the worse for wear, the man crawls into the cabin. The entire transfer from ground to air has taken only a few minutes.

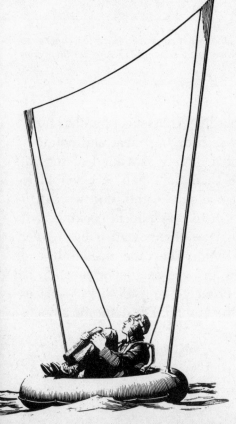

Air pick-up rescue device at sea. The stranded pilot sits in a raft facing oncoming plane. The poles are fastened into special sockets in the raft.

[271]

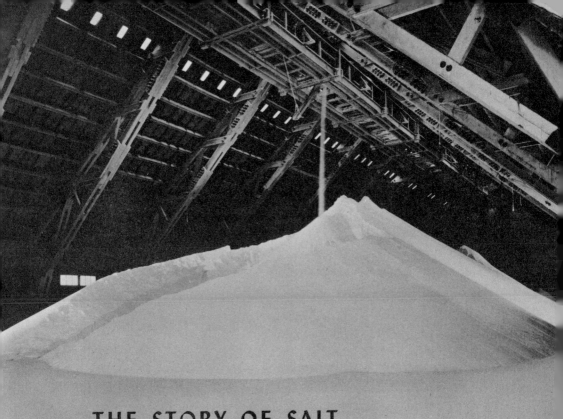

THE STORY OF SALT

After being crushed, ground and purified, the salt is carried to huge warehouses to be stored. Note the salt falling from the overhead conveyor. An under-floor conveyor removes the salt from the warehouse.

W E ALL know what salt looks like. In its most familiar form, fine white granules, it is used on our meat and potatoes, and perhaps we think of it merely as a kind of seasoning. But it is really much more than that. Salt is essential to human life, and while there is some salt in the food we eat, it is not enough. We have to add salt to our food in cooking it, if not at the table as well. What is true of mankind is even truer of some animals, domestic and wild. They too need salt and their food in some cases supplies an even smaller proportion of their need. Wild animals must often go to "salt licks"—places where rock salt is exposed above the ground. For domestic animals such as horses we provide pieces of rock salt that they can lick when necessary.

Salt, too, is a natural preservative for food, the first that man discovered, and still the most important. And salt is needed in many industrial processes. In fact, next to water, salt is the most-used substance on earth.

Where Do We Find Salt?

Nature provides salt for us in three different forms: first, in sea water solution; second, in salt springs; and third, in the form of salt rock.

From time immemorial man has obtained salt from sea water. This is still being done on our seacoasts, but the salt obtained by evaporating the water usually contains many impurities.

Inside the Kleer Salt Mine at Grand Saline, Texas. This is a low-cut gallery, the roof being only 30 feet high. Later it will be increased to 85 feet. Note the whiteness of the salt.

Salt of a better grade is obtainable from what are known as salt springs. These springs are formed by water flowing over a deposit of salt rock. The amount of salt obtained from evaporating this spring water is, however, so small that salt springs are an impractical source of supply when it comes to making salt for commercial purposes.

Rock salt forms the most common and practical source of supply. It is found in all parts of the world and reasonably near the surface. The deposit is said to be what is left of ancient salt seas. In the United States, the largest deposits of salt are found in the states of Michigan, New York, Ohio, Utah, Louisiana, Kansas, Texas, and California.

One of the largest sources of salt supply in Europe is at Wielizka in Poland. This deposit of salt is believed to be the largest in the world, the bed of salt rock being 500 miles long,

This room is 65 feet wide, 85 feet high and 700 feet long. Many a skyscraper could be placed in it. Notice the holes cut in the side walls to provide light.

A powerful drag line is used to bring salt from one of the wall faces after it has been blasted loose. The salt will be dumped through the grate where the workmen are standing, onto a large conveyor belt.

20 miles wide, and 1,200 feet thick. Some of the salt mines in Poland are very extensive, and it is said some of the miners spend their entire lives in these mines, never coming to the surface of the earth.

How Is Salt Mined?

The general way of obtaining salt from the earth is by means of salt wells. These wells are drilled in the same way that wells are bored for oil and gas. A pipe about six inches in diameter is lowered to the surface of the salt rock, and then an inside pipe is put down, water is forced down between the two pipes and the pressure exerted brings up the dissolved rock or salt brine through the inside pipe.

[275]

*In this tunnel, 700 feet below the surface, we see the main transportation belt bring-
ing salt from the working spaces to the shaft, where the salt is hauled up in elevators. The men are picking out large lumps of salt to be used for feeding cattle.
These lumps are cured and dried before shipping.*

How Is Salt Purified?

Most of the deposits of salt rock contain impurities that need
to be removed before the salt is fit for use commercially; however,
some deposits show a very pure salt rock, and when ground up,
this rock salt is suitable for table use. In general, however, the
salt made from crude salt rock is fit only for the crudest commercial uses. The most common impurity is gypsum, a substance
from which plaster is made.

As the salt brine reaches the surface, the salt is extracted from
it in various ways. At present, the crude open-pan system, where
the brine was poured into open pans and fires were built below

Salt dredging operations on the shores of Great Salt Lake, about fifteen miles west of Salt Lake City, Utah. Great Salt Lake is a virtually inexhaustible source of salt.

the pans, is almost obsolete. Today, salt is refined by the Grainer, Vacuum Pan, and Alberger systems.

The Grainer system is similar in its operation to the old open-pan system. The brine is run through long, shallow tanks, and the heat is applied through steam pipes inside of the pan. The salt settles to the bottom of the pan and large rakes, operated either by hand or machinery, collect the salt.

In the Vacuum Pan process, tiny cubes of salt are formed and settle to the bottom of the pan in which a vacuum has been created. The salt is then drained out and is ready for drying.

Variations of the two above processes make possible the production of certain grades of table salt. Oftentimes the brine is relieved of impurities through the action of certain chemicals. In some instances a chemical known as barium chloride is used, but the wisdom of this process has been much questioned, owing to the fact that barium chloride is a deadly poison.

The Alberger system of salt manufacture is a mechanical process that subjects the salt brine to a much higher temperature and removes the impurities by means of mechanical filters. This process makes a very pure salt and has been used for some time as a practical method for manufacturing high-grade dairy and table salt. Unlike the other two common methods of making salt, it forms tiny salt flakes instead of cubes or lumps.

After manufacturers obtain the salt from the brine, they usually put it through drying processes. After drying, the salt is sifted and the fine table salt is separated from the coarser products. When salt is sifted, it is ready for packing in bags or packages suitable for shipment to the consumer.

How Much Salt Do We Use?

According to recent government reports, it is estimated that the average consumption of salt per capita for all purposes is about one hundred and ten pounds per year. The salt industry is said to have reached a very stable basis, and the demand for salt in the United States is practically all supplied by American manufacturers. Salt can be put to a great many uses in addition to the usual requirements for table and cooking. It is used by food manufacturers and performs highly important functions in certain commercial fields.

What Is a Carat?

If you have heard such expressions as "an 18-carat gold watch" and "a 50-carat diamond," you must have been puzzled by the fact that the watch is much heavier than the diamond. The explanation is that the word "carat" has two meanings. It is a unit of weight used in connection with diamonds and other precious stones. But in connection with gold it is a measure of fineness, meaning literally a twenty-fourth part. Thus, "18-carat gold" means an alloy of which $18/24$ or three-quarters is pure gold, the rest some other metal. As gold is very heavy and soft, it is almost never used in pure form for jewelry or coinage. The commonest alloy is with copper.

What Is a Robot?

The word "robot" comes to us from the satirical drama "R.U.R." (Rossum's Universal Robots), by the Czech playwright, Karl Capek. In the play, Rossum's Universal Robots are machines in human form, hence the word "robot" has come to mean, in many languages, a working automaton apparently endowed with human intelligence.

THE STORY OF MINERALS

Before the days of modern motor transportation, loads of borax were hauled out of Death Valley by twenty-mule teams.

FOR many centuries, men have been digging into the ground in an effort to wrest treasure from the bosom of old Mother Earth. In fact, mining may very well have been one of the first of all human industries, following closely upon the heels of hunting and fishing. For the flint from which early men chipped their axes, spears, and arrow heads—the flint which furnished men with fire, tools and weapons for thousands of years—all had to be mined. At first, these mines were merely open pits which contained outcroppings of flint easy to get at. As the centuries passed and men continued to dig for the precious flint, these pits became sizable workings.

By the time the earliest civilizations were well established— the Egyptian along the River Nile and the Babylonian in the valley formed by the Tigris and Euphrates Rivers—mining was big business. Indeed, it was so profitable that mine owners were among the richest men of antiquity. Many of the mines were so very rich that jealous kings and priests took them away from their lawful owners and prospered on their ill-gotten wealth.

What Minerals Were Used in Ancient Times?

By this time, too, there was a surprisingly large variety of mines. Stone as well as clay bricks had come into widespread use for building palaces and temples. Building stone—granite and sandstone, as well as limestone—was mined in quarries. Marble was also quarried, for statues and to beautify temples and palaces. Lime was very important, since from it was manufactured much of the plaster employed in finishing individual rooms. Vast quantities of clay were taken from the clay pits for the making of cooking pots and vases and bricks. Clay was also used in Babylonia, instead of papyrus, for writing letters and business documents. And then there were the smaller mines whence came the gorgeous gem stones so beloved by the kings and ladies. Another product of those early mines was jade, a smooth green stone very useful in making chisels. Jade tools were even harder than the metal tools men possessed six thousand years ago.

How Do Minerals Compare with Metals?

In those days, the use as well as the value of these *non-metallic minerals*, as they are now called, far exceeded the use and value of the *metals* which were mined. One reason is that far more minerals than metals were known. The ancient metal craftsmen knew only gold, silver, copper, lead, and tin. Another reason was that metals had to be refined by long and tedious processes, whereas the minerals could be used much as they were taken from the ground.

Strangely enough, minerals still predominate over metals today. And it is also true that in the past century alone, a greater amount of every known mineral has been used than was mined in all the thousands of years preceding this one century! Not only that, but today far more metals and minerals are known than ever before. Some seventy metals have been discovered, and nearly one thousand substances which are classed as non-metallic minerals.

What Is the Difference Between Minerals and Metals?

A metal is a *chemical element*. All of the metals have a definite melting point; all have a "metallic sheen"; all can be hammered out into thin sheets and fine wire; and they possess many other such properties in common.

A mineral, however, is usually a *compound*. That is, it is made up of several *elements*, held together in a chemical combination. A mineral occurs naturally, whereas the metals are almost always found combined with one or more of the other elements. An *ore*, therefore, is a mineral from which one or more of the pure *metals*

A gypsum quarry. This abundant mineral has over eight hundred industrial uses.

A shop where patterns for casting of all sizes and shapes are made out of gypsum plaster.

can be extracted. The term *mineral* includes all rocks, stones, ores, gems, sands, and clays. In fact, the entire crust of our globe is composed of mineral substances!

Just to list the minerals that are not classified as ores, together with their industrial uses, would require volumes. Many of these mineral substances are well known by name. Aside from these, however, there are many other minerals whose names are practically unknown, although we use them in one form or another every day and without their aid would fare badly. Many manufactured products are of mineral origin, although they are often so disguised that most people do not realize the fact.

For instance, there are minerals that can be woven into cloth; minerals that once were waving trees and tall jungle ferns in the days of the earth's vanished youth. There is a kind of coal that will float on water; another kind of coal—carbon in the form of the diamond—that is one of the most expensive substances known. There is a mineral made up of the shells of microscopic animals that lived before humans, and which we use today in various forms as tooth powder and as paste for cleaning silverware.

What Is Gypsum?

What are some of these mineral substances with which we come in contact every day? One of the most useful is *gypsum,* a crystalline rock made up of calcium and sulphur. There are gypsum deposits in nearly all countries and great deserts of it in our own Southwest. Gypsum crystals contain what is called "water of crystallization." This water content is important in certain uses to which gypsum is now put.

Usually, the gypsum crystals are fairly large and so soft that they can be scratched with the thumbnail. Sometimes, however, chunks of gypsum are found in which the individual crystals making up the entire mass are tiny and packed closely together. This gives the rock a satiny appearance and hence it is known as "satin spar." Many minerals have the word "spar" as a part of their name. "Spar," however, is merely a slang term used by miners to indicate any of the nonmetallic minerals in general. "Satin spar" merely means "satin mineral."

Gypsum plaster, laid over lath or wallboard, is extensively used to make the walls of houses.

When a slab of gypsum is extremely fine-grained, it becomes the material which for ages has been used by poets to indicate the whiteness of a lady-love's brow—*alabaster*. Alabaster is prized as a material for making statues, vases, and other objects of art. Sometimes alabaster is pure white; at other times it is veined and tinted with blue, pink, and other delicate shades. Many temples and palaces of bygone ages owed much of their beauty to the alabaster statues gracing their halls—and to the white plaster made from the more common form of gypsum.

Ordinary gypsum becomes commercially valuable to industry after it has been heated and its water of crystallization driven off. It is thus reduced to a fine powder known as "Plaster of Paris," because for many years the world's supply came from huge gypsum quarries north of Paris. When water is added to this powder it soon "sets" (re-crystallizes) into whatever shape has been given it. It becomes a hard, rocklike mass because it has actually been

[283]

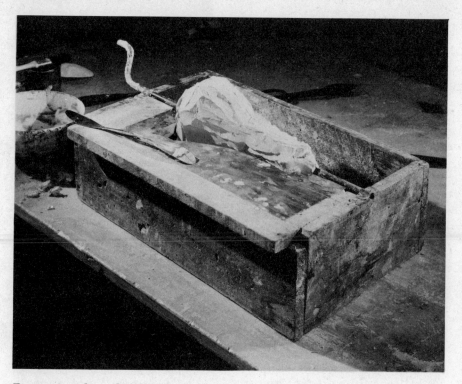

First step in the making of a gypsum pattern. Thick plaster is applied to a metal rod until the mass is in the rough shape of the wooden template.

transformed back again into the rock it was before! Plaster of Paris is important in making all kinds of casts and molds, such as those surgeons use for helping broken bones to set properly.

Cattle hair and goat hair are added to this "burned" gypsum to form building plaster. The hair helps hold the plaster together. The five million tons of gypsum mined each year in this country, however, are used for many other things besides building plaster. Glass makers use tons of it in making plate glass. Ordinary panes of "window" glass are set rigidly on iron tables by means of Plaster of Paris. The glass is then polished on both sides with sand and rouge, an operation that imparts the high sparkle characteristic of plate glass. Farmers use gypsum as fertilizer. Ground-up gypsum is put into paints and is also added to rubber to make this soft material harder and more durable. The chalk used in schools is not natural chalk at all, but gypsum molded

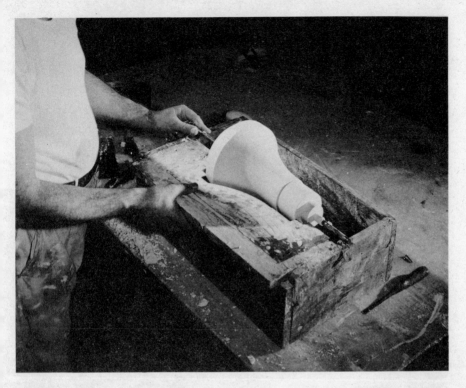

Turning against the template rounds the gypsum pattern to finished form. The pattern will be used to make a mold for casting an aircraft part of solid aluminum.

into sticks. One of the latest uses of this mineral is in the motion picture industry. Piled into heaps, or drifting on the wind caused by the wind machines, powdered gypsum gives a perfect imitation of snow.

What Is Asbestos?

Another mineral substance, *asbestos*, is widely known, although many people think that it is a cloth. Actually, it is a silicate rock—that is, made up mainly of the element silicon. The stone, as quarried, is composed of fine fibers, closely packed together. These fibers have to be fluffed out, after which they can be woven into all kinds of yarn, rope, and cloth.

The best-known application of asbestos is in making fireproof curtains for theaters, since asbestos, as everyone knows, is an

Clad in an asbestos suit, a firefighter approaches the very heart of the flames, without danger.

excellent heat-resisting material. More important ways in which asbestos daily safeguards our lives is in the brake bands and clutch facings of our automobiles, and in fireproof shingles for roofing houses.

Asbestos cloth is woven into suits of armor for the men who battle fires—fires from bombs, from airplane accidents, from oil refinery disasters, and many other causes. During the war, our country alone made something like 75,000 complete suits of asbestos armor for firefighters in all branches of the armed services.

The vast amount of asbestos used every year throughout the world—more than 300,000 tons a year—is ample proof of this mineral's importance. Although the United States produces only a small amount of what it needs, Canada has an ample supply together with well-developed mines and mining equipment.

What Is Mica?

Mica—a very complex mineral made up of aluminum silicates together with potassium, iron, lithium, magnesium, and hydrogen —is familiar to all of us because we have seen flakes of it sparkling under Christmas trees as artificial snow. Its greatest importance, however, is in the electrical industry. During the late war, mica was a "strategic" mineral because high grade mica is absolutely essential in making the best radio and aircraft magneto condensers. No mica, no magneto—and the magneto has proved to be the most reliable method of producing the sparks that keep an airplane engine running.

Mica is mined in big chunks, which split easily into thin leaves that have a high resistance to the flow of an electrical current. This is why the heating wires on electric toasters are wrapped around sheets of mica. The uses of mica in the manufacture of electrical appliances are legion. Mica is also employed to give wallpaper a shiny appearance; in the manufacture of rubber; as a lubricant; and in making certain kinds of roofing shingles.

What Is Graphite?

Graphite, one of the pure forms of carbon, is most familiar through one of its less important uses. This greasy, greyish mineral is crushed, mixed with clay, and then molded into thin sticks which form the so-called "lead" in modern lead pencils. But there are three other uses which require far more than the 2,000 tons of graphite consumed yearly by our pencil industry.

Most important of graphite's uses is the work it does in metal casting. The liquid metal is poured into molds hollowed out of sand. The surfaces of the sand molds must be dusted with powdered graphite to keep the grains of sand from sticking to the metal after it cools and hardens—just as a cake pan is greased to keep the cake from sticking to it.

[287]

The second important use of graphite is as a pigment or a coloring compound in black paint. The third is its use in the manufacture of the large crucibles or pots in which brass and high-grade steels are melted. In fact, much of the quality of the steel from which cutting tools are made depends upon these graphite melting pots.

Several thousand tons of graphite are also used each year in making the brushes that furnish the electrical contact with the commutators of motors and electric generators. The advantage of graphite is that it wears evenly and decreases sparking. Another important use of this greasy mineral is as a lubricant. Sometimes it is mixed with oil or grease and sometimes it is used alone—as in pianos and organs—where oil or grease would be objectionable on moving parts made of wood.

Asbestos shingles not only decrease the fire hazard but also insulate the house from extremes of hot and cold weather.

What Is Talc?

Talc, when mentioned to most people, at once suggests face powder, just as graphite suggests pencils. But face powder is an unimportant use of talc from the standpoint of the amount used every year. Ground-up talc is used as a filler for paper; in rubber, paint, and in glass making; and to coat the surface of roofing material so that it will not stick together when rolled. Large slabs of talc are made into laundry tubs, sinks, and the acid-proof tops of laboratory work benches. Switchboard panels and many other things which must be nonconductors of electricity are also made from slabs of talc, because this stone can be easily bored and cut to shape. For these and many other uses, we mine around three million dollars worth of talc every year.

Safety and comfort are promoted by the use of asbestos Flexboard in the walls of the kitchen.

What Are the Uses of Sulphur?

One of the most common of all the nonmetallic minerals also happens to be one of the most important in our modern industrial world. This is the element *sulphur*, once commonly called "brimstone." This name means "burn stone" and was given to sulphur because it catches fire easily and is difficult to extinguish. Centuries ago, the priests of various pagan religions were so attracted by the bright blue flame which burning sulphur makes—as well as the pungent, penetrating odor it gives off—that they used this mineral extensively in their weird ceremonials in order to impress the common people.

The more practical men of the ancient races, however, found other uses for sulphur. They learned that sulphur is valuable in bleaching linen—that is, for making the newly woven cloth much whiter. Later, the Greeks found out that when sulphur is burned in a house, it cleans and purifies the air, making the atmosphere

A mass of rare asbestos fiber.

wholesome again after sickness. As early as 500 B. C. the Chinese were making gunpowder with sulphur, although so far as we can learn, this gunpowder was used merely in fireworks and not for warfare. The Roman doctors cured skin diseases with sulphur salves, and during the Middle Ages the alchemists, misled by the yellow color of this mineral, vainly tried to make gold out of sulphur!

The ancients, however, never used such huge quantities of sulphur as we do today. The United States used more than a million tons of this fluffy, yellow mineral a year in peace times; its use in war times is much greater.

Our country has vast amounts of sulphur, so much of it that no geologist will even attempt to estimate how much lying some thousand feet or so under the surface of Texas and Louisiana. To mine sulphur, several pipes (one inside the other) are forced down through the ground until the sulphur deposit is reached. Superheated steam is forced down through the outermost pipes and melts the sulphur. Hot blasts of air are then forced down through one of the inner pipes. This churns and whips up the melted sulphur so it becomes frothy and light. More air pressure forces the molten sulphur to the top of the ground through the centermost pipe. The sulphur is cooled and stored in bins.

Why Is Sulphuric Acid So Important?

Three-fourths of all the sulphur consumed in our country goes into the manufacture of sulphuric acid. This acid is so vital in industry that the amount produced is frequently referred to as the "measuring stick of business." This heavy, corrosive liquid has something to do with the manufacture, at one step or another, of more products than does any other single chemical in the world.

There is never a moment, day or night, when we are not using something which sulphuric acid has made possible. The clothes we wear; the paper in books and magazines—these were treated with sulphuric acid. Vegetables, fruit, and even bread owe a lasting debt to sulphuric acid, since the fertilizers used on farms were prepared with its help.

Borax is a white mineral that looks much like common salt. In this form it is called Priceite or Pandermite.

The crude oil that furnishes our cars and trucks with gasoline and oil contains a dark, smeary tar which must be removed before the petroleum products can be used. This tar is taken out of petroleum by mixing it with sulphuric acid and blowing compressed air through the combination in huge agitating tanks. Practically all articles made of iron and steel are "pickled" at some point in their manufacture—that is, given a bath in dilute sulphuric acid. Pickling removes all the dirt, rust, and grease which would otherwise cause trouble later on.

What Are the Uses of Borax?

Another old friend among the nonmetallic minerals that serve mankind faithfully is *borax*. This has long been used in soap and for adding to water used for washing. Its main present use is in the enamel applied to bath tubs and bathroom equipment in general. It is also employed extensively in making pottery, soap, glue, and glass and also for giving a fine glaze to paper. Large quantities are consumed in the manufacture of cloth and the

Kernite, also called Rasorite, is another form of borax. It somewhat resembles mica.

tanning of leather. Much of the borax we use comes from vast "dead lakes" in California—thousands of tons every year.

What Other Minerals Are Used in Large Quantity?

One of the problems in building construction that is familiar to everyone is that of heat insulation. In winter, much of the heat generated inside a home or any other kind of building immediately escapes, and the amount thus lost is so great as to make any effective heat insulator very valuable. A number of mineral substances compete for this "insulation service." One is "slag wool," produced by the effect of a jet of air on melted slag of the correct composition. Another is "diatomaceous earth." This is a deposit formed by an accumulation, over a period of many thousands of years, of the skeletons of plants known as "diatoms."

Diatoms are microscopic in size and have shells made of nearly pure silica. Diatoms were so numerous in ancient seas that today there are deposits of diatomaceous earth hundreds of feet deep. The tiny shells of the diatoms have extremely fine ridges, and so this material, made up into a paste, is also used for silver polish. The ridged shells act like minute files and scrape away the tarnish without marring the expensive silver beneath. Much diatomaceous earth is also used to strengthen cement and to increase the weather resistance of paint.

Feldspar is an unfamiliar mineral servant because it never appears "in person." It forms from one-tenth to one-third of the material from which porcelain, pottery, vitrified sanitary ware, and enameled brick are made. The enamel on iron bath tubs and other bathroom equipment is composed largely of feldspar, and artificial teeth are made of it. Not the least important of its numerous applications is its role as scouring powder for use on materials which sand will scratch. Hundreds of thousands of tons of feldspar are used each year and although the mineral costs only a few dollars a ton, the products made from it are many times more valuable.

There are many more non-metallic minerals which are of vital importance to us. For instance, there is *fluorspar*, a necessary addition to every batch of steel that is made. Among many others we may list building stone; limestone from which cement is prepared; sandstone from which grindstones are made; coal for fuel and for making thousands of "coal tar" products; diamonds for the important diamond-tipped tools used in machine shops; slate; pottery clays for the more humble dishes; and the more expensive clays for making automotive spark plugs which must resist terrific heat. Then there is asphalt, often called "versatile ooze" because it has hundreds of uses ranging from paints to runways for air fields. Lastly, we must mention *salt*, a mineral so important to human life that a separate article in this book is devoted to it.

How Did Your State Get Its Name?

Alabama is named after the Indian word which means "here we rest"; Alaska comes from the Eskimo word "Alakshak" or "Alayeska" and means "the main land"; Arizona is derived from the Indian word "Arizonac," meaning "small springs," or "few springs"; and Arkansas is sort of a mixture of the Indian "Kansas," which means "smoky water," and the French prefix "arc," meaning "bow" or "bend."

Californa comes from the Spanish words "Caliente Fornalla," or "hot furnace"; Colorado, also from the Spanish "colored," from the red color of the Colorado River; and Connecticut, in Indian, means "long river."

Delaware was named after Lord De la Warr; Florida originated from the Spanish "Pascua de Flores," which means "feast of flowers," because it was discovered on Easter Day; Georgia was called after King George II of England; and Hawaii is a name peculiar to the natives there, although Captain Cook called it part of the "Sandwich Islands," after Lord Sandwich.

Idaho is Indian, meaning "gem of the mountains"; Illinois is another mixture of Indian and French, the Indian word "illini" and the French suffix "ois" meaning "tribe of men"; and Indiana and Iowa are both plain Indian, the former standing for "indians' land," and the latter, "beautiful land."

Kansas and Kentucky are Indian, too, Kansas meaning "smoky water" and Kentucky "at the head of the river," or "the dark and bloody ground"; and Louisiana is named after Louis XIV of France.

Maine and Maryland each come from abroad, Maine being called after the Province of the same name in France, and Maryland after Queen Henrietta Maria of England, consort of Charles I; while Massachusetts, Michigan, Minnesota, Mississippi and Missouri are all from the native Indian language, meaning, in the order for which they are given, "place of great hills," "fish weir," sky-tinted water," "great fathers of waters" and "muddy"; and Montana traces back to the Latin word *Montanus,* meaning "mountainous."

Nebraska is another Indian name, and means "water valley"; while Nevada is Spanish, meaning "snow covered"; New Hampshire and New Jersey are both from across the water, the former after Hampshire County in England, and New Jersey after the island of Jersey at the time when Sir George Carteret was its governor; New York and both North and South Carolina were also named after monarchs of Europe, New York after the Duke of York in England, and the Carolinas after Charles IX of France; while North and South Dakota bring us back to the Indian language again, meaning "allies."

Ohio and Oklahoma are both Indian, too, Ohio meaning "beautiful river," and the latter, "home of the red men"; while Oregon is from the Spanish word *oregano,* which stands for the wild marjoram, a plant abundant on the coast; Pennsylvania traces back to the Latin, meaning "Penn's woody land"; the Philippine Islands come from the Spanish words "Islas Filipinas," after King Philip; and Puerto Rico is also Spanish, from "Puerto Rico," meaning "rich port."

Rhode Island is called after the island of Rhodes; Tennessee, Texas and Utah are all Indian, Tennessee meaning "river with the great bend," Texas coming from several different forms of very old Indian language, meaning "friends," and Utah after the tribe by that name, also called the "Utes"; Vermont is from the French, meaning "green mountains," and Virginia is called after Elizabeth, the "Virgin Queen" of England.

Washington gets its name from a good, straight American source—George Washington; West Virginia is so called because it was formerly the western part of Virginia; and Wisconsin and Wyoming are both Indian, the former meaning "gathering of the waters," and the latter, "great plains."

Where Is the Deepest Petroleum Well?

An oil well at Athens, in the Los Angeles basin, California—7,591 feet deep—is believed to be the deepest active oil well ever drilled. In the Olinda field in Orange County, in the same state, a hole was drilled to a depth of over 8,200 feet, but was later abandoned.

The deepest gas well was drilled near Ligonier, Pennsylvania, 7,756 feet.

THE STORY OF GLASS

Crystal Fish, designed by Sidney Waugh.

G LASS was probably discovered by the first smelters of iron and copper. The prehistoric man who first heated the ores to extract these metals must have noted that much of the "slag" cooled into a hard, brittle, translucent mass. In time, he learned to cast this viscous liquid into ornamental and useful shapes. Certain it is that the manufacture of glass is at least 3,000 years old.

Yet it was only in the nineteenth century that glassmaking graduated from the rule-of-thumb stage and became the subject of scientific inquiry and improvement. The establishment of a real science of chemistry brought a new era in glassmaking, as in so many other departments of human activity.

What is glass made of? From ancient times, and even today, most glass is composed of sand (silica), soda and lime, fused together by heat. The copybook definition of glass has long been: "An amorphous, transparent or translucent mixture of silicates, one of which is always an alkali." But modern glasses require a broader definition. In some, magnesia is substituted for lime. Soda is sometimes replaced by potash. There are even non-silicate glasses based on alumina. Some glass contains organic substances. And there are also alkali-free formulas.

A more realistic definition of glass is: "A supercooled liquid." This defines the form, rather than the ingredients — and the form is really the important thing. Modern scientists recognize that glass is not a single substance. but a *form of matter* intermediate between the solid and liquid states. We think of glass as solid, because when it has "set" it is hard to the touch. Yet it continues to have some of the characteristics of a liquid. Greek and Roman glassware, dug out of the earth after two thousand years, is sometimes found to have absorbed minerals from the soil, and to show clear evidence of a slow but continual flow of particles inside the glass.

Besides the variations in the major ingredients, glass is also widely varied in its physical properties by the accidental or intentional addition of small amounts of other chemicals, such as sulphates, chlorides, carbon dioxide, fluorides, titanium, iron oxide, boric acid. The demands of lens makers have led to the development of many different kinds of glasses, with different optical properties. Glass with lead substituted for lime has vital uses in X-ray work, electrical insulation, as well as optics, and was formerly in great demand for cut-glass tableware.

Even ordinary glass has a great resistance to crushing pressure. Its strength is greater than that of granite, concrete, clay brick, or even cast iron. It has been said that "glass maintains its shape under pressures that cause metals to flow like putty." Glass brick is becoming more and more popular in building construction, combining as it does great strength with translucency.

Here the story of glassmaking is told in pictures.

SODA ASH

LIME

SAND

The basic ingredients of most glass are silica, sand, lime, and soda ash, mixed in tank furnaces under high temperature. A certain amount of cullet (broken glass fragments) is added to help the raw materials fuse. The bulk of the glass is silica. The lime contributes chemical resistance and surface hardness. The soda acts as a flux to aid in melting.

This huge clay pot contains nearly 2,000 pounds of molten glass, which is about to be transferred from the furnace to a casting table, where it will be made into plate glass. By far the greatest use of glass is for window panes.

Molten glass poured out of the pot cascades through iron rollers to form an orange colored carpet about 12 feet wide and 40 feet long. Power knives cut this rough product into two "blanks," which are then moved into an annealing chamber or "lehr" for slow cooling under automatic temperature controls.

Workmen trim the blanks as they emerge from the annealing lehr, and start them along a horizontal conveyor.

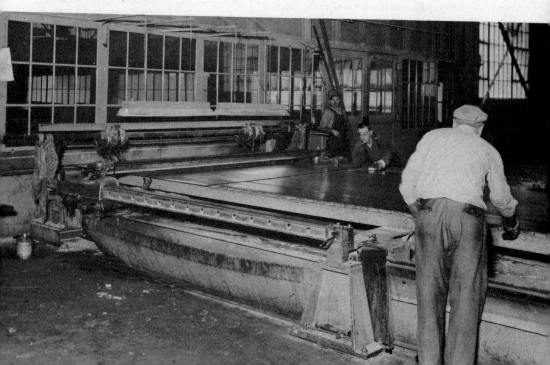

The conveyor moves the blanks under a crane, from which suction hoists are lowered to seize the blanks and transfer them to storage racks. A blank may be as large as 240 x 127 inches and weigh as much as 1,200 pounds.

Hundreds of blanks are stored here, waiting their turn to be ground and polished into fine plate glass for use in windows, mirrors, picture frames, wall panelling.

Two workmen in the background guide a blank as it is swung into position on the conveyor that will carry it to the finishing machines. In the foreground, another workman spreads a coat of Plaster of Paris on the conveyor. The plaster acts as an adhesive to hold the blank in place.

Both faces of the blank are ground to smoothness by a series of rotary soft iron disks, which are fed continuously with a sand solution. The sand progresses from coarse to fine as the glass moves down the line. After two trips down the grinding line, the blank is moved to the polishing line. Here, disks covered with soft felt polish the glass with "rouge" (iron oxide).

Cutting a finished glass blank into pieces of standard size. This task is not left to a machine, for the judgment of a skilled artisan is needed to avoid excessive waste.

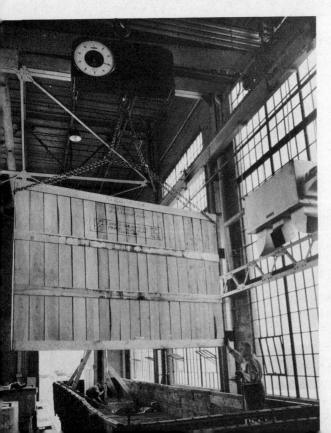

Plate glass, carefully crated and packed to withstand the shocks of travel, is loaded into railroad flatcars in the shipping shed of a glass factory. Note the workman in the rear nailing supports to hold a crate upright on the car. With the plate glass upright on edge, the jolting of the flatcar acts as a compression strain in the direction in which the glass is strongest.

A close-up of bottle-making molds. A measured amount of molten glass is poured into the "blank" mold at the right. Contact with the iron walls of the blank cavity chills the glass to correct forming temperature. The glass globule is then swung into the larger mold, shown on the left. Air blown into the glass presses it against the mold and forms the finished bottle, as shown on the extreme left.

Bottle-making in action. The two slugs of glass have just emerged from the blank mold and the finishing mold is swinging upon them from below. A blast of compressed air inside the slugs will bellow them out to the shape of a bottle.

Bottles and tumblers are placed in an annealing lehr immediately after being formed. A belt moves them slowly through gradually decreasing temperatures. This "tempering" prevents too rapid cooling, which would cause internal strains and excessive brittleness in the glass.

Expert inspectors examine glassware for cracks and other flaws after it emerges from the annealing lehr.

Individual craftsmanship is needed to make many types of glass vessels. The glass blower takes a gob of molten glass on one end of a steel tube and forms it into a bubble by blowing in the other end. He must watch the bubble and rotate the tube continuously in order to keep its walls of uniform thickness. Final shaping is made in an iron mold at his feet.

An expert glass blower shapes a large electronic tube. The girl is cooling the mold with a stream of water. The blow-pipe and tube must be rotated even while in the mold, so that the tube will show no mold marks or seams.

[305]

A heavy, clear glass called "crystal" is used in making artistic vases and other designs.

A craftsman puts the twist in what will be a vase in the shape of a cornucopia.

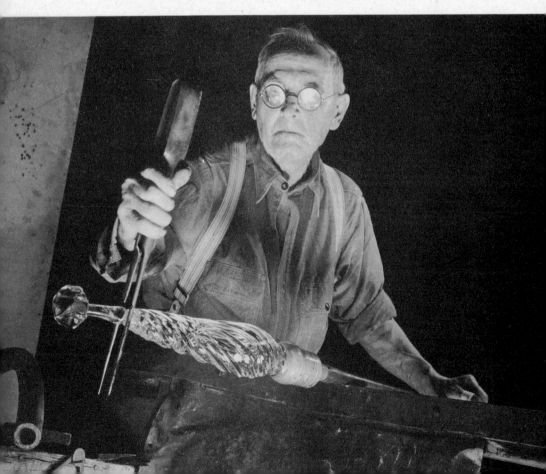

Grinding the rough edge around the mouth of a hand-blown glass vase. The "bubble ball" legs of the vase have been infused with air bubbles to add to the beauty of the finished piece. Modern hand-blown glass rivals the best of ancient times, when the secrets of fine glass-making were jealously guarded.

No mold was used in making this flare-mouth vase. The worker twirls the semi-molten glass on a pontil rod with his left hand, while his right forms it with special tools.

An example of artistic glass, this plate has the image of a white egret engraved on its underside. It is one of the "Audubon Series."

Beautiful craftsmanship in glass. Crystal horse, designed by Sidney Waugh.

Engraved crystal vase, designed by Peter Hurd. Many such beautiful pieces are treasured as works of art and collected by museums.

Glass block is often used to brighten stairways. It is translucent, and the ribbed design helps to diffuse sunlight. Glass block is hollow, with a partial vacuum inside, and therefore makes a good insulator against extremes of outdoor temperature.

Great increase in daylight illumination of schoolrooms is achieved by use of glass block. The block used in this Indiana high school are of special construction, containing tiny prisms that bend the light rays upward to the ceiling. Through reflection from the brightly painted ceiling, pupils farthest from the windows have almost as much daylight as those adjacent.

Fiberglass is a plastic with many uses. Drawn into fine threads like cotton wool, it makes a durable and highly heat-resistant insulator. Here are shown domestic water heaters receiving their insulating coats of Fiberglass.

Fiberglass can be woven into fabric to make blankets, sound-absorbing drapes, and the like. The girl in this picture is cutting out Fiberglass blankets, ten at a time.

Modern glass is tough. This picture made by a high-speed stroboscopic camera shows how a heat-treated glass tumbler bounces when it strikes the floor after falling off a table.

These Fiberglass-reinforced aircraft parts show the adaptability of the material to complex forms.

THE STORY OF MATCHES

Completed matches on an endless belt after dipping in the final coating bath.

Fire is one of the basic necessities of human life. We can only conjecture how primitive man first discovered the uses of fire, and obtained fire for his needs—perhaps from a volcano. During most of the historical era, only one fire-making device was used. This was flint and steel, which still survives in portable cigarette lighters and some other articles. Until the early nineteenth century, every family kept flint and steel on the hearth, every soldier carried a tinder box in his knapsack. Then the invention of matches put within reach of everyone a much cheaper, easier, and lighter device for making fire.

[313]

What Is Phosphorus?

The chemical basis of the match is phosphorus. Phosphorus is an element that oxidizes (burns) when exposed to air, generating enough heat to ignite paper or wood shavings. The element was discovered in 1669 by a Hamburg alchemist, Hannig Brandt, while he was experimenting with an olio that he hoped could reduce gold. The next 160 years saw many different attempts to utilize phosphorus in a practicable fire-making device.

What Were the Early Applications of Phosphorus?

In 1680, both Godfrey Haukwitz and Robert Boyle sold coarse sheets of paper coated with phosphorus, in combination with splinters of wood tipped with sulphur. When the splinters were drawn through a fold of the paper they burst into flame. Since the price of an ounce of phosphorus at that time was equivalent to $250 today, the clientele for these early matches was limited to the extremely wealthy. When the interest in the novelty ebbed, both the sales and experiments ceased.

In 1781 began a new cycle of inventions that culminated in the modern match. The first of these inventions was the Phosphoric Candle or Etherial Match, which appeared in France in that year. It consisted of paper tipped with phosphorus, sealed in a glass tube. Admission of air when the glass was broken set the paper to flaming. The Pocket Luminary (Italy, 1786) was a small bottle lined with oxide of phosphorus. Sulphur-tipped wood splints ignited when rubbed on this coating and withdrawn. The Instantaneous Light Box, invented in 1805, was highly popular with American gentlemen up to the time of the Mexican War, despite obvious dangers. Like the Luminary, it involved a small bottle, this one filled with sulphuric acid. The splints, treated with a composition of potassium chlorate, sugar and gum arabic, were called Empyrion or Oxymuriated Matches. The box and fifty splints retailed for two dollars.

The last of these elaborate early "matches" was the Electro-pneumatic Fire Producer, in which a fine jet of hydrogen gas was ignited by a spark from charged rosin. The chemist, Dobereiner, produced several types. He created gas by the action of sulphuric acid on zinc and directed it in a thin stream upon a platinum sponge in contact with the air. Several of Dobereiner's models still survive in museums.

How Else Has Phosphorus Been Applied?

Even after the birth of the match in its original modern form in 1827, inventors continued to contrive unusual means of producing fire. Self-lighting cigars of two types were introduced in Austria in 1839. In some of these a short splint of wood with a match head decorated with rosettes of linen were inserted in the tips. When the cigar was "struck," the smoker inhaled a combination of the fumes of match composition, burning wood and linen, but he had a light. Another type wore a frilly cap of treated paper much like the lacy "socks" placed on lamb chops in some restaurants. Pellet matches (1850) made of sawdust, flour and match

Graphic illustration of the steps in the manufacture of a box of matches, from the wood, chemicals and cardboard to the finished article.

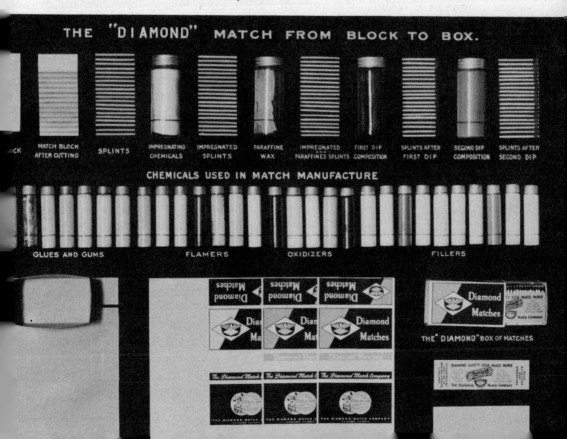

THE "DIAMOND" MATCH FROM BLOCK TO BOX.

MATCH BLOCK AFTER CUTTING · SPLINTS · IMPREGNATING CHEMICALS · IMPREGNATED SPLINTS · PARAFFINE WAX · IMPREGNATED AND PARAFFINED SPLINTS · FIRST DIP COMPOSITION · SPLINTS AFTER FIRST DIP · SECOND DIP COMPOSITION · SPLINTS AFTER SECOND DIP

CHEMICALS USED IN MATCH MANUFACTURE

GLUES AND GUMS · FLAMERS · OXIDIZERS · FILLERS

THE "DIAMOND" BOX OF MATCHES

composition were exploded by a plunger machine carried by users. Another pellet match came in strips like caps for a Fourth of July pistol and when detonated set fire to the paper holding them. "Wire Fixed Stars," "Chinese Lights," "Prussian War Fusees," and "Latchford's Bone Stem Cigar Lights Which Will Never Fall Off, Break Or Burn The Fingers In Using" are the names of some of the novel lights appearing in the 1860's.

In 1932, Foldi and Koenig, Austrian chemists, patented a "repeatedly ignitible rod" resembling a styptic pencil wrapped in cellophane. Actually it was an elongated match head, loaded with fire retardents to make it burn more slowly. Each of these matches was good for 40 lights if carefully nursed and were sold in Europe in packets of 3 for approximately 5 cents. Tried out in Holland, these repeatedly ignitible rods proved unsuccessful commercially.

Who Invented Friction Matches?

While Dobereiner was still manufacturing his elaborate Fire Producers, the first friction match had already been made and sold in England. The records of the apothecary, John Walker of Stockton-on-Tees, show that he sold to a Mr. Hixon "100 Sulphurata Hyperoxygeneta Frict." Later analysis indicated that Walker's matches were tipped with antimony sulfide, potassium chlorate, gum and starch. They were three inches long and were ignited by drawing them through a pleat of "glass paper."

Two years later, when Walker exhibited his matches to amazed Londoners, one of the spectators, Samuel Jones, was not too excited to note there was no protecting patent and he promptly set himself up in the match business. Jones named his matches "Lucifers." Their ignition was accompanied by a series of small showers of sparks and odors so offensive that this warning was printed on their boxes: "If possible, avoid inhaling gas that escapes from the combustion of the black composition. Persons whose lungs are delicate should by no means use Lucifers."

In 1830, about 160 years after its discovery, phosphorus was adapted by Dr. Charles Sauria, of France, as an ingredient for match heads. Sauria substituted it for antimony sulfide in the Walker formula and in so doing improved the efficiency of

The girl is feeding wooden blocks into a machine that cuts them into splints and sets the splints in an endless belt, which carries them upward to the impregnating baths.

matches, but also set off a wave of necrosis which was to exact a fearful toll of life among matchmakers and users for 80 years.

What Is Necrosis?

Necrosis is decay, particularly of the bones. It develops from the bodily absorption of small amounts of certain substances, of which phosphorus is one. Workers in match factories frequently developed "phossy jaw," so-called because the necrosis first attacked the jawbones.

This dreadful occupational hazard plagued American factories until 1911, when William A. Fairburn of the Diamond

Fixed in perforated metal blocks on the endless belt, these match sticks are about to be dipped in a chemical composition.

Match Company adapted harmless sesquisulfide of phosphorus to American climatic conditions. The new nonpoisonous formula was presented to the government for the use of all rival companies, a humanitarian gesture which won public commendation from President Taft and for which Mr. Fairburn and his company were given the Louis Livingston Seaman Medal "for the elimination of occupational disease."

Substitution of sesquisulfide of phosphorus in the formula accomplished other things. It raised the point of ignition more than 100 degrees, a considerable safety factor, and it ended fires caused by rodents. Experiments conducted by Mr. Fairburn proved conclusively that while rats and mice would gnaw on phosphorus matches, thus igniting them sometimes, they would not touch the new match heads even when starving.

Manufacture of the dangerous phosphorus matches began in America in 1836, when Alonzo Dwight Phillips, a Springfield, Massachusetts, powder maker, secured a patent for "new and useful improvements in modes of manufacturing friction matches for instantaneous light." Phillips made his phosphorus matches by hand and, when he had a wagon load, sold them himself from door to door, thus founding an industry which now produces about 500 billion matches each year in the United States.

What Is a Safety Match?

At that time, only one type of match existed, the wooden strike-anywhere that is sometimes called the "kitchen" match today. The discovery of red or amorphous phosphorus by Prof.

Anton von Schrotter in 1845 led to the development of another type of match, the safety, by Lundstrom ten years later. The safety match differs from the strike-anywhere only in one regard: part of the ingredients necessary to create fire are in the head of the safety match, part in the striking surface on the box.

When Did Book Matches Become Popular?

The third basic form of the modern match, the paper book kind, was the invention in 1892 of an attorney, Joshua Pussey. His books contained 50 matches, had the striking surface on the inside,

Black-tipped match sticks on the way to the final coating dip.

where sparks frequently ignited the remaining matches, a danger quickly corrected by the Diamond Match Company, which bought the patent in 1895. Unpopular at first and made by hand, book matches became big business in 1896, when a brewing company ordered 10,000,000 books to advertise their brews, forcing creation of machinery for swift production in volume. Today the industry manufactures 200 billion book matches annually in the United States, with about 196 billion being handed out free to customers of cigar stores, hotels, restaurants and railroads, a practice unknown in any other country.

When Were Machines Invented to Make Matches?

At the time of the Phillips patent, matches all over the world were made by hand on a piecework basis in the homes of the poor, a condition which led to the infection by necrosis of a considerable number of workers. This condition was alleviated by the invention of machines to replace hand labor.

[319]

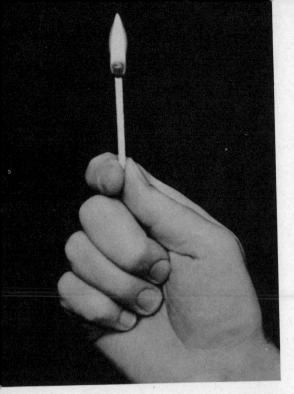

The first American patent for a machine to cut round splints was granted to Chauncey E. Warner in 1841. In 1842 came the invention of a machine by Reuben Partridge, which cut the wooden splints in bulk, ending tedious hand methods for this important process. Other inventors contributed to match machines, each performing a function, but real mechanical impetus came in 1883 when Ebenezer Beecher, of Connecticut, designed three "continuous" automatic matchmaking machines by combining all functions in one device. Beecher made these machines for Ohio Columbus Barber, of the newly formed Diamond Match Company, and they became the models for all future equipment in the industry.

The modern kitchen or "strike anywhere" match burns with a steady odorless flame. It solves once and for all one of the oldest of problems of man's civilization—how to obtain fire quickly, conveniently, and with a minimum of danger.

How Are Matches Made?

The methods used to manufacture all types of matches are basically the same. The wood or paper for the splints must be cut into proper size, dipped to create the heads, dried and assembled in books or boxes for retail sale. Hence the making of the strike-anywhere match on the modified Beecher machine gives a good overall picture of the processes involved.

The machines, 60 feet long, two stories high, convert blocks of straight-grained pine into packaged matches in 60 minutes at a rate as high as 1,125,000 an hour. The pine blocks, cured from 12 to 18 months, are fed into the head of the machine, where a row of from 42 to 57 dies cuts the splints and fixes them into perforations in an endless chain of metal plates, each with 12 rows of perforations. It is this operation which creates the visible indented collars at the holding tips of all round wooden matches.

The dies cut 350 rows of 42 to 57 splints each minute, setting them into the plates on which they ride through a series of five dips and baths which treat the wood against afterglow, provide a collar of paraffin to speed combustion, put on the main bulb and its "eye" and finally dip the heads with a solution which protects them from weather changes. Punched out of their plates after the final drying, the matches pour down a trough to drop into endless chains of boxes waiting for them. On the larger-size boxes an ingenious device turns the matches so that approximately half the heads are to the

Grinding chemicals to make the composition for match heads.

right, and the balance to the left, assuring a flat pack. The boxes, covers and wrappers for the matches are made in the same factories as the matches, synchronized so that matches and containers reach the packaging machinery simultaneously.

Some American factories have as many as 20 continuous automatic match machines, each capable of producing 10,000,000 matches in an eight-hour shift, a factory total of 200,000,000 each one-shift day. Shipment of a day's output would require five freight cars.

What Improvements Have Been Made in Matches?

Since the turn of the century match machinery has been constantly improved, and there have been three outstanding advances

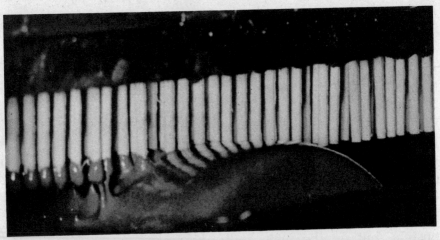

Close-up of the wood splints passing over the composition dip roll for their first chemical coating.

in American matches. The first of these, the nonpoisonous match, has already been discussed. The second was an improvement in the safety factor. It has been known, long before 1912, that match splints treated with an aqueous solution of ammonium phosphate retained no ember or afterglow when the match was blown out. Matches made under the veneer method (cut separately and dipped in composition in bundles) had been impregnated against afterglow simply by tossing them into vats of solution. But American matches were cut and made on a single machine which barred this method. But in 1912, fresh from his triumph with the nonpoisonous match, William A. Fairburn developed a spray attachment for the continuous match machine which would impregnate matches in course of manufacture. As with his previous development, Fairburn gave blue prints to the rivals of Diamond Match Company in the interests of fire prevention.

The war with the Axis powers resulted in another advance, the waterproof match, dream of match makers since the birth of the industry. The War Department needed a match that would function in the long rainy seasons of the South Pacific and called on the industry for help. Raymond Davis Cady, a chemist, produced a formula, approved by the Army, which resulted in matches that can still function after remaining under water for eight hours.

THE STORY OF TEXTILES

Creel room in a spinning mill. Creels are frames that guide the threads as they are fed into a loom.

THE NAME *textile* is applied to any woven material. Textiles are a vital part of our everyday living, in the form of clothes, blankets, curtains, rugs, chair coverings, mops. They are used to make many essential articles in commerce, industry, transportation; for example, in sails, tarpaulins, belting, parachutes. In addition, textiles form a part of a very long list of manufactured articles. To name just one item, think of the amount of thread that goes into insulating covers for electric wire.

Of What Are Textiles Made?

Until the present century, virtually all textiles were made from four natural products: flax, cotton, wool, and silk. The first two are of plant origin, and the others animal. Today, a fifth source has been added—plastics, which are man-made artificial products. Best-known of these new synthetic textiles are rayon and nylon.

There are three stages in the manufacture of a textile. The first is the gathering, cleaning, sorting, and other processing of the raw material. The second is *spinning*, in which the fibers of the raw material are twisted together to make continuous thread. The last stage is *weaving*, the manufacture of cloth out of thread.

What Is Flax?

Flax is a plant that grows from two to four feet high, with tapering green leaves and pale blue flowers. Few sights are lovelier than the shimmering blue carpet of a flax field in bloom. Flax grows best in a temperate climate, on level land with a plentiful supply of soft, fresh water. It has a great drawback as a cash crop, in that it can be harvested only once in seven years. After one yield, the land must be enriched for six years before it reaches a degree of fertility sufficient to grow another flax crop.

Ireland is thought of as the chief flax-producing country, for flax has been her major agricultural industry since the seventeenth century. But many other countries also produce flax, notably Russia, Belgium, Holland, Germany, and France.

What Is Linen?

The textile made from flax is called *linen*. The word comes from the Celtic *llin*. Records of the manufacture of llin or linen can be traced back to the thirteenth century in Ireland. But the linen industry did not become of prime importance to Ireland until 400 years later. Then the Irish were prohibited by the English from producing wool, so they turned to linen. They were aided by French Huguenot immigrants who had fled from France. Today, Belfast is the largest linen-manufacturing center in the world.

Beaming

Weaving

Carding

Gilling

Steps in the making of cloth.

Though the name linen is relatively recent, the cloth is the oldest we know. In the days of the Pharaohs, cloth made from flax was already the fabric of Egypt's aristocracy. The shrouds wrapped around the mummified bodies of Egyptian emperors, nobles, and priests are found to be of the finest linen.

The Romans manufactured linen too, and when they expanded northward into Europe they found flax under cultivation by the Gauls. The art of linen manufacture was carried into Britain by Roman imperial officers.

Throughout history, linen has held high rank among the textiles. Today it is used to make the finest grades of handkerchiefs, tablecloths, napkins, scarves, sheets, and towels. It is also used for light, heat-resistant clothing.

How Is Flax Processed?

The fibers of flax from which linen is made are imbedded in the woody core of the plant. The first step in dislodging the fibers is *retting*. The plants are soaked for seven days in warm water, until the wood is well rotted. Then it is passed through rollers that break the wood into pieces, and finally a kind of padding machine whips the wood away.

The fibers are cleaned, straightened, and combed. They are usually combed by hand first, then by a machine. After processing, the linen is dried in sunlight, which bleaches it to a pure white.

What Is Silk?

Silk is the fiber of a cocoon that the larva of the so-called silkworm spins around itself when it goes into its pupal stage. According to Chinese legend, silk was discovered about 2700 B.C., during the reign of the emperor Huang-ti. His wife, Si-ling-chi, while wandering in her garden, noticed a worm spinning itself a white shroud. Presently she found a completed cocoon. Taking it in her hands, she found that with great care she could unravel it into a single fine thread of great length. She nurtured the worms carefully, unwound many cocoons, and managed to spin the fine threads together to make a robe for the emperor.

Bolts of rayon cloth undergoing final inspection for flaws. Synthetic fibers can be woven, dyed and printed. They have largely replaced natural silk.

Whether this legend is true, it is certain that silk was woven into cloth by the Chinese many centuries before the Christian era. Silk culture was a jealously guarded industry, but the secret eventually leaked out. The story is that in A. D. 289 four Chinese girls were kidnapped and carried to Japan to teach the Japanese how to make silk. The industry flourished there and became one of the most important to the life of the country. Japan, too, tried to keep the secret of silk within its borders, but it leaked out to India, then Persia, and eventually to the whole world. But even today, the Far East remains the center of silk-making.

Silkworm culture is no easy task. The caterpillar subsists only on leaves of the mulberry tree, and eats an amazing amount. The trays of growing worms must be fed and cleaned. The worms

Nylon thread being wound on cones, preparatory for shipment to knitters and weavers.

must be moved from soiled to clean trays every day. The rooms in which they are housed must be kept constantly at a warm temperature.

The worm commences to spin its cocoon about thirty days after it has been hatched. The cocoon is finished in about four days. Then the silk farmer steams the cocoon, to kill the worm (now a moth) inside, and so prevent it from breaking the silk thread by emerging.

Each unbroken cocoon is made of a single long strand. Several strands must be wound together to make a thread strong enough for weaving.

Throughout the centuries, silk has been the aristocrat of textiles. The much-prized "cloth of gold" of the fourteenth, fifteenth and sixteenth centuries was made of a combination of gold and silk threads. Not until the very recent development of plastic textiles has any other rival to silk appeared for making the finest of women's clothing, stockings, as well as the costliest drapes and decorations.

What Is Cotton?

Cotton is the soft material taken from the boll (center section) of the cotton plant. Cotton grew wild in ancient India. Its value as a material for cloth was discovered about four thousand years ago. At the same time that the Egyptians were making linen and the Chinese were weaving silk, the people of India were spinning cotton.

The hangings in the Temple of King Solomon were of cotton. This cloth may have traveled all the way from India, or it may

Picking cotton in a Southern cotton field. Cotton holds a preëminent position not only as a natural textile but also as a base for many of the synthetic fibers.

have been woven in Mesopotamia from Indian cotton thread. Arabian traders, two thousand years ago, brought cotton cloth from India to Europe. The very word "cotton" comes from the Arabic *guton,* which later became the French *coton.*

Cotton fibers are shorter and finer than those of flax. The first cotton was therefore not spun with the heavy, hanging flax spindle, but with a small spindle set in a bowl of water. The spinner twisted the cotton and wrapped it around the spindle. This primitive Indian spindle grew into the great spinning machines of today. The spinning jenny, a machine that spins cotton many hundreds of times faster than any hand spinner can operate, was invented in England in the eighteenth century. Weaving machinery brought the industrial revolution to England, resulting in a great increase in her population and wealth.

Another great impetus to the use of cotton occurred in 1793, when an American, Eli Whitney, invented the cotton gin. This is a machine that separates the cotton seed from its fiber. A third great invention, made very recently, has completed the use of machinery in cotton-making from boll to cloth. This is the cotton picker, a harvester that at last solves the problem of separating cotton bolls from the plants. Mechanical cotton pickers are now being introduced in Southern States of the United States, replacing much hand labor.

America is the greatest producer of cotton, although the finest quality comes from Egypt. A remarkable thing about cotton is the variety of uses to which it has been put. In World War II, for example, the Quartermaster Corps of the United States Army stored more than 11,000 items made of cotton!

The basic raw material of rayon is cotton linters, the short fibers remaining on the cotton seed after the staple has been removed to make cotton yarn. Here cotton linters are being put into a chopping machine.

Sorting crude wool into different kinds and grades. Next it will be scoured, washed and dried.

As you read these lines, no matter where you are you can reach out and touch cotton. Whatever the textile of your clothing, it is largely put together with cotton thread. Your shoes are stitched with cotton. Your handkerchiefs and neckties and other accessories all contain cotton.

Sixty-five pounds of cotton are used in an automobile. All kinds of electric wires require cotton for insulation. Cottonseed oil is extensively used in cooking. During 1945-1946, the world produced over 21 million bales of cotton (a bale is 478 pounds). This was the smallest cotton crop in more than twenty years, but it was still far greater than the production of any other textile.

What Is Wool?

Wool is hair shorn from the backs of living sheep. These animals can produce a "crop" of wool over and over again.

Like the three other great textiles, wool traces its history back to ancient times. The English lake dwellers are known to have sheared wool from sheep for cloth-making. They drove their flocks into streams to wash them. The men stripped the wool from the sheep with sharp knives. Then the women carded the wool to remove impurities and spun it into thread. From these early times, wool has always been prized because it makes the most durable and warmest clothing.

Sheep are raised in almost every country, but Australia is by far the largest wool-producing country in the world. Australia produces twice as much wool as Argentina, her nearest rival in the industry. Other extensive producers are the United States, New Zealand, the Union of South Africa, Russia, and Uruguay.

Sheep were first introduced into the United States in 1609. The first American woolen mill was erected at Rowley, Massachusetts, thirty-five years later. Today there are estimated to be 55 million sheep in the country, some in every state.

Wool is also obtained from goats. The Angora goat, a native of Asia, and the Cashmere goat, of the Himalayan mountains, produce delicate and highly prized varieties of wool.

What Are Man-Made Textiles?

The modern invention of many different kinds of plastics has founded a new industry—the making of artificial textiles. These

are artificial in the sense that they are made of thread drawn from complicated chemical mixtures, instead of formed by natural fibers or natural hairs.

The most important of the new artificial textiles is *rayon*. It is made from cellulose, the chief substance in the cells of trees and all other woody plants. Purified pulp from spruce wood,

The synthetic Nylon mixture is forced through small holes in a metal plate, making fine filaments which are then wound together to form thread.

One of the notable developments made possible by synthetic fibers was a cloth with moiré markings that are permanent despite moisture. Here moiré-marked rayon is being rolled up as it comes from the loom.

Western hemlock, Southern pine and cotton plants is the raw material of rayon. Rayon thread is used both by itself and in combination with other textiles to make smooth, strong, and inexpensive fabric.

Nylon is an artificial textile produced solely by the E. I. du Pont de Nemours Company. Its best-known use is for women's stockings. When World War II cut off silk supplies from Japan, nylon and rayon stockings completely replaced silk. Nylon is also used in underwear, parachute fabric, sewing thread, etc.

Vinyon is made from natural gas and brine. Although its principal use is in industrial applications, it is also used in various kinds of clothing.

Even glass has now entered the textile field. The development of flexible glasses has produced a new textile with a fine, silklike appearance.

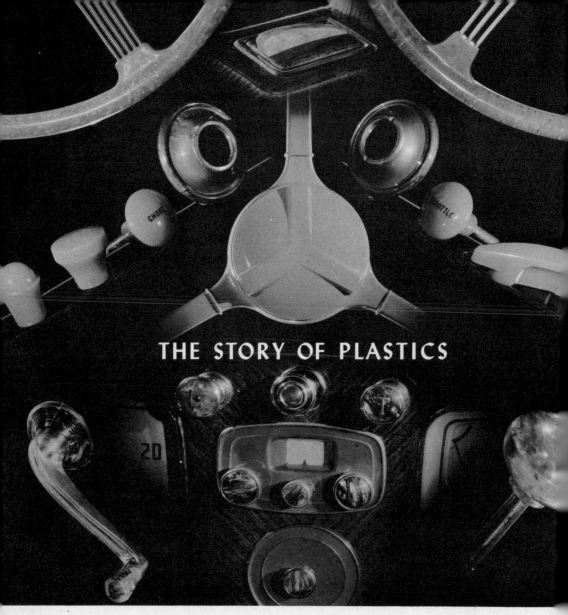

A few of the many parts of automobiles that are made from plastics.

THE creation of plastics is one of the great achievements of modern science. Thousands of articles that we use in daily life, as well as many others used in industry, are now made of plastics, replacing wood, glass, iron, steel and other substances. The growing list of plastics, already about a hundred, offers wide choice in weight, hardness, and toughness.

What Is a Plastic?

A plastic substance is one that can be molded to any desired shape. In this sense, common clay is a plastic. For most purposes, a plastic is widely useful only if, after being molded, it can be hardened so as to retain its shape. Clay is hardened by baking.

But the term "plastics" has been more narrowly defined in modern industry, as will be explained later. It now refers to certain artificial substances. But the great utility of plastics was shown long ago, when natural rubber first began to be used in industry. Rubber is a "natural plastic." It can be molded while soft, then hardened, and it can be given a variety of properties as to hardness, toughness, and so on, by mixture with different kinds and amounts of chemicals. It is, for example, "vulcanized" or made hard by the addition of sulphur. Hard rubber has long been used for electrical insulation, instrument panels, casings; we all know how vital rubber is in the manufacture of automobile tires; the very name "rubber" came from the use of soft rubber to rub out pencil marks.

Curiously enough, although this natural plastic, the sap of a tropical tree, has long been used, it was only recently that scientists began to make artificial plastics.

What Was the First Artificial Plastic?

The urgency that produced the first artificial plastic, which is to say, the first plastic in the modern sense, was the shortage of elephants in Africa! After the War Between the States, there was a great increase in the popularity of the game of billiards. Billiard balls had always been made of ivory, because of its extreme elasticity. Although hunters scoured Africa for elephants, or for elephant graveyards where there are large quantities of ivory, the demand for billiard balls outstripped the supply of ivory.

In desperation, an enterprising firm of billiard ball manufacturers offered a prize of ten thousand dollars to anyone who could produce a feasible substitute for ivory. Among others who set to work on the problem was John Wesley Hyatt, a young printer of Albany, N.Y. Hyatt ground up bits of wood, paper,

Even football helmets can be made of some of the new plastics.

rags, and mixed them with shellac and glue. But he found that this combination would not stick together adequately. In the course of his experiments he mixed cellulose and nitric acid. Since he was not a chemist, Hyatt did not realize that he was actually playing with guncotton, for nitrocellulose is the basis of many modern explosives. To this dangerous mixture, Hyatt finally tried adding camphor, and discovered that the substance could be molded and hardened satisfactorily. He christened it "celluloid." A vital fact about celluloid was that its final molecular structure was somehow different from that of the component nitrocellulose, no longer explosive. Although celluloid was unsuitable for billiard balls, and Hyatt did not win the prize, his discovery proved to be worth many times the value of the prize. He organized a company to make celluloid, and soon hundreds of articles were being made from this strange new substance. Celluloid film was the major factor in popularizing photography.

What Was the Second Plastic?

In 1889, the second plastic was created by a young Belgian, Leo Hendrik Bakeland. Bakeland was a brilliant inventor, whose first invention, a means of making a special photographic paper, was sold to an American company for a million dollars. In a laboratory at Yonkers, New York, he set out to create a synthetic shellac. In experimenting with a mixture of carbolic acid and formaldehyde, he discovered that this combination made a thick, syrupy substance that did not pour easily out of the test tube. He tried to soften it by heating it, but found that the heat only made it harder. He applied solvents and found to his astonishment that none took effect.

Bakeland began to study this strange dark substance he had created accidentally. He found it lighter in weight than metal or stone. It was chemically resistant and would not rust or corrode. It could be shaped by pouring it into a mold and letting it harden. Strangely enough, many years passed before this new plastic found a use. Not until 1907 was the so-called "Bakelite" manufactured for industrial use. Soon it came to be the standard material for telephone instruments and certain types of insulators.

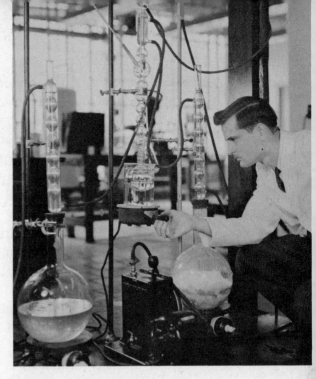

Behind the creation of every new plastic is long and patient work by chemists.

What Spurred the Development of Plastics?

During World War I new plastics began to appear as science and industry worked together to create new substances. The difficulty of obtaining certain raw materials made it vital to find substitutes. The search for a synthetic rubber began in earnest. The urgency was even greater in World War II, when Malaya, the chief source of rubber, and many other areas furnishing vital raw materials, were overrun. Government agencies joined forces with private industry in accelerated research for new plastics, many of which went into the making of munitions of war. With the coming of peace, dozens of these plastics were released for general use, such as rayon and nylon for women's stockings.

What Is a Modern Plastic?

The American Society for Testing Materials, which prepares standard tests for plastics, has defined a plastic as "any one of a large and varied group of materials, wholly or primarily organic in composition, which can be formed into useful shapes by the application, singly or together, of heat and pressure."

By "organic" is meant that these materials are composed largely of combinations of oxygen, hydrogen, nitrogen, and the other chief constituents of living matter. The raw materials from which plastics are synthesized are coal, air, water, lime, and vegetable by-products.

A classified list of commodities published by the Government contains approximately one hundred plastics, grouped into fourteen different types. Some familiar products made from seven of these types are as follows:

Phenolic—telephone handsets.
Polyamide—nylon stockings.
Alkyd—house paint.
Vinyl—shower curtains.
Acrylic—cigarette cases, compacts.
Cellulose—rayon fabrics.
Amino—closures for cosmetic jars and bottles.

These cotton linters are going into the making of a modern plastic.

A stage in the manufacture of a plastic fabric.

In What Forms Is Plastic Used?

Plastics differ widely in their characteristics: rigid, flexible; light, heavy; tough, brittle; opaque, translucent, transparent. They are colored black, white, green, blue, red, yellow, silver, and every other hue. They also differ in the form in which they are applied, but fall chiefly into four categories: molded or fabricated, laminated, fibrous, and liquid.

Most familiar to us are the molded plastics. Such articles as fountain pens, toothbrush handles, radio knobs, automobile steering wheels, are cast in molds and then hardened. Other articles are fabricated (tooled or finished) from rough castings. Some plastics are elastic and have a rubberlike consistency; they are

[339]

Plastic pellets are used to clean carbon from automobile engine pistons.

used for insulation on electric wiring, kitchen aprons, shoe soles. Synthetic rubber itself a plastic of this group.

Less familiar, because largely confined to industrial uses, is laminated plastic. It is so-called because layers (laminæ) of fabric, paper, wood, glass, or other material are pressed and bound together with plastic resins. This laminate is used to fabricate gears, pulleys, wheels, electrical parts, and many other like articles. Some laminates are made for decorative purposes, such as wall panels and table tops often seen in restaurants and night clubs. Laminates are even used for large-scale construction, as in boat hulls and airplane fuselages.

Fibers made of plastic go into rayon in all its varieties, nylon (in toothbrush bristles as well as stockings), upholstery fabrics, elastic belting for suspenders and belts, decorative fabrics in women's hats and handbags. Some of these fibrous plastics are derived from milk, soy beans, corn meal.

Liquid plastics are marketed to make coatings for other adhesives for binding paper, wood, metal; to make fire-proofing materials, such as paper, metal, wood, and textiles; to make water-proofing and wear-proofing agents.

What Are Commandos?

The word "Commando" was applied in South Africa to quasi-military expeditions of the Portuguese and Dutch Boers against the natives. It was revived by the British in 1941, during World War II, to denote picked and specially trained troops for such undertakings as surprise attacks on towns, undercover raids on power stations.

THE STORY OF THE TELESCOPE

The 40-inch telescope of the Yerkes Observatory. The entire floor under the telescope can be moved up or down. Shown here is the floor at its highest position.

For the men who study the stars, the telescope is the most important tool. With the glass, metal, and mirrors that make up the telescope, men can see thousands of times farther and more clearly than with the naked eye.

The word telescope comes from the Greek words *tele*, meaning "afar off," and *skopein*, "to view." Although men have studied the heavens for many centuries, the first telescope was made only a little more than 300 years ago.

The most important part of the first telescope was the glass that is used to magnify distant objects. While the ancient Egyptians made glass as far back as 3500 B. C., the first glass that could be seen through dates from 660 B. C. The lens is a piece of glass, in shape either concave (curving inward) or convex (curving outward) or a combination of both. The earliest description of the magnifying properties of the lens is recorded by Alhazen, an Arabian of the eleventh century.

Soon after this, lenses were shaped into spectacles, as an aid to poor eyesight. Spectacles spread rapidly through Europe, but

The floor of the Yerkes Observatory at its lowest point. At its highest point it is level with the circular balcony seen against the brick wall.

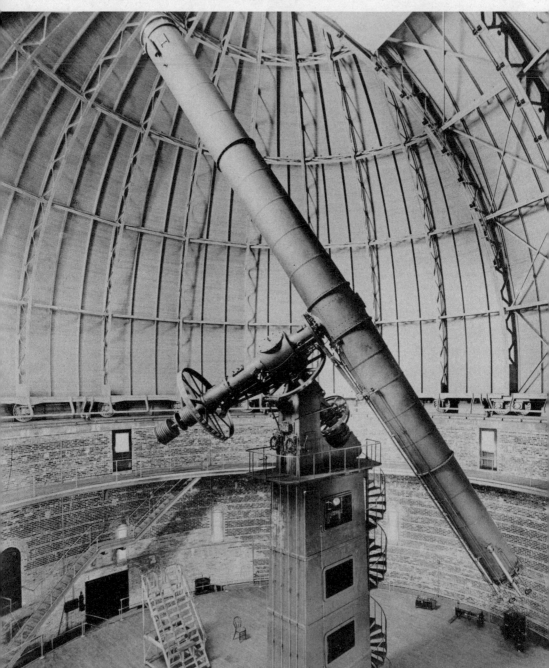

it was not until the early part of the seventeenth century that anyone saw the possibilities of a telescope made from these optical lenses. Then it took place quite by accident.

Who Invented the Telescope?

The story goes that Jan Lippershey, a spectacle lens maker of Middelburg, Holland, happened to hold a convex lens in one hand and a concave lens in the other. By chance he held them in a line and looked through them both at the village church steeple. He was surprised to notice that the steeple seemed much nearer and larger than when he looked at it without the lenses.

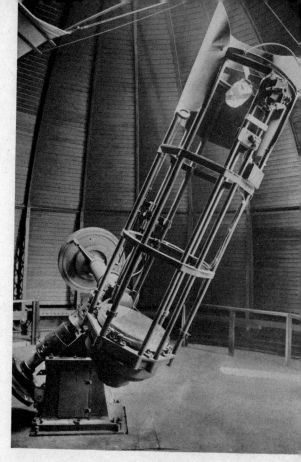

The 24-inch reflector telescope of the Yerkes Observatory, Wisconsin.

What Is a Refracting Telescope?

Lippershey was quick to act upon his discovery and designed the first telescope. He placed the two lenses at either end of a tube, probably made of paper. He used a large convex lens as the *objective* lens, through which the rays of light come. The concave lens, to which he put his eye, was called the *ocular*, or eyepiece. This was the first *refracting* telescope, so called because its lenses bend the light rays for the viewer.

The great Italian scientist, Galileo, first applied Lippershey's telescope to search out the mystery of the skies. Improving on the Dutchman's work, Galileo used the telescope to make many of his important astronomical discoveries. That is why the early instruments are known as Galilean telescopes.

[343]

The dome of the Mount Wilson Observatory in California. The upper half of the dome can turn in a complete circle. The curved shutters can be drawn together in bad weather.

Other improvements were made by Johannes Kepler, the famous German astronomer. He substituted a convex lens for the concave eyepiece used in the Galilean telescope. The change refracted light rays inwardly instead of outwardly, and so gave a larger field of view.

Before long, as larger and larger instruments were designed, telescope makers discovered that the images they created were no longer sharp and clear. Later this trouble was traced to spherical aberration, distortion caused by the break-up of light waves through the varying thicknesses of lenses. Another problem was posed by chromatic aberration, distortion caused by light rays breaking down into different colors. These problems were eventually solved, but not for another 100 years. In the meantime, experiments were made with clumsy, outdoor telescopes, sometimes strung on ropes and pulleys on a horizontal bar as long as 150 feet.

What Is a Reflecting Telescope?

Because of aberrations, the limit of the size of the refractors was soon reached. In 1663 a Scottish mathematician, James Gregory, announced his invention of a new type of instrument— the *reflecting* telescope—that employs mirrors to do most of its work. Gregory's telescope consisted of a large mirror to reflect the image of the sky. This image was reflected to a smaller mirror, which in turn reflected the light rays to a lens that served as eyepiece. Sir Isaac Newton and several others improved and modified Gregory's original reflector, until Sir William Herschel, a German who migrated to England, constructed a reflector in 1789 with a 48-inch mirror weighing more than a ton. The later reflectors eliminated the use of one of the mirrors.

The major difficulty encountered with reflecting telescopes was that the mirrors soon lost their polish and became dull and useless. While this difficulty was being solved, refractors (now equipped with fine optical glass to do away with aberrations) came into favor again during the 1800's. But in the past 50 years, reflectors have again become the more popular.

Today both types are used, each for special purposes. The reflector, because it can be made inexpensively, is the instrument of our many amateur astronomers. Our large observatories use

The 100-inch telescope at the Mount Wilson Observatory, Mount Wilson, California. The 100 inches referred to is the diameter of the big reflector at the base of the telescope.

Plastic model of the 200-inch Mount Palomar telescope in California with which the California Institute of Technology will study the skies.

Drawing of the 200-inch Mount Palomar telescope in the tremendous observatory that houses it. Through this giant telescope the moon will appear only 40 miles away.

The 200-inch Mount Palomar telescope pointing farthest north as seen from the control desk. Here the nose of the telescope is sunk into the horseshoe-shaped north end of the supports.

both kinds. The refractor is the better instrument when fine detail is wanted, as in the study of the planets. But there is a limit to the refractor's practical size. For viewing distant stars and exploring unknown regions of space, the reflector is preferred.

Where Are Our Largest Telescopes?

The greatest giant of all telescopes is located on Mount Palomar, 125 miles east of Pasadena, California. Its mirror is twice as large as the next biggest telescope "eye," the 100-inch telescope on Mount Wilson, also in California. The new glass giant will explore 27 per cent more of the universe and will photograph stars far, far away, stars we cannot now see. It will take pictures of stars more than 100,000 times fainter than the faintest star now visible to our eyes.

The Palomar reflecting telescope will not magnify much more than the 100-inch instrument, but it will gather far more light and will make many more stars and nebulæ visible for the study of our astronomers. Construction started in 1935, but was interrupted because of the war. It cost $6,000,000, weighs almost 500 tons, and is housed in an observatory more than 10 stories high. It is set on a 5,568-foot mountain far from any cities, and it may bring forth new truths about our universe never dreamed of up to the present.

Other large reflecting telescopes are located at the University of Michigan, the University of Texas, and the University of Toronto, Canada. In the Southern Hemisphere, where

This drawing shows how astronomers are lifted by a special elevator to the rear end of the 200-inch telescope. The ribbed structure of the underside of the great mirror can be seen above the hanging platform to which the elevator rises.

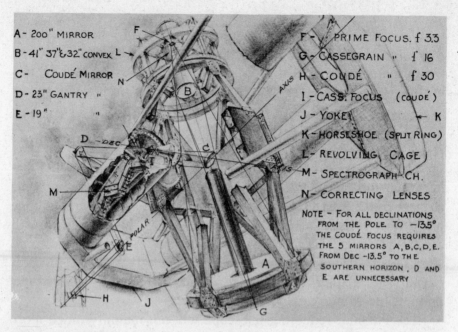

A - 200" MIRROR
B - 41" 37" & 32" CONVEX
C - COUDÉ MIRROR
D - 23" GANTRY "
E - 19" "

F - PRIME FOCUS. f 3.3
G - CASSEGRAIN " f 16
H - COUDÉ " f 30
I - CASS. FOCUS (COUDÉ)
J - YOKE
K - HORSESHOE. (SPLIT RING)
L - REVOLVING CAGE
M - SPECTROGRAPH CH.
N - CORRECTING LENSES

NOTE – FOR ALL DECLINATIONS
FROM THE POLE TO –13.5°
THE COUDÉ FOCUS REQUIRES
THE 5 MIRRORS A, B, C, D, E.
FROM DEC –13.5° TO THE
SOUTHERN HORIZON, D AND
E ARE UNNECESSARY

Diagram showing the many different combinations of mirrors that can be used in the 200-inch telescope. Points A, B, C, D, and E are all mirror lenses of different diameters.

astronomers see a different set of stars, the largest observatories are located near Bloemfontein, South Africa; Cordoba, Argentina; and Melbourne, Australia. Russia, Sweden, Italy, Germany, Scotland, and England have reflectors ranging from 36 to 48 inches.

The largest refractor telescope is at Yerkes Observatory, Williams Bay, Wisconsin. One of the oldest astronomical centers is the Royal Observatory of Great Britain. Located at Greenwich, near London, it was founded by King Charles II in 1675. It is the point from which the earth's longitude is reckoned. Many important astronomical and navigational discoveries were made at the Royal Observatory, which is directed by an Astronomer Royal appointed by the king.

The science of radar and electronics may soon add many new devices to improve our telescopes. And, with the coming of rocket space-ships, astronomers are thinking hopefully of the day when an observatory can be established on the moon. Without clouds and with a low gravitational pull, the moon would be an ideal location.

[348]

THE STORY OF THE STARS

This spiral nebula in the constellation of Andromeda is an "Island Universe." Light traveling from it at the rate of 186,000 miles a second reaches us in 900,000 years.

THE sun is one of the most familiar things in our lives, yet very few of us realize how vital it is to our existence. Its rays are the source of all our light and heat. From the sun come all the life and energy on the earth. Without it, there would be no food, no flowers or trees, no animal life. When we use coal and oil to heat our homes and run our automobiles and factories, we are really using the sun's energy.

Although it is difficult to believe, we know that our sun is a star, just like the others in the sky. It appears so much larger simply because it is closer to us than any other star. It is

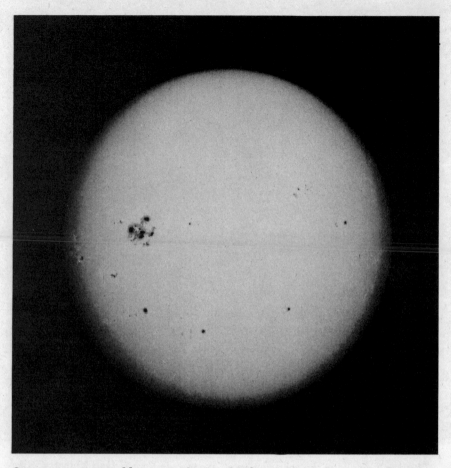

Our sun is a star just like many others in the sky. It appears larger to us because it is closer to us than any other star. The sun's surface temperature is about 10,000 degrees Fahrenheit. The spots visible in this picture are thought to be explosions of gases that burst through the sun's surface.

93,000,000 miles from the earth. Although this is a great distance, light travels so quickly that the sun's rays reach the earth in a little more than eight minutes.

How Large Is the Sun?

It would take more than a million earths to make a star as large as the sun. The sun has a diameter of 866,000 miles, but it is hundreds of times smaller than Antares or Betelgeuse, two of the brightest stars. The sun's surface has an estimated temperature

The moon has many craters on its surface. Temperatures on the moon rise as high as 265° Fahrenheit and fall to 116° below zero at night. There is no ice, no wind, and no running water on the still, dead surface of the moon.

of 10,000° Fahrenheit, and its center is much hotter. To generate as much heat as the sun radiates, a power station on earth would have to burn many thousands of millions of tons of coal every second.

A photograph of the moon taken through the 40-inch Yerkes Observatory telescope at Williams Bay, Wisconsin. The large crater in the center of the photograph has a diameter of 64 miles and its walls rise to a height of 18,000 feet.

Scientists can recognize in the sun many elements which we know on earth. These have been detected in the gases on the sun's surface by the use of an instrument called a spectograph. More than sixty of the chemical elements, such as hydrogen, oxygen and helium, are found on the sun. So are elements such as iron, copper, aluminum, nickel, silver and lead. Because of the sun's intense heat, these are present in gaseous form instead of as metals.

What Is the Solar System?

By the solar system we mean the earth and the other eight planets, and their moons, or satellites. They are the sun's family, rotating in a regular course about the sun, just as the moon goes around the earth. The sun holds its family in place by the force of gravity. The planets, which get their name from the Greek word meaning wanderer, have no light of their own. When we see a planet, we are really seeing the reflected light of the sun's rays.

[352]

The nine planets of the solar system, in order of their distance from the sun, are Mercury, Venus, the earth, Mars, Jupiter, Saturn, Uranus, Neptune and Pluto. They get their names from the gods of ancient Roman mythology.

Mercury, smallest of the planets, is difficult to see. It is less than half the earth's size, and takes only eighty-eight days to go around the sun. Venus is often called the earth's twin because it is almost the same size as the planet we inhabit. It is visible early in the evening, when it is called the evening star. When seen just before dawn, it is called the morning star. Venus is covered with dense clouds, and it has a higher temperature than the earth because it is nearer the sun.

This is not the moon but a crescent phase of the planet Venus. Often called the earth's twin because it is almost the same size, the planet Venus is covered with dense clouds and has a higher temperature than the earth because it is nearer to the sun.

We can distinguish Mars in the sky because it shines with a red light. It gets its color from the soil on its surface, believed to contain large quantities of iron rust. This planet is only half the earth's size, but is similar in several ways. It is the planet which scientists believe is the most likely to have animal life. Like the earth, Mars has polar ice caps. It has two small moons revolving about it.

Between Mars and its next neighbor, Jupiter, there is a vast space containing hundreds of tiny worlds called planetoids or asteroids. A powerful telescope is necessary to see even the largest of them.

Jupiter is the largest of the nine planets, and has eleven moons. Saturn is the next largest planet. It is a beautiful pale orange color and is surrounded by three rings. Besides these rings, Saturn has nine moons. Saturn, nine times the earth's size, is composed of materials lighter than water. Uranus, with its

Occasional visitors to the sun's family of planets are the comets that flash through the sky. They are composed of flaming particles and gases. Seen above is Brooks's Comet, which was first photographed in 1911. The tail of this comet, composed of luminous vapors, was 35 million miles long.

four moons, is nearly two billion miles from the earth. It takes eighty-four of our years to make one complete journey around the sun.

Neptune is so far from the sun that its temperature is as low as 364° below zero Fahrenheit. It was thought to be the planet farthest from the sun, but in 1930, astronomers discovered Pluto. There may be still more planets beyond Pluto, waiting to be discovered by astronomers.

What Are Comets?

There are also occasional visitors to the sun's family, outside of the planets and their moons. These are called comets, large masses of small particles and gases. They have long tails, and look like flaming snakes hurtling through the sky. The most famous of them is Halley's Comet, which can be seen every seventy-five years. You may be able to see it on its next visit in 1985.

[354]

How Was the Solar System Formed?

No one knows exactly how the solar system was formed. No one could even tell you very much about the origin of the earth, which is at least three billion years old. One theory about the solar system says that a star came extremely close to the star which is now our sun. Great masses of matter were attracted away from the sun by this star. These burning masses were drawn so far out that the sun did not have enough power to draw them all the way back. But they did stay within the gravitational pull of the sun. They gradually cooled off, condensed, and became the planets.

What Do We Know About the Moon?

Through the gigantic Mount Palomar 200-inch telescope, the moon appears to be only thirty miles away. Actually, its distance from the earth is 238,000 miles. The moon is ¼ the size of the earth, with a diameter of 2,163 miles. We can see clearly its mountains, craters and plains. But we have become acquainted with only one side of the moon. During the time it revolves about the earth, once every 27⅓ days, it always keeps the same side toward us. This is because it rotates on its own axis at the same rate that it travels around the earth.

There is no life on the moon—and it would be thoroughly uncomfortable if there were, to say the least. Because there are no air or clouds on the moon, it is at the complete mercy of the sun's rays. Its temperature rises to 265° Fahrenheit during the day, and falls to 116° below zero at night. With no ice, wind or running water, the surface of the moon does not change as our earth's face does.

What Causes the Tides?

The earth holds the moon in its orbit by the force of gravity. In the same way, the moon exerts force on the earth. We can see this most easily in the rise and fall of the water on the shores of our oceans. These tides are caused by the pull of the moon,

[355]

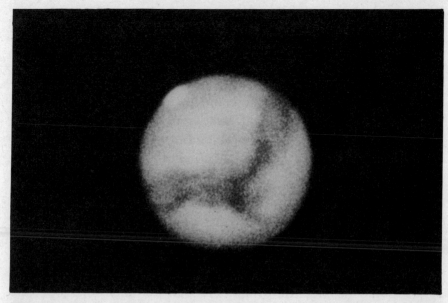

The planet Mars is farther from the sun than our earth. Only half the earth's size, it is the planet most likely to have animal life. The round, white spot noticeable in this picture is thought by scientists to be one of Mars's polar ice caps, similar to those on our earth.

and, to a lesser degree, by the pull of the sun. All parts of the earth are attracted by these forces. But water, which covers three-quarters of the earth, reacts most freely. There are two low and two high tides in each twenty-four hours and fifty minutes. Highest tides of the month, called spring tides, occur when the moon is full and at the time of the new moon. These are the days when the moon and sun are both exerting their gravitational pull upon the earth in the same direction.

Why Does the Moon Wax and Wane?

This relation between the moon and sun explains something about the different phases of the moon, its varying appearance. We can see only the part of the moon's surface which is facing toward the sun. When the moon is nearly in the west at sunset, it is almost directly between us and the sun. The sun is then shining on the moon's side mostly away from us, and only a tiny crescent of the half facing us is illuminated.

We can see the full moon, with its entire face shining, rising in the east just before the sun sets. The new moon, with no light reflected from its surface, also rises in the east, at dawn. By evening it has crossed to the western sky. Each night after that we see it twelve degrees of the compass farther east, as it waxes, or shows more light. By two weeks later, it has become a full moon, rising in the east at sundown. Then for another two weeks it wanes, or shows less light, until it is once again a new moon. The moon rises fifty minutes later each day. For this reason, high and low tides at any one point also occur fifty minutes later each day.

The largest of all planets is Jupiter. It has eleven moons and is farther away from the sun than Mars. This photograph was made through the 60-inch reflector telescope at the Mount Wilson Observatory, California, using ultraviolet light.

[357]

Saturn is a beautiful pale orange color and is surrounded by three strange rings. It is nine times the size of the earth and has nine moons. Saturn is the second largest planet and is composed of materials lighter than water.

What Do the Stars Mean to Us?

On a dry, clear evening you can look up and see one of the most beautiful sights of nature—the stars in their unending glory. We can add much to our enjoyment and wonder of the star-filled heavens if we learn to recognize some of the constellations, or star groups. Since the stars remain in the same position relative to each other, these constellations were known to our ancestors just as we know them today. But as the earth moves, we see different sections of the sky. People living in South America see entirely different constellations from people living in North America.

Among the most familiar constellations are the Big Bear (Ursa Major) and the Little Bear (Ursa Minor). We know seven stars of the Big Bear as the Big Dipper. The handle and bowl of the dipper are quite distinct. The two stars at the bowl's end are called the pointers. They always point toward Polaris, the North Star. You can get your direction if you remember that Polaris is always directly north.

Parts of the Little Bear make up the Little Dipper. Polaris is the end star in the handle of the Little Dipper. Other prominent constellations we can recognize easily were named after animals—the horse, the dog, the bull, the lion, the goat and the whale. Many star groups were given the names of Greek and Roman heroes and heroines, such as Perseus, Andromeda and Cassiopeia.

While gazing into the sky, you may have been startled by a shooting star, or meteor. These meteors race through the sky, usually burning themselves out. Although millions of meteors enter the earth's atmosphere every day, only a very few ever strike the earth. When they do, they are called meteorites. The largest meteorite in the United States weighs 15½ tons.

Situated in the midst of the constellation called Orion is an immense mass of luminous gas known as the Great Nebula. It is the largest of all the nebulæ and can be seen with the naked eye. The gases in it are mostly helium, oxygen, hydrogen and nitrogen.

There are about three thousand stars visible to the eye on a clear night. With field glasses and telescopes, we can see even more. With the one hundred-inch telescope on Mount Wilson in California, one billion stars have been photographed.

We also have planetariums to give us an indoor view of the heavens. Planetariums are optical instruments, placed in large buildings with dome-shaped ceilings. On these ceilings, a projection lantern flashes views of the heavens, pictures of what we might see in the actual sky. By showing us different views, the planetarium can bring us a picture of the sky as it appears in the various seasons, or in other parts of the world. The planetarium experts can figure out how the sky looked centuries ago, or how it will look in the future—and show it all to us on the ceiling as we sit comfortably in the darkened room.

Stars have practical uses, too. They have been helpmates to seafarers for centuries. By carefully observing the stars and moon, sailors can determine the exact positions of their ships. By using a sighting device called a sextant, ships' navigators "shoot" the sun, and have still another way of determining their location.

What Is an Eclipse?

An eclipse is an interception or obscuration of the light of the sun, moon or other heavenly body by the intervention of ancther and nonluminous heavenly body. Stars and planets may suffer eclipse, but the principal eclipses are those of the sun and the moon.

An eclipse of the moon is an obscuration of the light of the moon occasioned by the interposition of the earth between the sun and the moon; consequently all eclipses of the moon happen at full moon; for it is only when the moon is on that side of the earth which is turned away from the sun, and directly opposite, that it can come within the earth's shadow. Further, the moon must at that time be in the same plane as the earth's shadow; that is, the plane of the ecliptic in which the latter always moves. But as the moon's orbit makes an angle of more than five degrees with the plane of the ecliptic, it frequently happens that though the moon is in opposition it does not come within the shadow of the earth.

The theory of lunar eclipses will be understood from Figure 1, where S represents the sun, E the earth, and M the moon. If the sun were a point of light, there would be a sharply outlined shadow of umbra only, but since the luminous surface is so large, there is always a region in which the light of the sun is only partially cut off by the earth, which region is known as the penumbra $(P\ P)$. Hence during a lunar eclipse the moon first enters the penumbra, then is totally eclipsed by the umbra, and then emerges again through the penumbra.

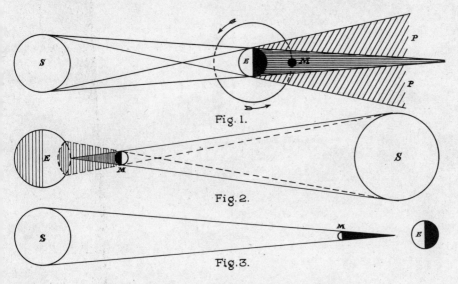

Diagrams Illustrating the Theory of Eclipses

An eclipse of the sun is an occultation of the whole or part of the face of the sun occasioned by an interposition of the moon between the earth and the sun; thus all eclipses of the sun happen at the time of new moon.

Figure 2 is a diagram showing the principle of a solar eclipse. The dark or central part of the moon's shadow, where the sun's rays are wholly intercepted, is here the umbra, and the light part, where only a part of them are intercepted, is the penumbra; and it is evident that if a spectator be situated on that part of the earth where the umbra falls there will be a total eclipse of the sun at that place; in the penumbra there will be a partial eclipse, and beyond the penumbra there will be no eclipse.

As the earth is not always at the same distance from the moon, and as the moon is a comparatively small body, if an eclipse should happen when the earth is so far from the moon that the moon's shadow falls short of the earth, a spectator situated on the earth in a direct line between the centers of the sun and moon would see a ring of light around the dark body of the moon; such an eclipse is called annular, as shown in Figure 3; when this happens there can be no total eclipse anywhere, because the moon's umbra does not reach the earth.

The average number of eclipses in a year is four, two of the sun and two of the moon; and as the sun and moon are as long below the horizon of any particular place as they are above it, the average number of visible eclipses in a year is two, one of the sun and one of the moon.

THE STORY OF THE WEATHER

Stratocumulus clouds are low and usually bring rain. They occur locally and usually do not cover a large area.

OUR world is built on the bottom of a vast ocean of gases that cling to the earth in its spinning flight through space. This ocean of air reaches into our daily lives in many different and often unnoticed ways. Its strange, variable character affects the clothes we wear, the cost of the food we eat, our health, and our habits. Even our occupations and ways of life depend on it.

What Is Air Made Of?

The ocean of air is an enormous but delicate mixture of the lightest things on earth. About one-fifth of it at the earth's surface is oxygen, the element that sustains all animal life. With much more or much less oxygen, man would not be able to survive.

Clouds are classified according to a system agreed upon internationally in 1932. These are cirrus clouds in parallel trails and small patches.

Most of the rest is nitrogen, which furnishes nourishment to plants and dilutes the oxygen to the correct proportion for man's needs. Only 3 parts in 10,000 are carbon dioxide, but without this element all plant life would perish, dooming man and the entire animal kingdom. Small, varying proportions of water vapor protect us from the sun's intense heat and bring rain to the farmers.

What Is the Pressure of the Air?

We seldom think of air as having weight, but a cubic yard of it weighs more than 2 pounds. The sky above us contains more than 5½ million billion tons of air. That is more than the weight of the entire Mediterranean Sea! Air is so heavy that it presses

Fleecy, cottonlike clouds are typical of periods of good weather in summer. This type is called the cumulus or fair weather cloud.

against us in all directions with a force of about 15 pounds on every square inch, more than a ton on every square foot.

How Is Air Pressure Measured?

At any given spot on the earth, the pressure of air varies from time to time, and these variations are very important to the weather man, or meteorologist, in helping him forecast the weather. To measure these variations, he uses an instrument called a barometer. A mercury barometer, the most accurate instrument of this kind, enables him to determine air pressure simply by measuring the height of a column of mercury enclosed in a glass tube. Mercury is the heaviest fluid we know, but at sea level, air pressure ordinarily supports a column of mercury about 30 inches high.

Sometimes, however, the column of mercury falls below 30 inches, indicating that pressure is "low." At other times it rises to

Cumulus and cumulonimbus cloud. The large cloud has just grown into a cumulonimbus. This type usually precedes thunderstorms in summer. In winter it produces hail, rain or snow.

perhaps as high as 31 inches. Then the pressure is "high." To the weather man, a falling barometer usually means an approaching storm, while a rising barometer means that cooler, clearer weather is coming.

What Causes Wind?

Air pressure also varies from place to place, and these variations are the cause of winds. The pressure of air is the force it exerts not only downward but in every direction. The force is greater where the pressure is high, so that air from high-pressure areas pushes its way into regions of lower pressure.

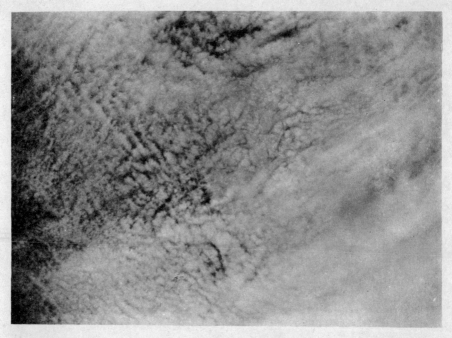

Cirrocumulus cloud. This type is composed of ice crystals and usually appears at altitudes between 20,000 and 40,000 feet. The air within such a cloud is rough and turbulent.

The earth has seven main pressure belts. At the North and South Poles, where air is cold and heavy, average barometer readings are high. Around the Arctic and Antarctic Circles, the readings are generally low. Around the horse latitudes, just north of the Tropic of Cancer and south of the Tropic of Capricorn, the pressure is high, while around the equator it is low.

We can, therefore, draw a general picture of how the great masses of air circulate on the earth's surface. In every case, wind blows from a high-pressure region to a low-pressure region, but because of the rotation of the earth it swerves to the right in the Northern Hemisphere and to the left in the Southern Hemisphere.

In the Northern Hemisphere, there are three main wind belts. Winds in the Arctic generally blow from the northeast. In the temperate zone, they blow from the southwest and west—the "prevailing westerlies." In the tropics, the so-called trade winds blow from the northeast. Similarly, in the Southern Hemisphere there are three main winds: the southeasterlies in the Antarctic,

[366]

Altocumulus cloud. The laminated form results from degeneration of the cloud sheet. This type is found at medium altitudes, between 6,500 and 20,000 feet. Altocumulus clouds often appear at different levels at the same time, and the air beneath them is often hazy.

Making a snow survey in the Chequamegon National Forest, Wisconsin. The snow sampler tube with its core of snow is weighed, and from the figures the Weather Bureau can calculate how much underground water there will be in the surrounding watershed during the following summer.

the prevailing westerlies of the temperate zone, and the southeasterly trade winds of the tropics.

Air above certain parts of the world takes on characteristics of the surface below and then rides these winds, carrying weather conditions from place to place. In winter, for example, a great mass of heavy, cold air forms over Canada's ice-cold MacKenzie Valley. This is a large high-pressure area, and sometimes it stretches down into the United States where a piece of it may break off and drift eastward in the prevailing westerly wind, bringing cold, clear weather. Such a vagrant mass of polar air forms a local high-pressure area.

In summer, northern Mexico and the southwestern areas of the United States receive hot, direct rays from the sun. The air above becomes hot and dry, pushes northeastward in the prevailing westerly wind, and brings summer hot spells with dry southwesterly winds.

A hurricane in Florida. Note how the trees bend before the driving wind. Hurricanes are storms that start at sea and are accompanied by heavy rains.

What Causes Rain and Snow?

Above seas and oceans, air becomes loaded with invisible water vapor. The warmer the air the more water vapor it can hold. Thirty-five cubic feet of air at a temperature of 84 degrees Fahrenheit can hold about an ounce of water, but if the temperature is reduced to 62 degrees, the same amount of air can hold only about half an ounce. The actual amount of water vapor the air contains is called its specific humidity. Relative humidity, usually expressed as a percentage, is the amount of water vapor the air actually holds divided by the amount it could hold if it were completely saturated or loaded with water vapor.

[369]

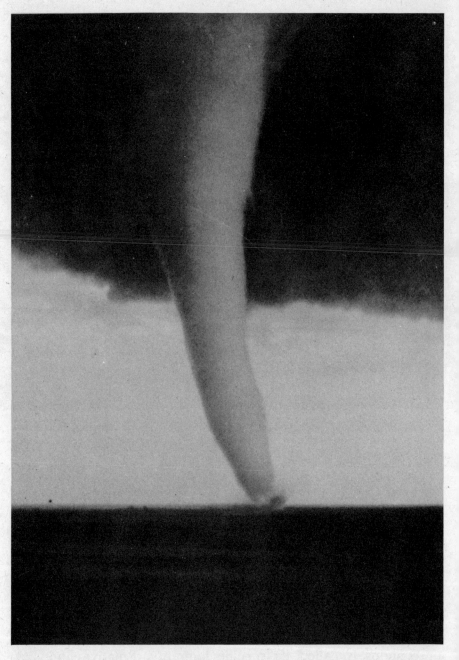

A Kansas "twister"—a tornado racing across the prairies. Tornadoes are whirlwinds that move with great speed, destroying everything in their path. Houses, trees, and many other objects are sometimes sucked up inside the cone and carried many miles away from their original locations.

[370]

A waterspout seen from an airplane during a storm at sea. A sudden shift in air pressure over a body of water will sometimes start a column of water whirling with terrific speed. A waterspout can easily destroy a ship. Warships have been known to stop a waterspout by firing a shell through the twisting column of water.

The relative humidity of air over the Gulf of Mexico and the Sargasso Sea is high, and when masses of this moist, tropical air push north and east over the United States, they are often cooled to the point where they give up some water vapor. Especially when such a mass of air meets polar air from Canada, water vapor condenses out of it, and rain or snow falls.

Cold and warm air masses wage war the year round over the United States, the cold gaining victories in winter and the warm in summer. The two types of air use different tactics. Along what is called the cold front, a cold, heavy air mass slides under a mass of lighter warm air, forming a long, thin wedge that forces the

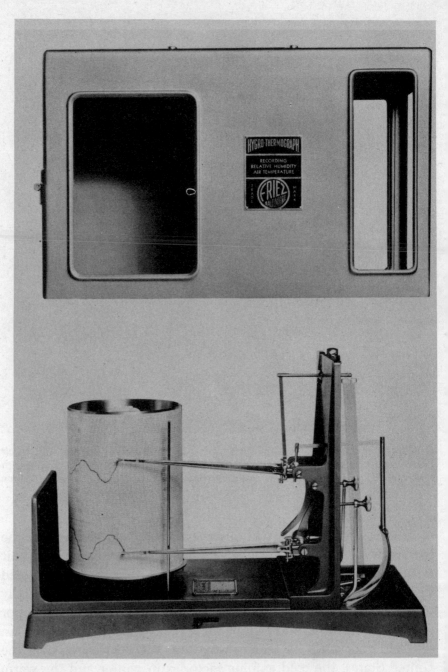

A hygro-thermograph. The cover has been removed to show the inside mechanism. This instrument tells the weather man the temperature and the relative humidity.

warm air up. Along what is called the warm front, a warm air mass, using a pushing, rushing form of attack, rolls the wedge of cold air back.

When air masses are active, storms occur. To a meteorologist, a storm does not necessarily mean rain or snow. It is merely an active field of combat where warm air has made a dent in the cold front. This forms a round or oval low-pressure storm area, anywhere from 300 to 2,000 miles in diameter, with the winds revolving around it counterclockwise and spiraling slowly towards the center.

A four-cup anemometer for measuring wind velocity. The wind catches the cups and spins them around. A geared dial below gives a direct reading of wind speed in miles per hour.

The barograph records atmospheric pressure. Low pressures indicate rain and storms; high pressures indicate good weather.

Releasing a balloon with a parachute and radiosonde attached. The man at the left is holding the radiosonde, which has an automatic radio transmitter. The balloon carries the equipment to a prefixed height, as much as 50,000 feet, where it explodes, releasing the parachute, which brings the radiosonde safely to the ground. During the ascent, the transmitter sends out signals that are picked up by radio receivers on the ground. These signals indicate the temperature, humidity, and barometric pressure at high altitudes.

Rains sometimes fall along the fronts in this "low" and are carried across the country by the prevailing westerly winds. Along the warm front, the onrushing warm air climbs over and pushes back the wedge of cold air. As it rises, it cools and gives up its moisture. Clouds form as billions of tiny water droplets, only about four ten-thousandths of an inch across, condense out of the air, and cling to microscopic bits of dust. Then, as the droplets grow in size, they fall and we have rain—or if they freeze on the way down, we have sleet, or if they form crystals of ice while they are still in the cloud, we have snow.

Changes are usually sharper along the cold front. The warm air is pushed upward suddenly, and huge quantities of water, often thousands of tons, condense out of it to form towering thunderheads. The familiar line squall, that whirling cloud at the base of the thunderhead, is right between the two turbulent air masses. The cold air rushing down one side of it and the warm air rushing up the other give it its familiar spin.

Sometimes the updraft of warm air is so sudden and violent that rain, instead of falling, is lifted miles high in the air, where it freezes and falls as hail. Frequently it is lifted up many times before it reaches the earth, each time taking on another coat of

A tipping bucket rain gauge. Rain water is collected in the cylinder and measured to determine the amount of a rainfall.

ice. When they finally fall to the ground, the chunks of ice are sometimes as large as baseballs.

By studying the air masses—where they come from, what their temperature and humidity is, in which direction and how rapidly they are moving, over what kind of surface they are moving and how that surface may warm or cool them, where and how active their fronts are, where low-pressure areas are likely to form, and in which direction they are likely to move—by studying all these facts and putting the data on weather maps, the weather man is able to make his forecast.

(Reprinted in part, by permission, from Man's Heritage of the Skies, *by Thomas Spooner, copyright by Westinghouse Electric Corporation.)*

There are millions of volts in this spectacular flash of lightning.

THE STORY OF LIGHTNING

L IGHTNING, striking with a roar and a blinding flash, uprooting trees, fusing metals, bringing destruction and even death in its wake, has commanded the attention and awe of man since the beginning of time. There are many records of early observations of lightning by ancient scientists. Pliny the Elder, in 23 B.C.,

[376]

made an effort to describe different types of lightning when he wrote: "Of thunderbolts themselves several variations are reported. Those that come with a dry flash do not cause fire, but an explosion. The smoky ones do not burn, but blacken. There is a third sort called 'bright thunderbolts' of an extremely remarkable nature; this kind draws casks dry without damaging their lids and without leaving any other trace melts gold and copper and silver in their bags without singeing the seal."

Though lightning continued to fascinate learned men throughout the centuries, the blinding bolts from the heavens inspired only fear and superstition in most people. Benjamin Franklin's celebrated experiment with the kite awakened an interest in the whole phenomenon of electricity, but the behavior of lightning continued to be a mystery, even to scientists, for nearly another century and a half.

Who First Made Artificial Lightning?

One August afternoon in 1920, Dr. Charles P. Steinmetz, the famous mathematical and electrical wizard, was on his way to his summer camp with a laboratory assistant. A sudden storm prevented them from going to the camp immediately, and when they reached it they discovered that lightning had struck it. The table where Steinmetz usually worked was smashed. Trees were splintered, two-by-fours were smashed, wires were fused, lights were burned out, and a mirror was broken into fragments.

This incident brought about the first serious study of lightning ever undertaken by a great scientist. Steinmetz went over the ground with the thoroughness of a detective. He observed that the bolt had first struck a tree a foot away from the camp window. Then it had broken the window and leaped inside. There it had splintered the table and jumped to the far side of the camp, where it shattered the mirror. Steinmetz collected the pieces of mirror and fitted them together between two sheets of glass, so that the pattern struck off by the lightning charge could be studied. This pattern was perhaps the first "portrait" ever preserved of lightning's effect. The scientific study of lightning had begun.

Three million volts of man-made lightning strike a miniature house set up in a laboratory.

Steinmetz knew well the importance of that study. He knew that each year several hundred persons are struck by lightning in the United States. He knew that the power industry loses millions of dollars through interruptions caused by lightning when it strikes power lines. Steinmetz hoped that with more knowledge of lightning's behavior, both lives and dollars could be saved through the development of protective devices.

Steinmetz was confronted immediately by the problem that had baffled other men who had wanted to study lightning. To study it you have to see it, but no one knows just when and where lightning will strike. Why, asked Steinmetz, cannot man make his own lightning and control it? He set to work to make the world's first artificial lightning generator. The first crude generator he built could create lightning which was about one-five-hundredth as powerful as natural lightning, with a potential of 120,000 volts and 1,000,000 horsepower.

This big machine, first demonstrated in the winter of 1922, was a queer sight. There were stacks of large glass plates coated with metal foil, connected by wires to a power source, and wired to a discharge path. This discharge was accompanied by a loud crash of artificial thunder. For the first time scientists and engineers had a form of lightning very much like natural lightning, controlled so that they knew when and where it would strike.

Of What Use Is Artificial Lightning?

After the death of Steinmetz, other scientists carried on his work. One of them created a giant impulse generator capable of producing 10,000,000 volts of artificial lightning. Its power output, in a discharge lasting ten-millionths of a second, was more than 13 times the total electric power developed at Niagara Falls!

The perfection of this giant artificial lightning producer meant that the two greatest difficulties encountered in the study of natural lightning had been overcome. With the new apparatus, lightning could be studied while discharging and it could be measured. Measurement was accomplished by the use of a sphere gap, a device consisting of two large metal spheres, properly supported and separated by an air gap across which an electric arc is made to jump. The distance which the arc jumps is the measurement of its voltage.

How Is Natural Lightning Studied?

When ways of creating and dissecting *artificial* lightning had been found, the lightning hunters turned once more to the study of *natural* lightning. Here they faced the old problem of catching nature's outlaw, so they resorted to photography. Here the ordi-

nary camera is of little use, for it fails to indicate how long the discharge lasted, whether more than one discharge occurred, or whether the stroke was initiated in the cloud or on the ground. So a special camera was built, with a rapidly moving film, thus supplying the necessary time dimension. The film velocity of the camera was a mile a minute!

An aërial wire attracts a bolt of lightning, and so saves the house below. This is the principle of the "lightning rod."

Picture of a lightning flash, taken from a high rock above the city of Spokane.

Now they had to find a place which lightning would strike frequently. Curiously enough, they found it first in the heart of New York City, high up in the tower of the Empire State Building. This building, projecting high above the others in New York, acts as a needle electrode, and nearly all the discharges in the near-by area are guided to its tower. Equipment to register the lightning strokes was installed in the building and photographic equipment was located in another tall building eight blocks away. From this vantage point, cameras snapped many pictures of the world's largest building being struck by lightning. Only a few of the bolts were visible from the street, more than 1,200 feet below.

Other engineers established a camp in the Tennessee Mountains near Knoxville. Apparatus was set up along the route of high-tension electric power lines. Day after day, trained observers at these camps patiently awaited the coming of severe electrical storms. In an entire summer they got one picture of a really big bolt of lightning striking a power line. Considering the money that went into advance preparations, salaries of the scientists, and apparatus, that single photograph cost $150,000!

In Pittsburgh, atop the 535-foot tower of the Cathedral of Learning, another laboratory was set up. It consisted of a 50-foot steel mast, a lightning arrester connected so that all of the lightnings stroke would have to pass through it, and two special recording devices.

In Montana, a trap was set for lightning in the smoke stacks of two smelters. The trap was baited with 20 copper rods, mounted in a copper ring 60 feet in diameter which encircled the top of the stack. Into one of these traps hurtled a giant stroke that was estimated to have a momentary energy of two and one-half billion kilowatts. If such an immense amount of energy could be produced steadily at some gargantuan power plant, output of that plant would be approximately 57 times greater than the total capacity of all the nation's generating stations!

How Is Lightning Measured?

To measure the lightning's force, the scientists use a whirligig magnetic lightning surge recorder known as a "fulchronograph." The word is a combination of the Latin *fulmen,* meaning "lightning," and the Greek *chrono,* meaning "time," and *graphos,* a "writing" or "picture."

The fulchronograph is a motor and a slotted aluminum wheel filled with laminated permanent magnet steel, projecting like fins from each side of the wheel and rotating through two coils which carry the total surge current from the lightning stroke being measured.

Current in the coils produces a magnetic field proportional to the surge current at any instant, and the magnetic steel slot or fin on the recording wheel that happens to be passing in that magnetic field is magnetized in proportion to the amount of current that is carried by the stroke in time divisions as brief as 40-millionths of a second.

Two such recorder units are used at lightning research stations. One is a high-speed wheel containing about 400 iron fins and whirling continuously more than 3,400 times per minute, completing a cycle in 1/60 of a second or 17,000 microseconds (millionths of a second). The spacing of the fins and the rapidity of the wheel enable it to make a record every 40 microseconds or 40-millionths of a second. The result is a schematic picture of the wave shape and surges of a single lightning stroke. The second wheel is relatively slow; it revolves only once every second and is capable of making a record on its fins every 2,400 microseconds to determine the magnitude and sequence of lightning bolts when more than one strikes in the same place. This slow-motion device gives the crest value of each stroke, separates the strokes, and enables the investigators to analyze the multi-stroke impressions on the high-speed wheel.

What Are the Characteristics of a Lightning Stroke?

With their scientific equipment for studying lightning, scientists were able to make many discoveries about this startling phenomenon of nature. They found that a discharge of a lightning stroke has two important characteristics. It starts out by having a very high current which does not, however, last very long. This part of the stroke discharge produces the violent action of the stroke. It is responsible for the thunder and the shattering and splintering action when trees and houses are struck. It will not, however, cause fires. It is the second part of the discharge, the flow of smaller current for a much longer time, which produces fires and other thermal effects. For this reason, strokes that have this part of the discharge to a great enough degree to cause burning are called "hot" lightning. Those which do not are called "cold" lightning. It is the "hot" lightning which causes forest fires and the burning of barns and other inflammable objects.

What looks like a single stroke of lightning may really consist of many discharges. One bolt striking the 580 smokestack at Anaconda, Montana, consisted of 22 separate discharges, which passed down the same pathway for about three-fourths of a second. Actually, a flash of lightning resembles a swift game of follow-the-leader. A weak, almost invisible, preliminary stroke picks its way haltingly through the air at the relatively slow speed of 100 miles per second. When the path to earth has thus

Artificial lightning jumps a fifteen-foot gap in a laboratory demonstration.

been broken, a full fledged, powerful stroke comes charging along the same route at nearly 20,000 miles per second. On its heels comes another, perhaps many more, at the same speed.

What Causes Lightning?

What is lightning? Of course, everybody knows that it is a discharge of electricity, but most people do not know that this electricity comes from the earth originally. The normal electrical charge of the earth is about 500,000 coulombs (a coulomb is the amount of current carried by one ampere in one second). Were air a perfect insulator, this charge could not leak off the earth.

[383]

This fiery arc demonstrates what happens when high voltage electricity leaps to the ground.

But air becomes ionized, a condition which permits it to conduct electricity. Thus the electrons leak gradually away from the earth into the surrounding clouds. This flow of electrons from the earth is only 5 microamperes per square mile, but on a clear day this represents about 1,000 amperes. In fair weather, if this rate of loss were maintained, the earth would lose its negative charge in less than ten minutes.

It is lightning that returns these escaping electrons to earth. To accomplish this, the earth's surface must be struck by lightning 50 times per second—more than two billion times a year. This means that the average number of strokes per square mile is 7 or 8 per year.

What Causes Thunder?

Not every flash of lightning is accompanied by a clap of thunder as popularly supposed. Flashes that have little or no thunder may appear to be just as bright as the ordinary stroke, but their destructive force is less. Thunder, as well as the physical rending and tearing created by the lightning stroke, is the result of the sudden expansion of air created by a fast moving discharge. Since all flashes do not release energy with the same speed, the expansion of the air is sometimes too slow to create thunder. Most thunder does not reach the ears as a single crack because of the slow speed at which sound travels compared with the speed of the lightning itself. For instance, one portion of a lightning discharge may be six seconds away, while the portion of the stroke near the earth may be only one second away. Thus the sound reaches the ear as a continuous rumble rather than as a sharp single explosion.

Can Lightning Strike Upward from the Ground?

Lightning can strike *up* as well as *down*. During a thunderstorm a downward lightning stroke will distribute its negative charges from cloud to ground along its path. As these negative charges come closer and closer to the earth, the positive charges on the ground become more and more concentrated until, as the stroke comes within a few hundred feet of the ground, streamers may rise out of the earth to a considerable height. Thus, many people who have been struck by lightning have been struck up out of the ground rather than struck down from the sky.

How Does Lightning Help Man?

Lightning is not completely destructive. It is a benefactor to agriculture in a little-known manner. Natural lightning produces about one hundred million tons of fixed nitrogen over the earth's surface. The air, composed roughly of four parts of nitrogen to one part of oxygen, is broken down by the passage of a lightning bolt, and fixed nitrogen is desposited in the soil with the rain. When men manufacture fixed nitrogen, electric sparks 15 or 20 feet long are employed. Nature's spark lightning may be thousands of feet in length, and if it were not for the extremely short duration of the lightning current it would produce immensely greater quantities of this essential agricultural chemical.

Because men have found a way to create their own power, they no longer need to dream of harnessing lightning. But they are determined to tame it, to stop it from destruction of man-made structures, so the lightning hunters continue their quest to find out more about nature's most brilliant electrical display.

Brown bear; Rainier National Park

WHEN THE English, French and Dutch colonists first came to America, they found a continent teeming with wildlife — birds, beasts, and fish in abundance. These animals furnished food to the early settlers, and for many years were more important than corn and other cereal crops. As the continent became dotted with cities and towns, and the huge forest reserves were depleted, the living space for this wildlife became more and more constricted, while the indiscriminate slaughter of animals continued. By the middle of the last century, there was real alarm about this great "natural resource." Unless a halt were called, whole stocks of wild creatures would be entirely exterminated.

The states then began to pass laws limiting hunting and fishing to certain seasons, certain areas, and limiting the number of animals that might be taken. The Federal government embarked on a long-term program not only to conserve the existing wildlife but also to replenish it in game preserves and fish hatcheries.

Many large national parks were set aside where wildlife might expand without molestation. Artificial propagation came to the rescue when the protection of animals and fish during the mating and spawning seasons proved inadequate.

The directing agency in this work is the Fish and Wildlife Service of the Department of the Interior. Its activities include "Construction and development of wildlife refuges, fish hatcheries, and rearing ponds, stream and lake improvements; tree planting on refuges; range revegetation; marsh conditioning; and other management practices including controlled burning, as well as prevention and suppression of uncontrolled fires—all designed to improve living conditions for wildlife."

This agency, and the coöperating state agencies, have many

Bear cubs are friendly and playful. They like to climb trees.

notable achievements to their credit. By the end of the War Between the States, the buffalo or American bison was well on the way to extinction. Today, great herds of buffalo have been built up in several national parks. At one time, reckless lobster fishing had so depleted this stock that the catching of lobsters had to be banned along the New England coast. Government hatcheries not only repopulated the water so that the industry could be revived, but also continue to distribute young lobsters in the coastal waters as fast as mature lobsters are taken out.

Thanks to the awakened public conscience, an abundance of wildlife remains in our country. The following pages show in pictures a few of the many species of animals, birds, and fish.

Buffalo; Oklahoma. *Great herds of American bison populated the Midwest plains at the time of the westward expansion.*

Part of a buffalo herd in the Nebraska National Wildlife Refuge.

Herd of elk in the Elk Refuge at
Jackson, Wyoming.

A ranger makes an elk do tricks to
get his supper; Forest Ranger Station, Yellowstone National Park.

Longhorn steer; Wichita Mountains Wildlife Refuge, Oklahoma.

Four longhorn steers and a bull, in Big Bull Pasture, Oklahoma. The longhorn is relatively rare among the great herds that now furnish our beef.

Herd of antelope; Charles Sheldon Antelope Refuge, Nevada.

Pronghorned antelope; Wichita Mountains Wildlife Refuge, Oklahoma.

Doe and two fawns; Arkansas National Wildlife Refuge, Texas. Venison or deer meat has always been a favorite of man, and American deer were near extermination before drastic state and Federal laws came to their rescue.

Mountain lion; Colorado. The hunter who killed this animal with aid of the dog pack is employed by the government to protect other animals from this fierce carnivore. This big cat was tracked down and destroyed after it had killed the five-point buck on the ground below him.

A catch of coyotes. The coyote is a small animal resembling a wolf, found in great abundance on the prairies.

Rabbit at a government breeding station. The rabbit propagates fast and is a voracious eater; it does great damage to certain crops, but is prized for its fur.

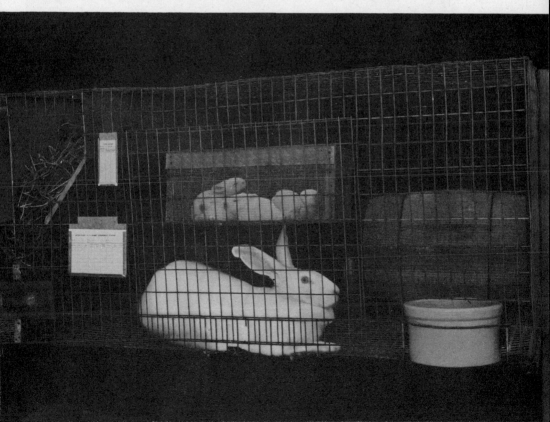

Male fox. Few wild foxes roam the country, but many are reared in fox farms for the value of their fur.

Beaver; Medford, Oregon. Note the broad flat tail, which the beaver uses with great skill in building dams to make pools which are his natural habitat.

Muskrat. This aquatic rodent provides more fur than any other animal in the United States. Many farmers and other landowners raise muskrats as a profitable side line. Muskrat fur in garments goes under a dozen different trade names.

Mink; Patuxent National Wildlife Refuge, Maryland. Mink is one of the costliest of furs, for so many pelts are needed to make one garment.

Fur-bearing seals; Polovina Rookery, St. Paul Island, Alaska. The larger, darker animals are males, each of which has a large "harem" of females. The great value of sealskin led to indiscriminate slaughter of thousands of animals prior to propagation, until sealing was limited by international treaties in 1910 and later.

Muskrat pelts on wire stretchers in a fur dealer's drying room.

Chinook salmon. The largest fishing industry in America is provided by the salmon that migrate from Pacific waters into the upper reaches of the Columbia River, Washington, to spawn. Conservation agencies as well as the fishing industry spend large sums to protect the salmon from water pollution, river barriers, and other hazards.

A catch of salmon is transferred to a larger boat, which will take it to the cannery. Salmon are caught in huge nets as they return down the Columbia River after spawning.

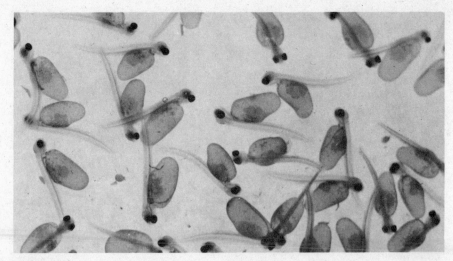

Newly hatched salmon fry get food from the attached yolk sac. These fry grow into fingerlings and migrate to salt water in three or four months.

A government salmon salvage operator taking samples of water for analysis with a field chemical unit, Nason Creek, Washington.

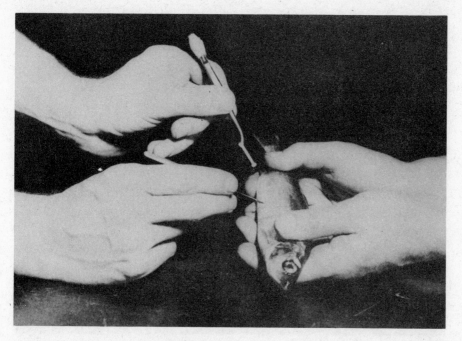

Inserting a tag in the abdominal cavity of a herring. The fish will be returned to the water, and the tag asks the finder to forward it to a government station. These tags help to determine the extent of fish migration.

String of bass taken in the Ocala National Forest, Florida.

Taking eggs from trout. Artificial propagation of trout is necessary to stock new areas and others where fishing pressure is heavy.

Biologist measuring a haddock, as indication of its age, on the Georges Banks out of Boston. The age of fish helps to determine its abundance.

Six hundred pounds of yellowfin tuna on the way to market. The tuna is one of the largest of food fishes.

Marlin being returned to the sea after tagging by government operators.

Planting oyster shells on a mud flat; Beaufort, South Carolina. The empty shells help young oysters to propagate, for they have to attach to solid objects to live.

Lobster encrusted with barnacles. In its natural state, the hard shell of the lobster is a mottled green; it turns red when boiled.

Alaska king crab. Crabmeat is prized as a delicacy, and the industry has been greatly advanced by experimental breeding.

American lobster in berry, the breeding stage where the abdomen of the female is covered with hundreds of eggs. Note the difference between the two big claws, which exists in all lobsters.

Pintail ducks; Sacramento Wildlife Refuge, California. Duck hunters have such refuges as this to thank for the abundance of wild fowl throughout the country.

Releasing diamond-back terrapin in the marshes near Beaufort, South Carolina. Grown from eggs in a government hatchery, these tiny turtles will grow to maturity in their natural habitat.

This goldfinch evidently does not mind the band placed on his foot. Through such tags, the migration of individual birds is determined.

A goldfinch nibbles sunflower seeds while a pine grosbeak stares at the camera. Though of no value as food, small birds are of utmost importance to man, for they live on insects that attack food crops. It has been said that if all the birds were destroyed, man would soon be extinct.

[405]

A tremendous blast loosens thousands of tons of rock.

THE STORY OF CEMENT

HROUGH the magic of man's imagination and mechanical genius, the nature-created bulk of mountains can be made into broad, smooth-riding highways, great bridges, towering skyscrapers, majestic cathedrals, massive dams. When you see a gleaming concrete structure, you may not realize that behind the seemingly commonplace material known as portland cement, there is a fascinating story of putting a mountain through a sieve.

What Is Portland Cement?

Portland cement is the basic ingredient of concrete—the material formed by carefully proportioning and mixing portland cement, sand, stone and water. The name "portland" has nothing to do with Portland, Maine, or the largest city in Oregon. It was the name given by the English stonemason who invented hydraulic cement in 1824. He thought that the cement looked like the natural stone quarried on the Isle of Portland. This inventor, Joseph Aspdin, was experimenting to produce a mortar that would harden under water. He achieved this by burning crushed limestone with clay or shale and pulverizing the resulting clinkerlike mass.

How Is Portland Cement Manufactured?

Where Aspdin's process was crude and his product variable, modern cement manufacture is controlled with laboratory accuracy, yet conducted on a gigantic scale. Today portland cement is produced from mountains of rock, clay and shale, all of which must go through some eighty different and carefully controlled operations. These include grinding, burning at a temperature that would melt steel, and regrinding to a fineness which permits nearly all of it to pass through a sieve with 40,000 openings to a square inch—a sieve fine enough to hold water!

Portland cement is made from limestone combined with other ingredients, such as clay, shale, or blast-furnace slag, and a small amount of gypsum. More than 600 pounds of raw materials, in addition to fuel, are required to make one barrel of portland cement that weighs 376 pounds.

The whole process starts with blasting. Rugged cliffs are blown to bits by powerful explosives. Sometimes one blast may loosen as much as 400,000 tons of stone — enough to fill about 8,000 standard railroad gondola cars.

Gigantic kilns like these are used in making cement.

Each year the cement industry in this country uses more than 23,000,000 pounds of explosives.

When the carloads of rock reach the cement factory, they are hauled up an inclined cable way. At the top a car stops and tilts its load of rocks into a steel-lined hopper at the bottom of which are the crunching jaws of a gyratory crusher which seems to swallow automobile-sized rocks as easily as an elephant swallows a peanut. Such a hopper is about sixteen feet across and can swallow a whole dump load of rock in two minutes.

The men who tend this tumbling giant evidence a wholesome respect for its power. They wear safety belts attached to chains from overhead, lest a misstep precipitate them into the monstrous, crunching jaws. The hungry giant needs tending because sometimes a load of rock clogs in the hopper and must be pried loose with long rods, like great furnace pokers.

The quarry rock leaves the primary crusher in pieces of varied size, some as large as a handball, and is carried by bucket or belt conveyors to additional crushers. These are usually hammer mills that crush the rock down to about ¾-inch pieces. A hammer mill consists of a series of hammers, extending like wheel spokes from a revolving plate. These hammers strike the pieces of rock as they pass over a heavy plate, reducing them to a size which will pass between narrowly spaced steel bars.

What Are "Ball Mills"?

From here, the pieces of rock go to the ball mills. These mills are giant revolving cylinders which are partly filled with heavy steel balls. As the cylinders revolve, the balls are carried upward by the centrifugal force holding them in place on the steel plates, or ribs, set into the sides of the cylinders. When the balls near the top of the mill they are hurled back by gravity onto the charge of raw material, which is ultimately ground to small particles.

Before the raw material is ground in the ball mills, it has been carefully proportioned to include the right amounts of limestone and clay, shale or slag.

The proportioning of the limestone and other ingredients is done under laboratory control by clever automatic devices. Thus,

The crunching jaws of this great crusher can swallow a whole carload of rock. Note the safety chain attached to the workman's belt.

any single sack of finished cement taken at random will have the identical characteristics of the day's output of the mill, even though the production is thousands of barrels.

After this mixing process, the combined materials are again ground to a fine powder in another battery of tube mills. These are sometimes divided into several compartments, the material passing through screens from one to another until just the right stage of fineness is reached.

What Is "Slurry"?

If the wet process is followed, enough water is added as the mixture enters the ball mills to give it a thick, creamy consistency, in which state it is called "slurry." The slurry is then pumped to large tanks where it is thoroughly mixed and agitated, ready to be pumped into great storage tanks to be held until needed for the burning operation.

The burning operation is a spectacular scene in cement manufacture. A rotary kiln, such as is used in all modern plants, is a mammoth steel cylinder lined with a thick layer of fire brick, sometimes 10 feet or more in inside diameter. An average-sized cement kiln, if set on end, would be taller than a 20 story building. Some in use are more than 400 feet long. In a large cement mill, kilns are usually installed in batteries in a separate building. These kilns are supported on giant roller bearings and rotate at an average rate of ¾ of a turn each minute. In order that the material will pass through continuously, the kilns are inclined from ½ to ¾ of an inch for each foot of length. Inside the kilns roaring tongues of flame, 30 or 40 feet long, create a temperature of 2700° Fahrenheit. Hot gases, from the flames in the lower end of the kilns, pass over the raw mixture as it is fed automatically, gradually drying out all the moisture, which in the wet process is from $\frac{1}{3}$ to $\frac{1}{5}$ the weight of slurry.

What Is "Clinker"?

As the material passes slowly down the kiln, its heat increases until it is in the "burning zone," the lower third of the kiln, where it becomes incandescent and takes the form of marble-sized, glass-hard balls called "clinker." In this burning zone it changes chemically as well as physically and emerges from the kiln as a new substance, harder than the rock from which it came. Workers, peering through slits in the kiln with colored glasses to protect their eyes, see a weirdly beautiful sight. Semimolten masses, ranging in shade from blinding incandescence through delicate purples and violets to oranges and reds, perpetually surge and roll from the rotating sides of the kiln in a brilliantly colored tide.

After its period in the flaming kilns, the clinker passes through a long tubular cooler before going into storage. The clinker is usually in excess of 2,000° Fahrenheit when it leaves the kiln, and gives off a great amount of heat as it moves through the rotating cooler. The heat is passed back into the kiln, saving fuel.

It took 7,000,000 tons of concrete to build Boulder Dam. Towering 726 feet over the foundation rock, this is the highest dam in the world. It holds back the waters of the Colorado River to form a lake more than 100 miles long.

The clinker is inert after it is cooled and may be stored for months without deterioration, thus allowing cement mills to build up reserves for the season when cement demand is greatest.

THE MANUFACTURE OF PORTLAND CEMENT

Converting rocks into portland cement—a structural material with a thousand uses—involves great quantities of heavy materials, mammoth machinery and precision control. Eighty-odd operations are graphically summarized below.

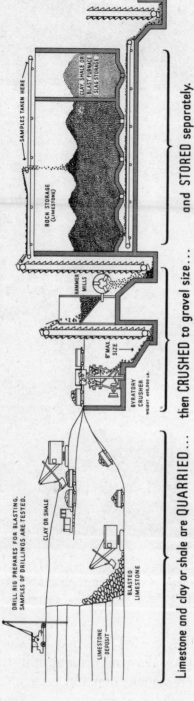

Limestone and clay or shale are QUARRIED . . .   then CRUSHED to gravel size . . .   and STORED separately.

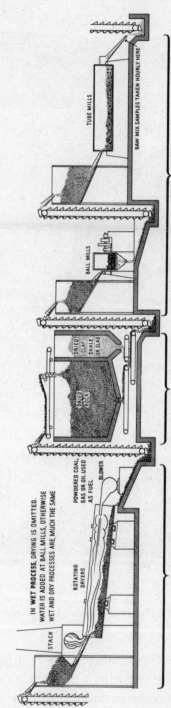

The two materials are DRIED . . . .   PROPORTIONED by weight . . .   and GROUND to fine powder called "raw mix."

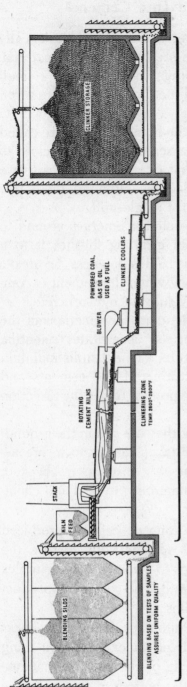

Thoroughly BLENDED...   mix is KILN BURNED to partial fusion at 2700°F., forms glass-hard cement clinker resembling pebbles.

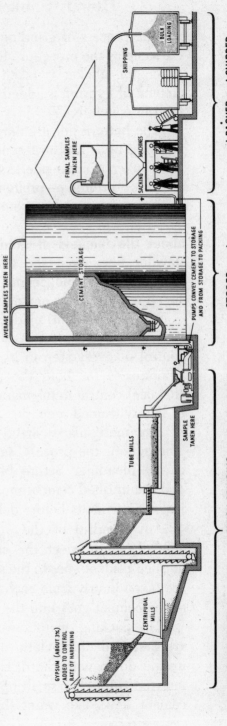

With GYPSUM ADDED, clinker undergoes FINISH GRINDING into portland cement...   is STORED in silos...   until PACKED and SHIPPED.

[413]

How Is Clinker Ground Into Cement?

The process of grinding the clinker into cement is practically the same as the procedure followed in preparing the raw material. When the clinker is taken from storage to be ground, a small amount of gypsum is added to control the time of hardening when used in concrete.

The batteries of grinders used in the final operation are called finishing mills and are generally in a separate building close to the clinker storage pile. As in the first operation, there are two stages of grinding—preliminary and final—although these two operations are often accomplished in a single mill.

From the first battery of mills the clinker emerges ground to about the fineness of sand. The final grinding finishes it to a powder finer than the average flour. This fineness assures a standard and homogeneous consistency when the cement is combined with water to make the bonding substance of concrete.

Portland cement, made to meet standard specifications of the American Society for Testing Materials, necessitates scientific control of every step in its manufacture. Cement mills maintain laboratories for both the physical testing of the cements and chemical control in the manufacturing process under the direction of highly trained men.

Raw materials are first tested while they are still in the ground. Throughout the process, samples are taken hourly to insure accurate blending. Before burning, the raw mixture is checked, and the finished cement must meet numerous physical and chemical requirements before delivery.

Any handful of the millions of tons of cement produced annually must meet the same rigid specifications. Before the finished cement goes to the storage silos to await packing, samples are taken hourly from each finishing mill. The composite product of the cement goes into the storage silos.

The packing operation is largely automatic. The empty sacks are first tied, if of cloth, or glued, if of paper, and then hung upside down with the discharge nozzle of the packing machine inserted through a small opening in the bottom of the sack. The cement flows like water through a one-inch nozzle, being shut off automatically when exactly ninety-four pounds of cement have entered the sack. Then the weight of the cement on a small flap inside the sack closes the opening as the sack is turned right side up. When cement is shipped in bulk it is pumped into box-cars similar to those used for carrying grain.

And so cement ends its long process and is ready to go into the making of bridges, dams, roads, buildings, ships, and many other structures of modern civilization.

What Is a Cyclone?

A cyclone is a circular or rotatory storm, or system of winds, varying from fifty to five hundred miles in diameter, revolving around a center, which advances at a rate that may be as high as forty miles an hour, and toward which the winds tend.

Cyclones of greatest violence occur within the tropics, and they revolve in opposite directions in the two hemispheres—in the southern with, and in the northern against, the hands of a watch—in consequence of which, and the progression of the center, the strength of the storm in the northern hemisphere is greater on the south of the line of progression and smaller on the north than it would if the center were stationary, the case being reversed in the southern hemisphere.

An anti-cyclone is a storm of opposite character, the general tendency of the winds in it being away from the center, while it also shifts within comparatively small limits. Cyclones are preceded by a singular calm and a great fall of the barometer.

What Is the Ninth Planet?

The nearest planet to the earth is Venus, from 25 to 160 million miles distant. Next is Mars, 35 to 248 million miles distant. Then Mercury, 50 to 136 million miles; Jupiter, 367 to 600 million miles; Saturn, 744 to 1,028 million miles; Uranus, 1,600 to 1,960 million miles; Neptune, 2,677 to 2,910 million miles. This gives eight planets: Earth, Venus, Mars, Mercury, Jupiter, Saturn, Uranus, and Neptune. But the discovery of a ninth planet, called Pluto, was announced in 1930 by the Lowell Observatory, Flagstaff, Arizona. The ninth planet Pluto swings in a tremendous orbit beyond Neptune. Its average distance from the sun is forty times that of our earth, about 3,700 million miles. The earth is only 91 to 94½ million miles from the sun; Neptune, 2,769 to 2,817 million miles. This new ninth planet Pluto is still farther away.

THE STORY OF DAMS

The Marshall Ford Dam on the Colorado River, Texas, is one of a great chain of works that harness this mighty stream to the use of man. Above the spillway of this dam is a steel bridge to carry traffic across the river.

FOR THOUSANDS of years man has built dams to tame rivers and regulate the flow of their waters to suit his needs. Traces of the earliest known dams have been found along the banks of the Nile River in Egypt.

The necessary water for ancient Egyptian agriculture was provided every year by the summer rise of water in the Nile. But the Egyptians found that their river was not reliable. In some years the river rose less than usual and failed to water the soil adequately. In other years, it rose higher than usual, and disastrous floods resulted.

Where Were the Most Ancient Dams?

Almost six thousand years ago, King Menes of Egypt planned the first recorded Nile dam. He undertook to build a large stone dam at Kosheish, 12 miles south of the site he had selected for his capital city of Memphis. This protected the city of Memphis from floods for centuries. When the dam fell into neglect, the city of Memphis was flooded. Later, other kings built storage dams, which created Lake Moeris. The Greek historian Herodotus describes the lake as having a shoreline of 400 miles and a depth of 300 feet.

The waters of the Tigris and Euphrates Rivers, in ancient Babylonia, were also dammed and controlled for irrigation purposes, as early as 4500 B.C. An elaborate system of canals and

Parker Dam, located about 155 miles below Boulder Dam on the Colorado River, serves a 242-mile aqueduct that carries billions of gallons of water annually to Los Angeles.

Mt. Shasta Dam has helped the farmers in the Sacramento valley, California, to double their acreage of irrigated rice. In the background is the snowy peak from which the dam takes its name.

Mt. Shasta Dam during construction of the central spillway. The spillway of a dam permits water to flow past before the water level reaches the top of the dam, and so acts to prevent floods in the area upstream from it.

ditches was constructed to distribute the precious water. Stone dams were built to divert the water, and gates were used to regulate the flow. When Alexander the Great invaded Babylonia in 350 B.C., he found the remains of masonry dams prevented the passage of his invasion ships.

If the records we have are correct, the greatest dam ever built was constructed about 1700 B.C. in Arabia. It was supposed to have been two miles long, 120 feet high and 500 feet thick at the base. Fifteen million cubic yards of masonary were needed. It lasted for almost two thousand years, and finally collapsed before the surge of a tremendous flood.

The Romans built many dams which lasted for centuries. The Emperor Nero directed the construction of one which lasted for

Downstream face of Friant Dam during construction. The roadway on stilts marks what will be the crest of the finished dam.

1,300 years. The Romans set a pattern for dam building which was followed for a long time. Their dams were made of cut stone laid in lime mortar, and were three times as wide at the base as their total height. In A.D. 913, the Moors built a dam in Spain with these same proportions.

What Purposes Do Dams Serve?

Dams are built for a wide variety of purposes, of which the principal are: storage of water, navigation, flood control, recreation, and conservation.

The storage dam itself, usually a high unit built to retain a great volume of water behind it, serves a number of purposes. The

[419]

Friant Dam Spillway, operating without the control gates. This dam impounds water in Millerton Lake that irrigates 358,000 acres of new land in the fertile San Joaquin Valley.

tremendous water pressure it stores serves to drive electric generators which provide power, light and heat often for hundreds of miles around. They may also simply provide the power for local factories which sometimes have their own dams. For local farmers, the storage dam creates a water supply which can provide an unending amount of water to irrigate their fields. Large cities are provided with their drinking water supply and with water for their sewage systems by storage dams, sometimes located miles away. Los Angeles, for example, goes 250 miles for its water.

Navigation dams make it possible for boats to use stretches of water into which they could not otherwise go. Flood control dams are vital in many portions of the country which have been regularly laid waste by recurring floods.

Recreation dams provide swimming or fishing facilities, while conservation dams simply maintain a water supply in a certain area, either to beautify the spot, or provide water for wildlife.

Many dams, of course, serve more than one of these purposes. Storage dams will be beneficial for flood control if the reservoirs are empty or low at the time of a flood. Storage dams for navigation and power are usually operated so as to be beneficial for sanitation. All high dams are utilized for water power.

The chain of dams built and developed by the Tennessee Valley Authority shows clearly just how widely the work of dams affects the surrounding communities. Farmers in the Tennessee Valley now have more electricity, finer farm land, and abundant recreational facilities. At the same time, new industries, taking advantage of the power, are springing up, and floods are effectively controlled.

Foundations of the Grand Coulee Dam, chief structure in the harnessing of the mighty Columbia River. Rectangular cofferdams used in building underwater foundations are visible on the upstream side.

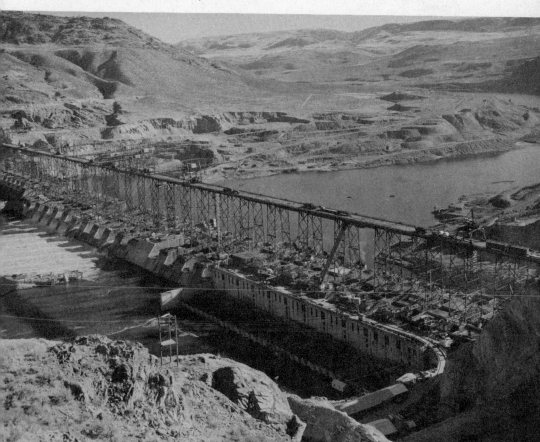

Grand Coulee Dam creates a reservoir of water 151 miles long, and generates more hydroelectric power than any other dam in the world. The boxlike structure at the base of the dam is one of the power houses where the giant water turbines are located.

How Is a Dam Built?

When we see one of our great dams, we are immediately impressed by its simple, but sweeping, beauty. As we stand in admiration and awe, we rarely think of the enormous preparations which go into building the dam. The location of the dam within the stream bed which will be the most effective in regulating the flow of water; the destruction of certain areas to store the water upstream; irrigation needs, the soil to be conserved, and the lives of the people nearby; all these must be considered.

The most important test which any dam will meet is its ability to withstand the tremendous pressure of water behind it. How to achieve this power has become a complicated engineering science, no matter how simple the resulting dam may seem.

Most large modern dams are made of masonry—concrete and stone—but there are other types still in use, such as those made

The Marshall Ford Dam on the Colorado River, Texas, during construction. This is the upstream face. For a downstream view of the finished dam, see the picture at the head of this chapter.

Marshall Ford Dam during construction of the steel bridge across the spillway.

Black Canyon in the Colorado River before the building of Boulder Dam.

of strongly supported earth, or rocks. The foundation of a masonry dam is dug until bedrock is reached, and sometimes the excavation is continued three to six feet more, in order to lock the foundation into the rock and make it almost impossible for the dam to slide.

Very high dams are generally built across the valleys of powerful streams. Perhaps the greatest difficulty which goes with their construction is the management of the flow of the stream while the dam is being built.

In some cases, a tunnel may sometimes be driven entirely around the site of the dam through which the river is turned. A big difficulty arises after the dam is completed, when the tunnel must be closed off and the water redirected to the dam.

[424]

Blasting channels in the precipitous walls of Black Canyon during construction of Boulder Dam.

The usual way of handling the water during construction is to carry it in a large flume, or artificial passage, directly over and across the foundation pit of the new dam. The danger here is that a flood or unexpected sudden flow of water may break or destroy the flume. In the case of a very wide excavation, whole new

[425]

stream beds are built far upstream to divert the stream during the period of dam construction.

After the foundations are solidly in place, engineers normally sink their pneumatic caissons, great air-tight boxes or steel drums. At the bottom of these caissons are great concrete blocks which serve as a cutting edge for the caisson to sink through the muck to make contact with the foundation.

What Is the Highest Dam in the World?

Boulder (Hoover) Dam, with one shoulder resting on Arizona and the other on Nevada, harnesses the Colorado River at Black Canyon. Third longest river in the United States, the Colorado flows high in the snow-capped mountains of Wyoming and Colorado, zigzags southwest for 1,700 miles, and finally pours into

Looking downstream from the crest of Boulder Dam. Visible are some sections of the power plants, the canyon wall outlet works, and cofferdam excavation.

Inside one of the tunnels gouged out of the rock walls of Black Canyon, to divert the waters of the Colorado River during construction of Boulder Dam.

Mexico's Gulf of California. The river's drainage basin covers 244,000 square miles, one-twelfth of the land area of our country.

The Dam, completed in 1936, cost $125,000,000. Millions upon millions of horsepower created at Boulder Dam help run the plants and factories of the Pacific Coast. The dam is 727 feet high, 660 feet thick at the base and 1,282 feet long at the crest. It is by far the highest dam in the world, outranking the Grand Coulee Dam in Washington (550 feet) and the Shasta Dam in California (560 feet). All three of these dams were built by the Bureau of Reclamation of the Department of the Interior.

For 115 miles behind Boulder Dam is a great inland sea, Lake Mead, large enough to float all the navies in the world. The shoreline of the lake is 550 miles long. The lake grew from the silt-laden Colorado, and every year great quantities of silt are carried into the lake from upstream. There is enough water in Lake Mead, which was nonexistent before the building of the dam, to cover the entire state of New York under one foot of water. The water in Lake Mead at times rises as high as the height of the Washington Monument.

When Was Boulder Dam Built?

Investigations on the control and use of the Colorado were made as early as 1902. The Boulder Canyon Project Act was passed by Congress in 1928, and the first concrete was placed in the dam in 1933. Two years later, the dam was completed and

Boulder Dam, highest dam in the world, straddles the Colorado River where it forms the boundary between Nevada and Arizona. The twin structures at each end of the upstream face are intake towers controlling the release of the impounded water.

Panoramic view of Lake Mead, the huge reservoir created by Boulder Dam, which is visible in the foreground. The jet of water is spurting from the penstock outlet after passing through the power turbines on the Nevada side of the canyon. Farther downstream, at the water level, can be seen the rectangular mouths of the spillways, which were built in part from the original diversion tunnels.

was dedicated by President Franklin D. Roosevelt on September 30, 1935. By 1939, there were nine electric generators in place, making Boulder's power plant the largest in the world at that time. It serves a hundred cities in a dozen states.

Materials for the dam were needed in quantities never before shipped to a single construction job in such a short time—five million barrels of cement; eight million tons of sand, gravel and cobbles; 45 million pounds of reinforcement steel; 18 million pounds of structural steel; 21 million pounds of gates and valves; 840 miles of pipe. All of this was hauled over newly built railroads in the first four years of construction.

Before the dam was built, four great diversion tunnels, each as high as a four-story building, were blasted through the canyon's rock. Then cofferdams, temporary structures, were built to

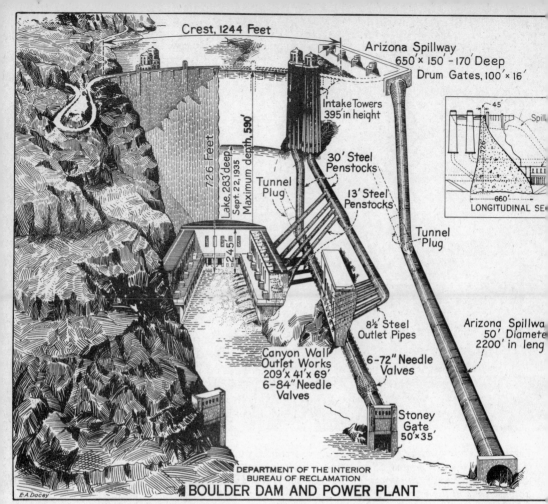

Crest, 1244 Feet

Arizona Spillway
650´ x 150´ - 170´ Deep
Drum Gates, 100´ x 16´

Intake Towers
395´ in height

30´ Steel
Penstocks

13´ Steel
Penstocks

Tunnel
Plug

Tunnel
Plug

726 Feet

Lake, 283 deep
Sept. 22, 1935
Maximum depth, 590´

245´

45

726

660

LONGITUDINAL SE

Spill

8½´ Steel
Outlet Pipes

Arizona Spillwa
50´ Diamete
2200´ in leng

Canyon Wall
Outlet Works
209´x 41´x 69´
6-84" Needle
Valves

6-72" Needle
Valves

Stoney
Gate
50´x35´

E.A.Dacey

DEPARTMENT OF THE INTERIOR
BUREAU OF RECLAMATION
BOULDER DAM AND POWER PLANT

Diagram of the Boulder Dam works on the Arizona side. At right is the spillway, a flume leading from the top of the dam to the old diversion tunnel. From the twin intake towers, steel penstocks feed water to the power turbines, which run huge electric generators. Similar diversion works are built into the Nevada wall of the canyon.

divert the water into these tunnels while the dam went up.

When complete, the dam included four intake towers, 260 feet above the river bed. Water from Lake Mead goes through these towers to the power station at the foot of the dam.

Why Was Boulder Dam Built?

When a Senate committee approved the Boulder Dam project, it said, "A mighty river, now a source of destruction, is to be curbed and put to work in the interests of society." Some of the work that the dam is doing includes these tasks:

[430]

This single huge generator at Boulder Dam can supply enough electricity to light an entire city.

The graceful intake towers of Boulder Dam, whose gates control the supply of water to the power houses.

It protects the lives and property of 100,000 people who lived at the mercy of the unbridled Colorado. It supplies water for the irrigation of nearly two million acres of land. It furnishes water for domestic, industrial and municipal use by the rapidly expanding population of the southern California coastal region. It eliminates, damaging, clogging silt deposits which previously had to be removed at a cost of one million dollars a year. It improves river navigation, provides a national playground and recreational area, as well as a new wildlife and bird refuge. And Boulder Dam, last but not least, is the source of an immense supply of low-cost electric power.

What Are Some of the Other Great Dams?

Grand Coulee Dam, which harnesses the Columbia River in Washington, is the world's biggest man-made structure, if it is measured by the amount of material it contains. It holds 11,000,000 cubic yards of concrete—more material than in any of our skycrapers. The reservoir extends 150 miles upstream, and irrigates more than a million acres. The power plant can produce eight billion kilowatt hours of electricity at low cost.

Among the great dams of the world, the most noted is the Assuan Dam on the Nile. Located at Assuan, about 700 miles from the mouth of the Nile, this dam was begun in 1898. It reaches a height of 146 feet, and is more than a mile in width. It cost $17,000,000—a fabulous sum in those days. Behind the granite dam can be stored 1,300,000,000 gallons of water, rivalling the reservoirs of today's greatest dams. Nowhere else in the world is a country so dependent on a single engineering project as Egypt is on its great Assuan dam.

The Senner Dam, on the Blue Nile in the Sudan, opened in 1926, is two miles long. The Burrinjack Dam in New South Wales, Australia, is 148 feet high and holds more than 251 billion gallons of water. In many countries, new dams are rising to provide cheap and plentiful electric power.

What Is a Planetarium?

With the discovery of the "new" planet, called Pluto, in 1930, there was renewed interest in the stars and planets. A "planetarium" is a mechanical device which makes the planetary system intelligible to an audience. In past centuries there have been many devices of similar character, though not so elaborate. The Franklin Institute, Philadelphia, has long had one of the old-time contrivances, a system of globes moved by clockwork, representing our immediate solar system. The modern planetarium was evolved by Oskar von Miller, director of the German Museum at Munich, and the first instrument was completed by the Carl Zeiss optical works, Jena, in 1924. It reproduces the stars and planets in motion in their relative size and brilliance.

The modern planetarium is a cylindrical machine on wheels, weighing 3,500 pounds, shaped much like an enormous dumb-bell, each end of which represents one hemisphere and contains a powerful electric lamp; 119 optical projectors portray the 5,400 stars of the two hemispheres (6.2 magnitude) normally visible to the naked eye. Sun, moon, and planets are projected individually from the center, since the bodies of the solar system do not travel at the same rate as the stars. The star projectors rotate about an axis parallel to the earth's axis; the earth-sun disk is perpendicular; the others are arranged at different angles corresponding to the actual respective angles of the orbits of the planets to the plane of the ecliptic (sun's orbit). The whole thing is operated by an enormous switchboard of electric pushbuttons.

The Adler Planetarium and Astronomical Museum is the first in America, Mr. Max Adler's $500,000 gift to Chicago. A miniature temple on an artificial island in Lake Michigan near the Field Museum of Natural History contains the famous Zeiss instrument. The building is small (160 feet diameter), twelve-sided, topped by a copper dome over a center hall, the planetarium room proper (75 feet diameter). Here 600 people may sit and watch the "drama of the heavens" portrayed by the strange looking instrument which projects the stars in motion on the interior surface of the darkened dome. The illusion is perfect.

The lecturer, with a light for a pointer, explains in one hour the daily phenomena of the celestial bodies. He has only to push a button: the sun sets, the moon rises, the stars shine in mysterious silence, the constellations and the planets course across the sky in accurate diurnal motion. The Milky Way appears, the misty nebula of Orion and the seven sister Pleiades. Earth, sun, and planets shown in accelerated rotation make plain in a few minutes what normally takes students years to observe and comprehend.

Should the speaker let four minutes equal one year, the time of Mars' journey around the sun is 7.2 minutes; Jupiter, 47.2 minutes; Saturn, 2 hours, 56 minutes. The far planets, Uranus and Neptune, are not included in the projector because they are never visible to the naked eye. As for the planets between the earth and sun, on this time scale Venus flits around in 148 seconds and Mercury breaks the speed record with 4+ revolutions in 58 seconds.

THE STORY OF DYNAMITE

An explosion of 54,463 pounds of dynamite at a trap rock quarry, Nonocacy, Pennsylvania. Explosions like this provide material for weeks of work.

EXPLOSIVES, blasting paths for the westward thrust of railroads and clearing forest acres for tillage, sparked the advance of America's expanding frontiers. Today explosives rank with electricity, steam and petroleum, as a motive force indispensable to the life of the community they helped to build.

What Was the First Explosive?

The earliest known explosive was black gunpowder, a mixture of powdered charcoal, sulphur and saltpeter (potassium nitrate). The Chinese are usually credited with having discovered gunpowder, and there is no doubt that they were making firecrackers with it at least 2,000 years ago. Marco Polo, who visited China about 1,200 years ago, noticed the explosive power of the black mixture, which was later called gunpowder, and learned how to make it.

[434]

The famous Franciscan friar, Roger Bacon, is thought to have made gunpowder in 1246. As early as 1346 gunpowder and wooden cannon helped the English defeat the French at the Battle of Crécy.

What Is Nitroglycerin?

An Italian chemist, Ascanio Sobrero, discovered in 1846 the basic substance used in most modern explosives. He found that by mixing glycerin with sulphuric and nitric acid he could make a strange liquid, nitroglycerin. In minute quantities, nitroglycerin is useful as a heart stimulant. In larger quantities, it is so unstable that a slight shock will cause it to explode with great violence. Invaluable as it is as a base for explosives, pure nitroglycerin can scarcely be used because of its extreme sensitivity.

What Is Dynamite?

It remained for a Swedish chemist, Alfred Nobel, to find a way to tame nitroglycerin. About twenty years after its discovery, Nobel hit upon the ingenious idea of mixing nitroglycerin with *kieselguhr*, a kind of sandy earth. He called the mixture "dynamite," after the Greek word *dynamis*, meaning power. Other substances were later used instead of *kieselguhr*—sawdust, flour, magnesia and sodium carbonate. The effect of these substances is to make the nitroglycerin much less sensitive, so that a much greater initial shock is required to detonate it.

After being mixed with inert substances, the dynamite becomes as plastic as putty and is pressed into sticks about two inches in diameter and about eight inches long. Each stick is then wrapped in paper and waterproofed. Usually the waterproofing consists in paraffining the paper-wrapped stick of dynamite.

Dynamite has certain limited uses in warfare. But it requires precautions in handling and transportation that are often impracticable. The staple explosive of warfare is the safer but less powerful TNT (trinitrotoluene). Nobel's invention has been used mostly for peaceful purposes, and it has greatly aided man's progress.

Here workmen are using a pneumatic drill to drive bore holes for dynamite. Each round of dynamite "shots" chips out several tons of rock and advances the tunnel about a yard. An advance of eighteen feet a day is considered very good in hard rock.

As a result of his discovery, Nobel became a millionaire many times over. Nobel realized that dynamite could become a deadly instrument for war and hoped that this would not happen. Hoping to encourage men in the ways of peace, Nobel established a fund in Sweden which awards yearly prizes for the persons all over the world who have made the greatest advances in the arts and sciences. The Nobel Peace Prize is awarded yearly to the person who has done most to advance world peace.

What Are the Uses of Dynamite?

Today factory, farm and mine; transport by air, rail, water and highway; commerce; the public services of power, light, gas, water and sewage—all the varied activities of the nation, whether at war or at peace—depend in some measure for their operation upon dynamite and similar explosives. The car you drive, the gasoline that powers it and the road it travels; the fuel that warms your home, fires the hearths and boilers of industry, all these are made ready for man's service through the help of explosives.

It takes a ton of dynamite to produce the surface material for each mile of an eighteen-foot highway. To mine the metal used in just a single light-model 1942 automobile required a pound, and millions of pounds go each year into prospecting for new petroleum sources and increasing the flow in old ones.

In aërial bombs, the accuracy of a war weapon in which explosives are the prime mover has been dramatized with stirring effect on popular imagination. But far more impressive is the

Cords of smokeless powder being collected in coils. These cords are next cut into suitable lengths. Dynamite is made in the same form except that the cords are about one inch in diameter, cut in certain standard lengths and wrapped in oiled paper.

constructive peacetime record achieved through the science of precision blasting, based on a profound study of the direction and force of explosive charges of all sizes.

What Can Precision Blasting Do?

Engineers have perfected more than two hundred forms of blasting agents and many techniques for their application in specialized functions. Using these forces, measurable often in thousands of horsepower, blasters frequently work to very close tolerances.

Through this science, dynamite became a sculptor's tool for the carving of the massive Rushmore Memorial. The late Gutzon Borglum, assisted by Du Pont experts, exploded charges as light as 1/64 of a pound of dynamite to mold the features of Washington, Jefferson, Lincoln, and Theodore Roosevelt from the rock facade of Mount Rushmore in South Dakota.

Borglum used 6,000 pounds of dynamite and 40,000 detonating caps to move 2,000 cubic yards of granite in the forming of the head of Washington. In shaping some of the more delicate traceries, a single electric cap exerted sufficient force.

In contrast, 750,000 pounds of dynamite provided the horsepower for plowing the transcontinental furrow through rock and mountains for "Big Inch." At river crossings in the construction of this world's largest pipe line, experts used dynamite with spectacular precision.

Thirty-one thousand pounds of dynamite exploded at a single blast as the experts dug the trench in the rock bed of the Susquehanna River at Marietta, Pennsylvania. Parallel rows of iron tubing, sunk deep in the rock bottom of the stream and projecting above its surface, marked the course of the crossing. Each tube was charged with 150 pounds of gelatin dynamite. When the eruption of rock, smoke and water subsided, the trench had been dug at a single blow by the terrific force of the explosion.

A typical instance of control over giant explosive forces was the damming of the Saguenay River in Canada for a hydroelectric project. The torrential rush of current balked several attempts to complete a cofferdam, the conventional method.

Sixteen thousand pounds of 60% gelatine dynamite were used to make this explosion in the bed of the Susquehanna River near Marietta, Pennsylvania. The blasting was done to dig a trench in the river bed for the world's biggest oil pipeline, which crosses the Susquehanna at this point.

[439]

So the dam was built outside the water, upon one bank of the river. Standing upright on end, the steel and concrete structure towered 95 feet in height, was 45 feet wide, and measured 40 feet where it was to plumb the river at its deepest point.

The problem was to drop its huge bulk into place in the stream. The margin between succcess and failure was rated in inches. A DuPont expert planted 1,000 pounds of gelatin dynamite in just the right spot to blow away the supports holding the dam upright. The entire charge exploded as a single shot. The tower toppled and fell. Five seconds after the blast, the huge dam rested squarely on the target.

Another time the creative genius of the dynamiter was challenged to meet a crisis was when floods threatened destruction to $25,000's worth of market-garden produce on a Florida farm. Unless the rising water could be diverted, the growing crops would be ruined. The experts charted courses for canals. The blasts were detonated. The flood followed man-made channels to natural watercourses. The crops were saved.

In this technique of ditching with dynamite, experts have given farmers a valuable time- and labor-saving method of reclaiming swamp land for cultivation or bringing water to dry areas. By blasting with varied types and charges, they have made it possible to excavate channels to exact dimensions with the single tool, dynamite.

Explosives have come a long way since primitive warriors combined charcoal, sulphur and saltpeter into the first incendiary bomb. The advances that have brought explosives to the perfection we know today have opened vast new areas to scientific explorers.

How Did the Term "Fifth Column" Originate?

During the civil war in Spain, 1936–39, General Emilio Mola was in command of Nationalist troops marching against Madrid. When asked about the disposition of his troops he is said to have replied: "We have four columns on the march outside the city. In the city we have a fifth column." He meant that in the city were people working undercover for the Nationalists and ready to spring into action when the opportunity came. The term "fifth column" came into popular use during World War II to denote undercover groups working secretly against their own country.

THE STORY OF TUNNELS

A Louisville and Nashville Railway passenger train entering a tunnel.

IN MANY areas of the earth, towering mountain chains stand as a mighty obstacle to the building of roads. The Alps straddle the northern border of Italy and separate it from the rest of Europe. The Urals split European Russia and Siberia. The tremendous chain of which our Rocky Mountains are a part isolate a strip of the west coasts of North and South America, from Hudson Bay to Patagonia. To establish communication across such obstacles, where no natural passes could be found, the ancients had to build long roads zigzagging up one slope and down another. Occasionally they tried boring right through the mountains, but they found the task of tunnel-building extremely difficult and extremely hazardous. To cut through solid rock, even for

[441]

short distances, was the work of years, and there was ever-present danger that the weight of rock above would crush the tunnel and snuff out many lives.

Modern power tools made it possible to bore tunnels of size and length that would have astonished the ancients. Concrete and steel construction has found ways to reduce the danger of cave-ins to a minimum. But the element of danger still remains, and the men who work back of the "shield" as the tunnel is driven through granite, clay or mud have to be men of courage.

What Was the First Long Tunnel in England?

Over a hundred years ago, the Great Western Railway wanted to lay a road from London to Bristol, England. The route chosen required a tunnel. The company went to Parliament for a charter. The Members of Parliament studied the plans for the proposed line and refused the railway permission to build it. Such a tunnel, nearly two miles long, was impossible to build, they said. But Brunel, the Great Western's great engineer, knew he could do it. He begged the lawmakers to give him the chance to prove his skill. After long hearings on the question, Parliament grudgingly gave its consent, and sat back, waiting for Brunel to fail.

But Brunel did not fail. He gathered the best construction men he could find and inspired them with his courage. They labored long, hard hours to do the job that "could not be done." Bit by bit, the tunnel grew, and five years later, superb engineering craftsmanship had won, and the Box Tunnel was completed. Today it stands as a massive monument to Brunel's brilliance and perseverance.

What Was the First Long Tunnel in the United States?

The first long tunnel built in the United States was the remarkable Hoosac Tunnel. In 1848, the State of Massachusetts asked the Troy and Greenfield Railroad Company to build a road from Greenfield to Williamstown. The towering Hoosac Mountain stood in the way. In 1851, work was started on the vast five-mile tunnel that was to bore through this forbidding obstacle. Skilled

An interior view of the Lincoln Tunnel near the New Jersey portal. Note the grilles in the ceiling through which air is exhausted and sucked out of the tunnel.

engineers guided the crews. They laid their plans with great care and precision, so that the workers digging through from one side would meet the men coming through from the other.

Previous to this time, only short tunnels had been tried, and they had been dug with pick and shovel. Engineers realized that it would take too long to penetrate the Hoosac Mountain with such inadequate tools, so they looked for a quicker, easier way to do the job. They utilized two tools that revolutionized tunnel building—the power drill and nitroglycerin. The coughing power drill bit its way fiercely into the rock, hewing a passageway in an astonishingly short time. Nitroglycerin gouged great rough chunks out of the mountain. In spite of these two mighty allies, construction of the first large-scale tunnel in the United States was a slow and costly process. The tunnel cost over $11,000,000 before it was finished in 1872, twenty-five years later.

What Is the "Shield Method" of Building a Tunnel?

As engineers gained experience in building tunnels, they began to use the "shield method." In this type of construction, the primary part of the tunnel structure consists of a tube or cylinder slightly larger in diameter than the tunnel it is intended to build. The front end of the shield has a bulkhead which can be opened at will. Behind this bulkhead are a number of hydraulic jacks arranged to thrust against the last erected iron wing, and so push the entire shield forward. To keep earth, rocks, and water from pouring through the opening faster than the workmen can dig it out, compressed air is used. A comparison may be made by saying that if the ceiling of a room were weak and threatening to fall, it could be kept from falling by filling the room with air at a great enough pressure. In tunnel work, air is supplied under compression from equipment on the surface. The workers, or "sand hogs," who work under this pressure, can stay on the job only a limited number of hours. They risk incurring the "bends," the same affliction that troubles deep-sea divers, who work under air pressure equal to the pressure of the water.

How Were Tunnels Built Through the Alps?

For hundreds of years the peaks of the mighty Alps had been an obstacle to trade between European countries. Goods had to go around by water, or over tortuous, precarious roads. In the middle of the nineteenth century, constantly expanding railroads made the French and Italian Governments eager for a direct rail connection. This meant tunneling through one of the rocky masses. The Government engineers chose Mont Cenis. Incredulous people scoffed. Tunnel eight miles through the Alps? Only fools would try it. But the Victor Emmanuel Railway Company, aware of the immensity of the job, started it in 1857. Fourteen years of weary backbreaking toil and stubborn patience went into the Mont Cenis Tunnel until, in 1870, the news flashed through Europe that the Alps had been conquered at last.

The success of the Mont Cenis started a wave of Alpine tunnel-building. Boring through St. Gotthard Pass started the next year. But the staccato power drills disturbed hidden mountain streams, and jets of water under high pressure spurted from every crevice. Sticks of dynamite were washed out as fast as the blasters could put them in. For nine long years the determined crews worked waist-deep in water, refusing to lay down their tools.

This obstacle was not the only one. Rock dust filled the hot, steamy air, and fumes from oil lamps and explosives crept stealthily through the cavern. Men breathed this air and collapsed like flies. Two hundred died, and there were days when two-thirds of the crew were sick and could not work. Disease ran rampant; workers who stayed at

Erecting a tunneling shield preparatory to driving the Lincoln Tunnel under the Hudson River to connect New York City and New Jersey.

their jobs for a year were invalids for the rest of their lives.

At many places along the way, veins of faulty rock buckled beneath the overwhelming pressure of tons of sound rock above it and smashed masonry walls that lined the tunnel. The workers threw up two masonry walls for reinforcement. Another cave-in shattered both linings. It finally took three sturdy masonry walls to hold up the rock at these points.

Working on the principle of lengthening the track to ease the grade, engineers built seven spiral loops inside the mountain, so that trains would not have to climb too steeply. Building the St. Gotthard was a fierce struggle against staggering odds, but courage and skill in planning and detail fought a good fight, and the nine-mile tunnel was opened in 1882.

Because they wanted a more direct route from Paris to Milan, the French and Italian officials chose Simplon Pass for the next tunnel. They proposed to dig through twelve and a half miles of rock in five and one-half years. Mont Cenis had taken fourteen years to build, St. Gotthard eight, and the Simplon was to be one and one-third times as long as the St. Gotthard. No one believed it could be done. But Brandt, the engineer, invented a rotary hydraulic drill that chewed through rock as if it were butter. And he had an ingenious plan of construction. He ran two bores side by side through the mountain; one the regular size for a single-track road; the other a small bore for ventilation, transportation of working materials, and drainage.

The Simplon, like the St. Gotthard, had its trouble with water, but these waters that shot into the cavern were hot! If Brandt had not had the extra tunnel for drainage, work on the Simplon would have stopped. At the Italian end, two million gallons of hot water swirled in during a single day. Workers cut a passage between the main tunnel and the small one to let the water out.

More trouble followed. The temperature of the air inside the rocky cavern soared to dizzying heights, reaching the unbearable peak of 131 degrees. Sprays of cold water failed to cool it. There was only one answer. The company installed a complete refrigerating system. This helped somewhat, but when the construction neared its end, the rock walls got so hot that no one could work near them. They cooled so slowly that the job had to halt for several days.

This longest tunnel in the world was opened in 1906. The men who had overcome such staggering obstacles were proud of their record of breaking twelve and one-half miles through a mountain in seven years.

How Was the Continental Divide Conquered?

At the beginning of the twentieth century, David Moffat was building his Denver, Northwestern and Pacific Railroad. He dreamed of laying a road straight through from Denver to the West Coast. But the massive Continental Divide loomed in his way, and to pass it, he would have to drill six miles through solid rock. This, of course, would be far too expensive a process. But Moffat, still envisioning a direct rail route, set about raising funds for the job, having already plunged his whole fortune into the road.

Moffat died penniless in 1911, but his scheme did not die with him. Two years later, the city of Denver appointed a Tunnel Commission to coöperate with the Denver and Salt Lake Railroad in building the tunnel. But the Colorado Springs Court outlawed the agreement, and the next nine years were spent in legal squabbles. Finally, the city decided to build the tunnel as a public work and to lease it to a railroad for operation.

With the double-bore method of the Simplon, the construction progressed rapidly. Its workmen set a record for fast tunneling. They burrowed 771 feet through the mountain in 15 days! Quickly the tunnel took shape. Officials congratulated themselves on the easiness of the task. They had run into none of the hazards met by the Alpine builders. In 1926 three-fourths of the tunnel was finished—then trouble shattered the streak of good luck. Drills struck an underground stream, and 3,000 gallons of water a minute burst into the cavern! Drenched, mud-covered men went on drilling grimly, while others struggled to get the drainage systems working. Soon afterwards, a crew of six laborers were bracing the roof of a section of tunnel to prevent a cave-in. In the middle of their work they heard an ominous rumble. Before they could leap to safety, tons of hurtling rock crashed down and buried them.

Despite these disasters, the Moffat Tunnel was finally finished, and the first train ran through it in 1928. David Moffat's dream had come true. Instead of taking seven hours to cross the Divide, trains streaked through the Tunnel in seven minutes! The Moffat Tunnel, 10,000 feet above sea level, linked Eastern industry to the West, and saved precious hours in transcontinental traveling.

What Is the Longest Tunnel in the United States?

While the Moffat Tunnel was being built in Colorado, the Great Northern Railway was having its trouble with its small, two-and-one-half-mile bore under Stevens Pass in Washington. The road's traffic had skyrocketed, and heavy trains had a hard time over the long grades. In 1925 the company decided to build a new Cascade Tunnel, almost eight miles long, and set an impressive time limit of three years for the job. The company bought

Lincoln Tunnel, showing the upper side of the ceiling slab in the south tube. The men are assembling glass tiles upon gummed paper before concreting.

the most modern machinery and best equipment it could find. Compressed air, electricty, and dynamite, backed by delicate engineering calculations, broke all speed records. Construction crews worked as fast as they could, with their quota for each day's work figured to the minute. Month after month, they bored their way through gray, solid granite at a terrific pace. Water roaring in at ten thousand gallons a minute could not stop them. Within three years, their inspired perseverance had finished the longest tunnel in America.

How Were Tunnels Bored Under the Hudson River?

The building of the Hudson River tunnels was probably one of the most daring engineering feats ever accomplished. As is well known, the Hudson River, for the length of Manhattan Island, is approximately a mile wide, reducing in width at the Palisades north of Hoboken. In consequence of the unusual geographical situation, all trunk lines and other transit facilities in New Jersey terminated on the western shore of the Hudson, and passengers were compelled to use ferries to reach New York. As far back as 1873, a company was organized to construct a tunnel under the river, but it met with numerous and most discouraging obstacles, so that it was finally compelled to abandon the work, although it succeeded in building a considerable length of structure. Efforts were made at various times after that date to revive the work, with no success. In 1902, however, work was resumed and a few years later was pushed to a successful end.

In tunneling under the river, nearly every conceivable combination of rocks and soils were met, but for the most part the material was silt. In such material, with a pressure of 5,000 pounds per square inch on the shield jacks, the shield was pushed through the ground as though one pushed a stick into a heap of snow. The silt was pushed aside, thus obviating the necessity of removing any excavated material. Sand or gravel, or any material which would not flow or become displaced by the shield, was excavated ahead of the shield, and removed from the heading prior to pushing it forward. In the silt, the most satisfactory and economic progress was attained, and a record was made of 72 feet of finished tunnel, completely lined with iron, in one day of 24 hours.

The most difficult combination that had to be dealt with under the river was when the bottom consisted of rock and the top of silt and wet sand. In such cases, and there were many of them, the upper section of soft ground was first excavated and the exposed face securely supported with timbers ahead of the shield; then the rock underlying it was drilled and blasted. This was very tedious and expensive work. Exceedingly small charges of dynamite had to be used and the procedure conducted with the utmost caution.

A catastrophe occurred in the south tunnel of the uptown tubes. When the shield had advanced 115 feet from the Jersey side, the night superintendent, in his anxiety to push the work, disobeyed instructions. The tunnel got away from him and was

[449]

Driving a water tunnel through the bedrock of Manhattan to bring water to New York City. In the background can be seen a completed portion of the tunnel.

flooded, and his men had a narrow escape with their lives. Several schemes were considered in order to reclaim the tunnel, including that of dredging out the bed of the river just in advance of the shield, to a sufficient depth to enable a diver to go down and timber up the exterior opening of the doorway, where the silt and mud had come through and filled the tunnel. This plan had to be abandoned, as the river above was almost entirely occupied by shipping that could not well be interrupted.

Finally the situation was met by the use of two large and heavy mainsails, which made a double canvas cover measuring about sixty by forty feet. This canvas cover was spread on a flat barge, and small sections of pig iron were attached to its edges. Ropes were carried to fixed points to hold it in exact position. The barge was then withdrawn, and the canvas cover dropped to the bed of the river. It settled over the point where the leak had occurred, and a large number of bags of dirt were then deposited on it. An opening was made in the bulkhead of the tunnel below, and for eight days material, under hydrostatic pressure, forced its way into the tunnel, where it was loaded on cars. Finally the canvas was drawn into the hole, stopping it up. Additional material was then deposited into the river to fill the cavity. The tunnel was recovered, pumped out, and work resumed.

Probably the most unique and interesting pieces of construction are the three junctions on the Jersey side of the river, where the uptown tunnels from New York diverge, north to Hoboken and south to Jersey City and New York downtown. For safe and expeditious operation of trains, where the headway is only one

[450]

A sectional view of the ventilating system of the Lincoln Tunnel. Actually, there are two tunnels, each of which carries one-way traffic. The seven-story building is completely occupied with blower and suction fan equipment. Fresh air is forced into the tunnel under the roadbed. It rises through openings in the sides of the road and is sucked out through the open grilles in the ceiling slab of the tunnel.

and one-half minutes, it was imperative that grade crossings should be avoided. (A grade crossing is a point where the tracks of one service cross the tracks of another at the same level.) At the point in question, this was a knotty problem to solve, owing to the unusual operating conditions which had to be met, there being six separate and distinct operating classes of trains to be handled around this triangle.

To meet this situation, three massive reinforced concrete caissons were built on the surface. They were virtually large two-story houses, each being over 100 feet in length, about 50 feet in height, and about 45 feet in width at their widest point. The bottom edges were sharp, and, with the use of air pressure and great weights, the three structures were sunk in the ground to the same grade as the intercepting tunnels, and the tunnels were then driven into them.

Where Are There Tunnels for Automobiles?

Although most tunnels are built for railroads, there are two remarkable tunnels which have been built for automobile traffic. They are the Holland and Lincoln tunnels into New York City. The first of the vehicular underriver tubes was the Holland Tunnel, connecting lower Manhattan with Jersey City, opened in 1927. The second was the Lincoln Tunnel, connecting mid-town Manhattan with Weehauken, N. J., one tube of which was opened for traffic in 1937. The Lincoln Tunnel has twin tubes enclosing double-track, one-way boulevards, one tube for east-bound vehicles, with one lane for fast and one lane for less fast traffic; and the other tube for west-bound vehicles, with two lanes for traffic of different speeds. These wonderful underriver highways, well lighted and well ventilated, are marvels of engineering.

The idea of the first vehicular tunnel under the Hudson River, to connect New York and Jersey City, was conceived about the year 1907, and gradually received favorable consideration. In 1919 a commission was appointed, and on October 12, 1920, actual work was started on the construction. Clifford Milburn Holland (1883-1924) was appointed chief engineer, and in recognition of his untiring efforts the project was named the Holland Tunnel.

A huge shield was used to bore out the north tunnel on the Jersey side and another for the New York side. The first shield was erected in the Canal Street shaft in New York on October 26, 1922, compressed air was introduced into the shield chamber, and tunneling was begun. Each shield was 30 feet, 2 inches in outside diameter, 16 feet, 4 inches long, and the upper half was equipped

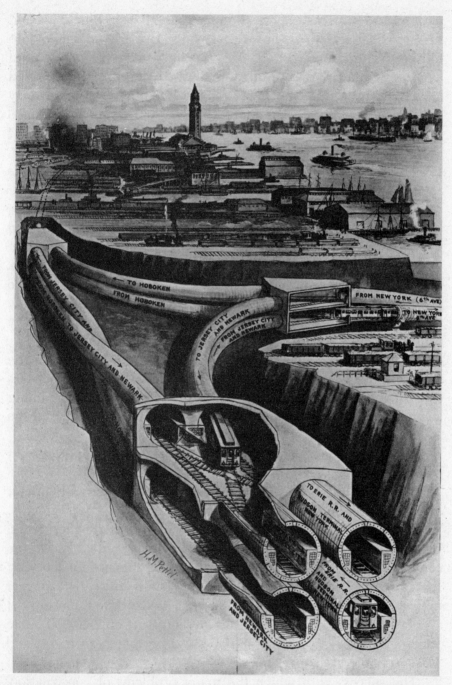

A cut-away drawing showing the complicated system of railroad tunnels that connect New York City with various cities on the New Jersey side of the Hudson River.

[453]

with a hood projecting 2 feet, 6 inches ahead of the shield proper. Five vertical and three horizontal walls divided the shield into thirteen compartments, and in these the workmen, called "sand hogs," dug out the rock, mud, and silt as the cutting shield bored its way into the river strata. The shield was equipped with thirty 10-inch jacks, having a combined thrust of 6,000 tons. The tunnel lining was composed of rings 2 feet, 6 inches wide, consisting of 14 segments each approximately 6 feet long, with a key 1 foot long, bolted together. Inside the lining was an inner lining of concrete 19 inches thick.

As the shield advanced and the lining was erected behind it, the space due to the difference in the diameter of the shield and the rings forming the lining was filled by forcing mortar made of cement and sand in equal parts into the void under high pressure. For this purpose each segment was provided with a mortar hole fitted with a screw plug. The lining was made water-tight by placing hemp wads soaked in red lead around the bolts, and by caulking lead-wire grooves between the segments.

As the steel cutting shield bored into the earth and rock at the rate of about twenty-five feet a day, the lining of the tunnel was constructed, the giant erector lifting the rings of the steel lining and putting them into place. This work followed right behind the shields, the riveters bolting the huge rings together.

The north tube shields met on October 24, 1924, and those of the south tube on December 7, 1924.

The tunnels are cylindrical in form, have an external diameter of 29 feet, 6 inches, made up of the fourteen cast-iron segments. The inside of each tunnel is lined with square white tile blocks. The road bed is concrete, the roadway of granite blocks, the ceiling, of concrete. The total length of the tunnel is 9,250 feet; length of underriver portion, 5,480 feet. The roadways are 20 feet wide, with 13 feet, 6 inches head room. The depth to top of tunnel at mean high-water level is 72 feet. In construction, 500,000 cubic yards were excavated, and 115,000 tons of cast-iron segments and 130,000 cubic yards of concrete used.

The success with which the many problems of construction, ventilation and maintenance were solved in the Holland and Lincoln Tunnels has led to the planning of other vehicular tunnels, in New York and elsewhere.

What Happens When Animals Hibernate?

We have all heard of certain animals sleeping through the long winter months and most of us have probably wondered what happens to them when they do this.

This hiding away for a long sleep, or hibernation, as it is called, commences when the food of the animal begins to get scarce, and the length and depth of the sleep depends on the habit and constitution of the animal.

Bats, bears, some animals of the rodent order, such as the porcupine, the dormouse, some squirrels, etc., all the animals belonging to the classes of *Amphibia* and *Reptilia,* such as tortoises, lizards, snakes, frogs, etc., and many species of mollusks and insects, hibernate more or less completely, retiring to suitable places of concealment—the bat to dark caves, the hedgehog to fern-brakes, snakes to holes in trees, etc.

During hibernation there is a great decrease of heat in the bodies of the the animals, the temperature sometimes sinking to 40° or even 20° F., or in general to a point a little above that of the surrounding atmosphere. The respiration as well as the pulsation of the heart is exceedingly slow, and the irritability of the animal often so low that in some cases it can be awakened only by strong electric shocks.

With frogs and amphibious reptiles the dormant state is very common, and if the temperature is kept low by artificial means they may remain dormant for years.

The term "æstivation" has been used to describe a similar condition into which certain animals, such as serpents and crocodiles, in tropical countries pass during the hottest months of the year.

When Were Women Taken Into the American Armed Forces?

During World War II, voluntary auxiliary services of women were added to the armed forces. The Women's Army Auxiliary Corps (WAACS) was established in the War Department by executive order of May 15, 1942, following an Act of Congress. In July, 1943, the WAACS became full-fledged members of the Army instead of mere auxiliaries. The title was changed to Women's Army Corps (WACS), officers being given regular military titles.

The Women's Reserve, a branch of the Naval Reserve, composed of Women Appointed for Volunteer Emergency Service (WAVES), was established by law on July 30, 1942. It was created to release male officers and men of the naval service for duty at sea. It provides ratings corresponding to those of the regular Navy. An Act of Congress, approved November 22, 1942, established the Women's Reserve of the Coast Guard Reserve, the members of which are known as SPARS (from the Coast Guard motto, "Semper Paratus—Always Ready").

THE STORY OF BRIDGES

The Baltimore and Ohio Bridge over the Susquehanna River. An example of the deck girder type, it is over a mile long.

THE first bridge was the trunk of a tree thrown across a channel, or a large slab placed upon stepping-stones in a stream. Rope bridges, hammock bridges of vines, pontoon bridges with boats for supports—these were among the types of bridges used in olden days, and still used in emergency or in out-of-the-way places of the world. In the course of time came the arch bridge, the materials being either wood or brick, then stone. Excavations on the site of Nineveh and Babylon show remains of brick arches dating back to four thousand years before Christ. A brick arch bridge, over six hundred feet long, is said to have been built over the Euphrates River within the city of Babylon about 200 B.C. It was composed of wooden platforms laid on stone piers. The first bridge to be composed entirely of iron was built in 1776 in England. Later, wrought iron took the place of cast iron, and about 1862 the first steel bridge appeared. The first steel arch, and the first steel railway bridge in America was the Eads Bridge over the Mississippi at St. Louis (1869-1874).

New York City's Hell Gate Bridge. The steel arch seen here has a span of 977½ feet and stands 140 feet above the water.

What Are the Chief Types of Bridges?

The principal types of bridges now in use include: the stone arch bridge, the steel arch bridge, the plate girder bridge, the simple wooden or steel truss bridge, the ribbed arch bridge, the various types of drawbridge, and the suspension and cantilever bridges.

The last two are designed for long spans. A cantilever is a bracket, projecting from a wall to support a balcony. A cantilever bridge is built on this principle, with piers, each of which has two cantilevers. Long girders connect the cantilever with adjacent piers. In many cases, as in the Quebec Bridge, there is a separate central span, which is joined to the cantilever arms.

The suspension bridge is so-called because the deck is suspended from cables that stretch between towers at each end of the span. Longer spans can be built by this method than by any other.

[457]

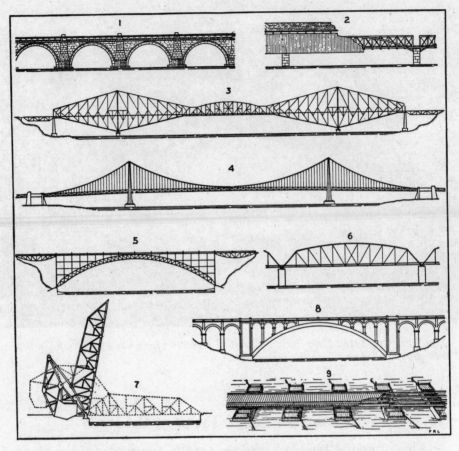

Principal types of bridges: 1, stone arch (Roman); 2, wood covered (Colonial); 3, steel cantilever; 4, steel suspension; 5, steel arch; 6, steel truss; 7, steel bascule, a form of drawbridge; 8, concrete arch; 9, wood pontoon (military).

What Were the Earliest Railroad Bridges?

Railroad construction engineers, seeking short cuts across valleys, rivers and mountain gorges have been among the foremost builders of bridges. These bridges have played a tremendous part in the development of railroading. Their story is a fascinating one, and goes back to the days when pioneer railroad builders hewed great rough timbers from America's virgin forests and laid them across streams to hold tracks. But when people began

One of the many stone arch bridges that carry London's traffic across the Thames River. Some of them are over three hundred years old.

to use trains for shipping goods, the timber bridges were not sturdy enough to carry freight.

Skilled stonecutters set to work under the direction of engineers and laid one great stone slab on top of another to form the first masonry arch bridge, which is about as solid a structure as man has achieved. This first railroad stone arch bridge, built in north Britain over two hundred years ago, is standing today! The oldest one still in use, the single arch built over Gwynn's Falls at Baltimore in 1829, today carries loads one hundred times greater than those for which it was built.

The most remarkable of the old stone bridges is the 612-foot viaduct at Relay, Maryland, now 110 years old, over which lay the

A view of the Thames River in England. In the foreground is the remarkable London Bridge—a combination of suspension and drawbridge. The center span opens to allow river traffic to pass. The next span across the river is a stone arch bridge.

route of the first trains ever operated in America. The railroad company gave the job of building it to an Irishman named John McCartney, who searched the country for the finest masons and the best construction men he could find. When the bridge was finished, the railroad engineers were astounded to find that the completed structure did not deviate a quarter of an inch from the plans, a feat unheard of in engineering history.

What Were the Earliest Girder Bridges?

Masonry bridges, although the strongest and most permanent of all, had three disadvantages: they were costly, their span was

White's Creek Bridge in Fraser Canyon, British Columbia, a deck girder bridge on stone masonry piles.

limited, and they were "fixed," that is, they could not be altered to accommodate the river traffic passing below. The girder span and the truss bridge solved the first two problems.

In the girder span, built first of timber, then of iron and later of steel, beams are laid on edge side by side with the track carried on top. This is known as a "deck girder span." A "through girder span" has girders laid on both sides of the span, with a floor between them on which the tracks run through the bridge instead of on top of it. The best example of this is the Britannia Bridge in North Wales, where four masonry piers support iron girders over 1,500 feet long. Here girders cross the longest opening in the world—a distance of 460 feet.

The first iron railroad bridge in the United States is believed to have been built for the Reading Railroad in 1845. In 1846-1847

[461]

a boiler plate tubular girder, 55 feet in length, was built at Bolton, Maryland, for the Baltimore and Ohio Railroad, and an iron Howe truss bridge, with 30-foot spans, was built near Pittsfield, Massachusetts, for the Boston and Albany Railroad. The first all-steel railway bridge was a 2,700-foot structure completed at Glasgow, Missouri, in 1879, for the Chicago and Alton Railroad.

Girder and truss spans are often combined, each chosen for the kind of work it has to do. The Zambesi Bridge in Africa has 40 spans and stretches over nearly 2 miles of water.

When Were Caissons First Used?

Captain James Eads began the first metal arch across the Mississippi River at St. Louis. This pioneer builder sank pneumatic caissons through the mud of the Mississippi bottom to bed rock, 100 feet below the surface. This new method of building foundations made possible such tremendous structures as the 3½ mile Hell Gate Bridge, built in New York in 1915, to perform the vital task of providing a link between New York and New England. The steel arch of this bridge has a span of 977½ feet, and trains rush across it 140 feet above the river.

Where Are the Largest Cantilever Bridges?

The cantilever is most often used to cross wide openings. Stretch a plank out from each side of a stream until they meet, weight the ends on the banks with rocks to balance the part over water, and you have a simple cantilever.

The Quebec Bridge, one of the longest spans in the world, is a cantilever. Tragedy stalked its building. In 1907, when a third of it was done, 19,000 tons of twisted steel snapped from its foundation and crashed down into the river, taking 70 men to their death. The plans had been so miscalculated that even this much of the bridge couldn't hold up its own weight. The builders spent nine years reinforcing what was left of the foundations and rebuilding the bridge itself. In 1916, ten thousand cheering people gathered on the banks of the St. Lawrence to watch the raising of the central span to position and what they thought

The cantilever Firth of Forth Bridge seen at sunset from a British battleship.

would be the completion of the bridge. But the 640-foot span had risen scarcely two feet when it slipped and plunged into the river.

World War I was in full swing then, and the armies in Europe needed supplies. Bridging the St. Lawrence would get the supplies there faster, so work was begun on another span to replace the one that now lay at the bottom of the river. After a year's work, another great crowd, this time silent, gathered to see the third attempt to finish the bridge. It took three days to raise the second span—inches at a time—but finally it touched the north and south arms of the bridge; a man at each end drove the bolts to fasten it, and completed the longest single span bridge in the world.

Runner-up to the Quebec Bridge is the massive Firth of Forth cantilever in Scotland, which was completed in 1890. Over 6,000,000 rivets fasten together 50,000 tons of steel in this tremendous structure, towering so high above the river that the biggest battleships can pass beneath it. The Forth Bridge Railway Company has 50 full-time employees, and 30 of these are the traditional Forth Bridge painters. They start at one end of the bridge to paint the 145 acres of metal, and it takes them three years to reach the other side! By that time the first end needs painting again; so they start all over. These men and their sons after them, spend their lives painting the Forth Bridge.

[463]

A steel gauge at one end of the bridge bears out the amazing fact that the bridge grows five inches during the day and that it shrinks back at night.

How Do Boats Pass Low Bridges?

Many rivers have heavy boat traffic, and railroad bridges must be either high enough for the boats to go under, or they must be "movable," that is, part of the bridge must lift up to let the boats through. Sometimes one end of the span is hinged, and the other end raises up like a jackknife. The swing span turns around horizontally on a center span, while the lift bridge is pulled up between elevator towers. The Pennsylvania's lift bridge at Newark can be raised 135 feet in less than 1½ minutes.

London Bridge is a notable example of a lift bridge, set in the middle of a suspension span.

Where Are the Chief Suspension Bridges?

One of the earliest suspension bridges, made with wire cables, was erected at Fairmount, Philadelphia, in 1816. The famous Brooklyn Bridge—the first of several over the East River at New York—was not completed until 1883.

In modern suspension bridges a stiffening truss is used, which causes any load on the bridge to be transmitted by a large number of hangers to the main suspension cables, thus reducing the local deflection. A bridge of the suspension type may seem to be solid when you motor or walk across it, but as a matter of fact it is a flexible thing—so flexible, indeed, that an army marching over it has to break step, for the bridge will vibrate and swing to the rhythm of the marching feet.

Some great examples of bridges are: the George Washington Bridge across the Hudson at New York, which has a span of 3,500 feet; the Delaware River Bridge at Philadelphia, 1,750 ft.; San Francisco's bridges, Golden Gate Bridge, 4,200 ft. span, and the San Francisco-Oakland Bridge, through Yerba Buena Island, part suspension (2,400 ft. spans), part cantilever (1,400 ft. span), completed in 1937.

[464]

Burnside Street Bridge, Portland, Oregon. This is a bascule type of drawbridge. In the background is another type, having a single central span that rises vertically between two steel towers.

Burnside Street Bridge with its center section open. This type of drawbridge saves the expense of building high bridges.

Combining the features of a trestle bridge with those of a drawbridge, this span is used by Southern Pacific streamliners.

How Is a Suspension Bridge Built?

In building a suspension bridge, the first task is to erect the great steel or masonry towers over which the cables will pass, and the masonry anchorage in which the ends of the cables will be embedded. From tower to tower, and from the anchorages to the towers, a slender thread of wire is suspended, and on this an ingenious device called a "spider" crawls back and forth, weaving a giant cable.

As day by day you watch the spider on its journey to and fro across the river, you see the strand of wire grow bigger and bigger until the cable has reached the proportions specified by the designer, who, long before the foundations of the tower are constructed, has studied the character of river and land, the velocities of the wind, the changes in temperature, the tensile strength of the materials and how much traffic the structure will have to bear; and has built up in his imagination a picture of the bridge that is to be. Two (or four) of these steel cables, each of them perhaps having eighteen thousand galvanized wires, as in the case of the great Delaware River Bridge, are flung out from anchorage to tower, then across the stream to the opposite tower, and embedded in the anchorage on the farther shore.

Supported by graceful concrete piles, the Goethals Bridge in New York is an example of the truss and girder type.

With the great cables in position, the next step is to provide for the roadway. At intervals along the cable, smaller steel ropes or rods are suspended. Viewed from the river, they look like threads hanging down fringelike from the larger thread. These are of graded length, the long ones being close to the towers where the main cables are highest above the water. The shortest of the hanging wire ropes are those in the center of the span—at the bottom of the great curve made by the suspension cables. At the bottom of these dangling ropes the steel girders are attached horizontally. These form the basis of the roadway.

Girder after girder is fixed in position. All over the structure men are at work on their several specified tasks, placing, riveting, hammering, painting; some of them perched along the curving cables; others on top of the towers; some of them in dangerous positions on the girders out over the water; some of them riding the great steel beams as they are hoisted to their lofty positions by puffing derricks.

Finally the great lengthwise girders are united by cross beams; the bridge begins to assume practical shape; the various roadbeds are laid, some for pedestrians, some for vehicular traffic, others perhaps for trolleys and trains. It is a gigantic task, and it involves the most careful calculation beforehand, as well as efficient work

[467]

San Francisco's Golden Gate Bridge, the highest, longest-spanned suspension bridge in the world. The towers rise to the height of a 65-story building. The center span is 4,200 feet long.

in actual construction. The suspension bridge is a marvel of engineering skill, but it is more than this, for there is also in its lines something of exquisite beauty.

Which Is the Longest Suspension Bridge?

Silhouetted against the sky, and spectacularly flung across California's far-famed Golden Gate, the Golden Gate Bridge frames a majestic portal for the entrance to San Francisco Bay, greatest harbor on the greatest ocean on the face of the globe.

Its successful construction climaxes centuries of progress in engineering science. Like the single appeal of a classic painting,

The George Washington Bridge over the Hudson River. One of the greatest suspension bridges in the world, it connects New York City with the opposite New Jersey shore.

the graceful, inverted arc of its main span wins premier acclaim at first sight—4,200 feet long, or 700 feet longer than that of the George Washington Memorial Bridge of New York, thus making the Golden Gate Bridge the longest clear span ever constructed.

The marvelous structure spans the narrowest stretch of the Golden Gate between Fort Point on the Presidio shore line and Lime Point on the Marin side and yet the bridge proper is 1¼ miles long. With north and south approaches, the project embraces 7 miles. It joins the San Francisco peninsula with the north coast counties of the Redwood Empire, breaking the last major water barrier in the Canada-Mexico coast highway.

The mighty single span is hung between the world's tallest bridge towers, each a labyrinth of individual steel cells and each rising 746 feet above water. The south tower, including its foundation, is 846 feet high. The two cables, each 36½ inches in diameter, are the largest ever spun and have 27,572 strands each—a total of 80,000 miles.

[469]

The minimum clearance of the main span above high water is 220 feet, more than sufficient for the greatest ships afloat. The bridge is built to withstand a wind velocity of 90 miles an hour, although 58 miles is the record to date. The center span may sway as much as 20 feet without damage, while expansion and contraction, due to atmospheric changes, may raise and lower the center of the bridge as much as 10 feet in one day.

The supporting piers of the two gigantic towers are huge concrete monoliths. The north pier, really a block of synthetic stone, weighs 90,000,000 pounds. The south pier, 1,200 feet offshore, is the first major bridge pier ever built in the open sea. Its foundations, where rock was blasted under water despite swirling tides racing at 7 knots, cover more than an acre.

The bridge is a single deck structure, 90 feet wide, with 6 lanes for automobiles, having an estimated maximum capacity

A railroad trestle bridge over the Feather River Canyon, California. Western railroads often use trestle bridges to reach across the steep gorges of the Rocky Mountains.

New York's Triborough Bridge, which connects the three boroughs of Queens, Bronx, and Manhattan. It starts from Astoria, L. I., crosses the Sound, swings over Randall's Island, paralleling the course of the Hell Gate Railroad Bridge, and on to the Bronx, or connecting with Manhattan by bridge across the Harlem River.

of 260,000 machines in 24 hours. It also has two pedestrian sidewalks—more in demand for sight-seeing than for traffic.

The roadway is brightly illuminated, the great towers flood lighted, and a lighthouse installed in the south tower, while air travelers are protected by aërial beacons and by lights outlining the cables. Thus the bridge creates a brilliant and impressive night display.

THE STORY OF RAILROADING

The most powerful electric locomotive in the world, the famed GG-1. The first man to demonstrate a successful electric locomotive was Frank J. Sprague, a young American naval officer. In 1885 Sprague made a successful run on the Manhattan El in New York City. The first section of New York's four-track subway, opened in 1904, was modeled on Sprague's designs.

THE STORY of railroading is one of adventure, courage, and engineering genius. Pioneers, struggling against incredible hardships, have covered the United States with a vast web of steel rails. Into the building of railroads has gone all the skill and science that man has acquired during centuries of progress.

To speed the advance of the iron horse, men have built amazing bridges of many kinds, have bored tunnels miles long through towering rocky walls, have employed all their knowledge of metallurgy, mechanical and electrical engineering, and have used innumerable inventions. The following pages tell the story of railroading in pictures.

[472]

John Stevens, an American inventor, designed this locomotive in 1825. Stevens was quick to see the possibilities of railroads. In February, 1815, the New Jersey legislature granted him a charter to build a railroad from New Brunswick to Trenton. This was the first charter ever issued for a railroad in the United States. Later Stevens built a railroad between Philadelphia and Columbia, a distance of 82 miles, which were covered by horse-drawn trains in nine hours.

The Stourbridge Lion was an English locomotive brought to America by a young American engineer, Horatio Allen. After a successful three-mile run over the shaky rails of the time, Allen reversed his engine and brought it back to the starting point at Honesdale, Pennsylvania. Crowds of spectators cheered as he stepped down from the locomotive. Allen was the first engineer to pilot a commercial locomotive. But the Stourbridge Lion was a failure, for it was not strong enough to pull the heavy coal carts of the time.

The first locomotive built in America was so tiny that its inventor, Peter Cooper, called it the Tom Thumb. Cooper's engine was the first that was able to negotiate the sharp turns on the Baltimore & Ohio Railroad. The picture shows the Tom Thumb in a race against a horse, which the horse won when the engine broke down. Nevertheless, Cooper's engine was a success. It was the first to make use of tubes in the boiler system.

At Promontory, Utah, in 1869, the rails of the Central Pacific were joined with those of the Union Pacific to form America's first transcontinental railroad. There was great rivalry between the two companies and each side drove its construction gangs hard, the Central Pacific from the West and the Union Pacific from the East. A Central Pacific crew laid ten miles of track in one day to win a $10,000 wager from the Union Pacific.

In 1870 it took eight days to cross the continent. As locomotives were improved, their speed increased. Diamond stacker engines like this 1870 model broke many speed records. The Jarrett and Palmer Special made a run across the continent in three and a half days, in 1876, and this record stood until the Union Pacific in 1934 sent a streamlined train from Los Angeles to New York in 56 hours and 55 minutes.

Curious skyscraper trains were sometimes used to house the men working on the Western railroads. Labor was a big problem during the building of the transcontinental railroads. Men were continually lured away from the roads by rumors of gold strikes. Some Indian tribes resisted the invasion of their lands, and the construction crews frequently had to lay down their tools to defend themselves with rifles.

"Smash the world record!" That was the order given to the famous engineer, Charlie Hogan, of the New York Central, when a new locomotive, the 999, rolled from the shops. On May 11, 1893, Hogan opened the throttle of the 999 and hurtled forward at a speed of 112.5 miles per hour. This new record in turn was broken on June 12, 1905, by a Pennsylvania passenger train, which covered three miles in 85 seconds—an average of 127 miles per hour!

The locomotive, with its terrific power, its noise and smoke, is indeed a dramatic sight. But it would be nothing without the steel rails that stretch motionless toward the horizon. And without the modern steel rail our giant high-speed locomotives could not run. The rails take such a terrific pounding that the equivalent of 5,000 to 10,000 miles of high-grade track must be replaced each year.

Tracks are no longer laid by hand. Derrick booms rigged on heavy cars swing tracks into place. Spikes are driven into the ties, to hold the tracks in place, by powerful pneumatic hammers. By the use of power-driven rooters, spreaders, ditchers, bulldozers, shovels, and drag-line excavators, tracks can now be laid at a very rapid pace.

Winter means a continuous battle to keep the tracks clear of snow. Winter weather played havoc with railroad schedules until the invention of the rotary snow plow by Lewis Bergendahl in 1885. This plow consists of a nine-foot wheel, weighing many tons, encased in a cylinder which scoops up the snow and feeds it to the wheel to be cut to pieces. Then the snow goes to a hopper and is blown a hundred feet from the track.

The modern locomotive is a marvel of mechanical efficiency. The fireman no longer shovels tons of coal from the tender into the firebox; he tends an automatic stoker that spreads a thin and uniform fire over the broad grates of the huge new locomotives. A screw conveyor under the coal bunker carries the coal to the firebox, raises it above the fire bed, and sprinkles it uniformly over the fire.

The iron horse has been streamlined to improve its appearance and speed. This passenger locomotive of 4-6-2 type, designed by Pennsylvania Railroad engineers together with Raymond Loewy, shows a reduction of one-third in wind resistance at mile-a-minute speeds. At maximum speeds the saving is equal to almost 300 horsepower.

Locomotives are identified by the arrangement of their wheels. The huge passenger locomotive here illustrated is of type 4-8-4. This means that it has four "idler" wheels in front (two pairs), followed by four pairs of driving wheels, then two pairs of small idlers in the rear. The small wheels are necessary to distribute the weight of the locomotive. The big wheels (70 to 80 inches in diameter) are driven by a rod connected to the shaft of the steam piston. The cylinder in which the piston moves is located between the small forward wheels in this type of locomotive.

Diesel locomotives are being used more and more for both freight and passenger haulage. The horizontal shock absorbers and low center of gravity of Diesel-engined trains enable them to sweep around curves at much higher speeds than steam locomotives. Lightweight bodies and low fuel consumption permit more economical operation.

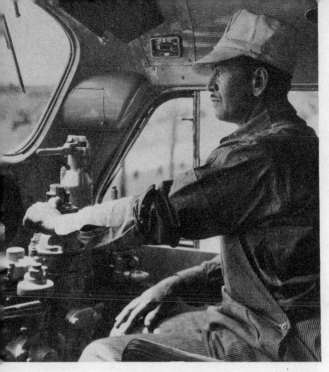

An engineer at the controls of a powerful Diesel locomotive. The controls resemble those of a trolley car. The cab is clean, comfortable, and sound-proofed. The engineer's right foot rests on the "dead man's pedal." If he should remove his foot, because of sickness or accident, the pedal would spring up and the train would stop automatically.

Electric locomotives are also used to haul freight. During the first decade of this century, railroads began to electrify tunnels to eliminate the danger of smoke poisoning. Since 1929, most electric railroads have used overhead power transmission at 3,000 or 11,000 volts.

Semaphore signals high in the Canadian Rockies. Semaphores and the Morse telegraph were used in the old block system after 1851. Each block was one to seven miles long. As the train entered each block, the towerman put down his semaphore and notified the next tower by telegraph that rang a bell. After the train left his block, the towerman returned his semaphore to the safe position.

Color-light signals were introduced in 1912. Red, yellow and green were used to indicate, respectively: stop, proceed with caution, clear. Three years later the Pennsylvania introduced position-light signals, reproducing the positions of the semaphore with amber lights in rows of three. Later the Baltimore & Ohio combined the position and color lights, using two green lights vertically for clear, two amber diagonally for caution, and two red horizontally for stop.

Semaphores above the track guide the engineer. A modern signal system is coördinated with track switches and is operated from a remote signal tower. Here an operator watches an electric diagram that shows the movements of all trains in his section. By pressing two buttons on his control board, he can line up a whole series of switches and signals, and thus control the entire route of a train.

A post office on wheels. The volume of mail carried by the railroads is tremendous. Mail cars are owned by the railroads, but are built according to the specifications of the United States Post Office Department. Look closely at any mail car and you will see a regular drop on each side. Here you can post a letter as you would at a post office.

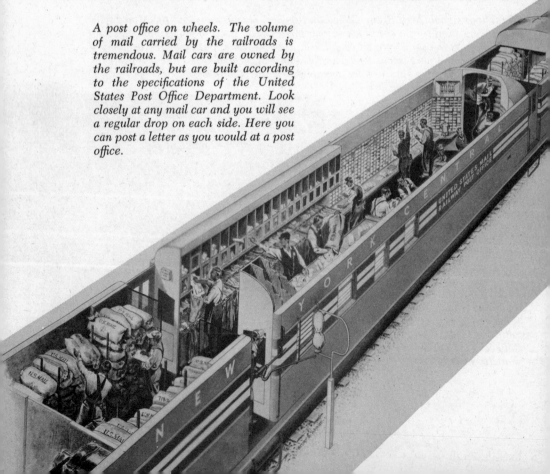

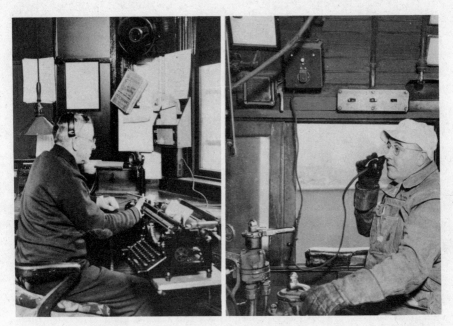

A dispatcher talking to a locomotive engineer in his cab by means of the inductive telephone. For more than half a century, inventors have dreamed of a station-to-train telephone. Today it is a reality. The inductive telephone is a wired radio-telephone. A radio wave from the telephone in the engine cab leaps to the telephone or telegraph wires along the track (or even to a rail), from which it is picked up by the aërial of the radio-telephone in the dispatcher's office.

The man behind every train order is the dispatcher. Orders from dispatchers formerly went out over telegraph lines, but today two-thirds of American railroad dispatching is done by telephone. Operators stationed along the line report to the dispatcher on the movements of all trains in his district, and relay his orders to engineers and conductors.

Odd-sized cargoes are carried on special flat cars. Here a giant electrical transformer, 18 feet high, is carried on a flat car with a sunken platform between its wheels. Trains carrying oversize cargoes must often go by roundabout routes to avoid tunnels and low bridges. One train moving boilers 18 feet high had to make a 100-mile detour and travel on the lines of the New York Central, Delaware and Hudson, Rutland, Canadian Pacific, Maine Central, and Boston and Maine.

End of a railroad journey—Grand Central Station, New York City. Each year, no less than 54,000,000 passengers pass through this enormous terminal. Five hundred trains arrive and leave every day. In one busy year, its employees handled 638 billion tons of freight. The terminal has two levels. Forty-one tracks carry through traffic on the upper level, while suburban trains use the lower level. Tracks and switches in its underground caverns stretch out for seventy-nine acres.

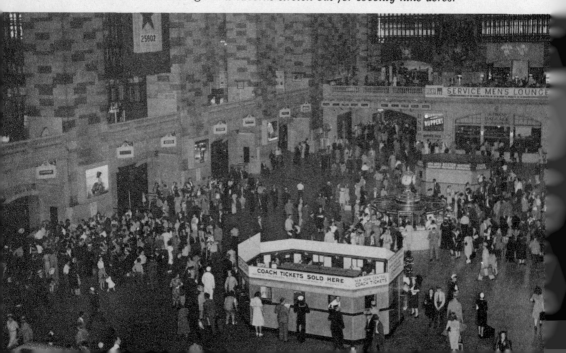

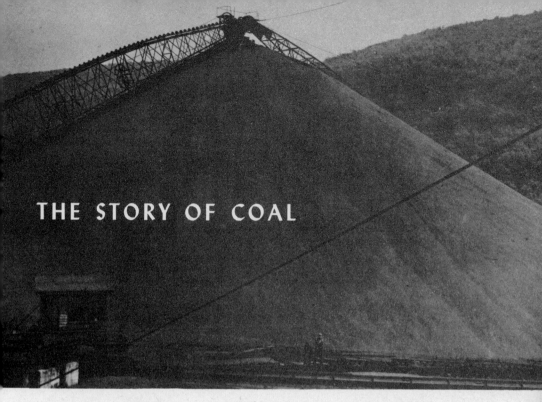

THE STORY OF COAL

A coal storage pile. Carloads of coal brought in on the tracks are dumped into hoppers and are carried to the top of the piles by conveyors. Other conveyors at the base of each pile reload the coal into cars for shipment to consumers.

NATURE guarded the secret of coal through the mists of centuries long before man, at some dim, unrecorded period in history, stumbled upon its use as a priceless fuel and an almost unlimited reservoir of energy.

For years that stagger the imagination—geologists estimate them at perhaps three hundred millions—coal has been forming in the earth through the gradual crushing and burial of dense masses of partially decomposed vegetation under layers of sand, clay and slime.

The beginnings were ages before the first faint dawn of civilization, chiefly in what the scientists now call the Carboniferous Age. It was in an age, difficult for modern man to vizualize, when queer, monstrous, now extinct beasts, birds and reptiles hopped, flew or crawled over the desolate crust of a comparatively young earth.

Men of science believe that the world was surrounded then by a gas, possibly carbonic acid, unfit for human life. They

A coal age (carboniferous) landscape of three hundred million years ago. No flowers, birds or human beings lived in this gloomy, damp, heat-saturated world. Its inhabitants were giant dragon flies with wings a yard wide, giant cockroaches that were five inches long, locusts, beetles and enormous spiders, and 50-foot salamanders.

picture the surface as split by gigantic cracks from which huge volumes of gases hissed continuously from a fiery interior. There were seas, lakes and rivers of warm waters. In that humid, congenial atmosphere the first vegetation thrived and developed to a wondrous extent.

From fossil remains found in comparatively modern times it is now possible to learn something very definite about the giant trees, strange plants, luxuriant ferns and thick mosses upon which human eyes never gazed. About two thousand species have been carefully studied and classified. The great majority of them belong to the flowerless division.

[486]

Where Does Coal Come From?

As countless centuries rolled by, the slow process of vegetable decomposition went forward in those steaming jungles. There were no seasonal changes to retard growth. In time, the muck became hundreds of feet thick. The decomposed mass next felt the tremendous erosive pressure of successive layers of silt, sand and mud. As the celluloselike mixture sank beneath the surface, the air gradually was forced out of the layers, aided occasionally by intense heat. Eventually, compact masses of carbon—or coal —were left imbedded among the rocks in seams. In these early stages of decomposition, before hardness sets in, such a mass is now known as peat.

At later, uncharted periods in history, there were terrific subterranean convulsions of nature that tossed up these seams of coal, forming elevations and depressions of great magnitude. Some layers sank beneath the level of the sea. The swamps themselves were submerged, tossed upward and buried again and again. Small particles of lime seeped through; sand was deposited over the coal seams. The silt became shale; the sand became sandstone; the lime became limestone—all familiar in the underground coal mines today. An idea of these catastrophic changes in the earth's crust may be gained from the fact that the geologists have counted thirty such separate seams of coal in some sections of the United States.

But coal did not form everywhere over the surface. Only occasionally, in the long history of the world, have coal-forming swamps existed. The most important formation era, known as "the Pennsylvania period," lasted for at least thirty-five millions of years.

Today, in the Dismal Swamp of Virginia, in the Florida Everglades, in the bogs in Ireland and in the Netherlands, peat is found. Conceivably, this would some day turn into coal under proper conditions; but the areas are relatively small and the present age is not considered as an important coal-forming period.

How long coal lay in the earth unnoticed by man is not known. So far as the written record goes, it was not used until comparatively recently. It passed the attention of the early writers and historians.

These ferns, found in coal deposits, are about three hundred million years old. Ferns were the dominant plant during the carboniferous age and formed giant forests. As they decayed and fell into the stagnant waters of ancient swamps, they became buried in the ancient mud and silt which gradually became rock. Under the heavy pressure of these ancient rock layers, the plant material turned into the coal we burn today.

When Was Coal First Used?

The Bible contains numerous references to coal. The Greeks made mention of it three centuries before the birth of Christ. There is evidence that the Chinese used coal long before the Christian era. Marco Polo, the greatest of the medieval travelers, who visited China about A.D. 1275, wrote of "rocks that burn."

It is known that the Britons used coal prior to the Roman invasion. In A. D. 852, the Abbey of Peterborough, England, signed a receipt for "twelve cartloads of cole" as rent from tenants.

The first real coal mines were started in England, and to this day coal mining is one of the most important industries of that nation. In fact, Britain's wealth and industry has been built up largely through her natural resources of coal and the maintenance of her sea power.

Those early English mines were primitive, little more than quarries. In later years the pits and underground workings extended over many parts of the island, and some are even under the sea. Today the coastal regions are dotted by hundreds of pits, many of them abandoned because all the coal has been dug out.

But before mining was started on a semblance of a plan in England, women and children laboriously gathered lumps of coal along the rocky shores of the North Sea, and elsewhere, and sold them as fuel to replace the dwindling supply of wood. This coal came from outcroppings of seams battered by wind and tide. It was aptly called "sea coal" for hundreds of years. Indeed, it is still called by that name in some parts of England.

English mining methods naturally improved as the years passed. They were copied and improved upon in other countries, notably in the United States. Generations of British miners have since grown up in the pits, sons following fathers in the profession and preferring no other occupation.

On the North American continent, coal was discovered by the explorer, Sebastian Cabot, on Cape Breton Island in 1498, but it was not until many years later that the discovery was put to practical use.

Did the American Indians Know About Coal?

Some historians believe that the American Indians used coal as a fuel long before the white man came to these shores, but there is no positive evidence to support this belief. It is known, however, that as early as about A. D. 1000, the Hopi tribe in Arizona used lignite (brown coal) for burning pottery. Many Indian tribes, especially along the Atlantic coast, who found coal in the outcroppings in the forests, polished fragments for ornaments or crushed them to form black pigments for painting themselves.

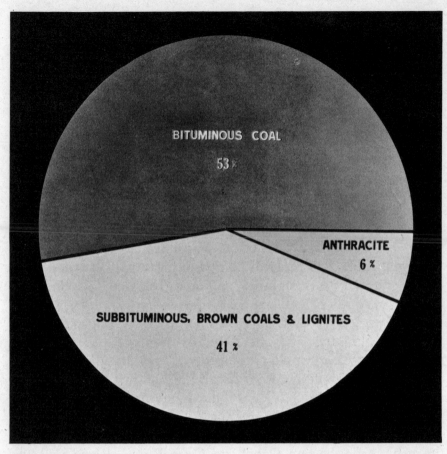

Total coal resources of the world, divided according to kinds. The known reserves are estimated at about eight trillion short tons (8 followed by twelve zeros). At an average annual consumption of one and one-half billion tons, these reserves would last until A.D. 7000. But the higher grade coals conveniently located for exploitation will, it is believed, be exhausted within 500 years. Pennsylvania anthracite will last less than 100 years.

The actual discovery of coal in the United States did not come until 1673 by the French explorers, Joliet and Marquette. Marquette's map of the Mississippi River, published with his journal in 1681, noted "Charbon de terra" near what is now the city of Utica, Illinois. Father Louis Hennepin, the French Jesuit missionary who was chaplain of La Salle's expedition in 1680, published a map showing a "cole mine."

While the early travelers in the new world made frequent mention of coal in their diaries and letters—mostly as a curiosity and never as a fuel—old maps showing coal locations are rare. In fact, after the first maps by the French, the next one of record did not appear until 1736 when Benjamin Winslow charted a mine on the upper Potomac River.

Why Didn't American Colonists Use Coal?

The hardy American colonists, engrossed in blazing a new civilization and fighting Indians in the meantime, paid little, if any, attention to coal. This is not surprising, for the struggling new nation was largely agricultural, with few large-scale industries. The endless, unbroken forests provided ample supplies of wood for heating and cooking for generations unborn. Indeed, it is extremely doubtful if anyone ever gave a thought to any other kind of fuel than wood.

So it was not until 1750 that the first coal mine was established in the colonies. Located near the James River near Richmond, Virginia, it was operated by an English company. Negro slaves were then in common use in the South and the first miners were slaves. The coal from this mine, dug from near the surface, was bituminous. Anthracite was not mined until nearly forty years later, in Pennsylvania.

George Washington, writing in 1770 in his "Journal of a Tour of the Ohio River" took note of a coal mine near the river bank where "the coal seemed to be of the very best kind, burning freely and an abundance of it."

Generally, native coal was not widely used in the sparsely populated colonies. Up to the time of the Revolutionary War, most of it came from England or Nova Scotia for limited industrial uses in towns along the Atlantic coast.

With supplies curtailed during the long war, some use of native coal was made by the blacksmiths for making munitions for the Continental Army. After the Revolution, the infant industry expanded slowly, mostly in areas adjacent to the mines. There was a practical reason for this—coal could not be marketed profitably to distant interior towns because of the lack of transportation facilities. The roads in those days were little more than rutted, winding paths through the wilderness. There were few

Although most drilling is done by machinery, some is still done by hand. Here a miner is drilling holes into a coal face. Dynamite or other explosive is inserted into the holes drilled and fired electrically. After the blast the miners wait for the air to be cleared of gases, then return to shovel the coal onto waiting rail cars or conveyors.

carting conveyances or animals that could be spared from the farm to draw them. The railroads had not yet come.

It also was something of a problem to convince a skeptical public of the value of the new-fangled fuel. Word had come from France in a roundabout way that a law had been passed there forbidding any workman from burning coal in Paris, under heavy penalty, because it was believed that coal fumes had caused serious epidemics of disease! It was an age when superstitions ran high; the pious colonists believed that "black rocks that burn" were instruments of the devil himself.

How Did Coal Come Into General Use?

On one occasion, some hardy persons who tried to sell coal from door to door in Philadelphia were obliged to flee to escape arrest. It is also related that in later years some workmen, after trying all night to start a fire with coal in a blast furnace, gave up the attempt in disgust and slammed the door shut. When they returned, a few hours later, they were astonished to find a brisk blaze. They had not realized that all that was needed was to leave the coals alone long enough for them to ignite and spread.

In the course of time, however, coal came to be used more and more. As bituminous coal was found close to the surface and required little expense to dig, farmers in their spare time peddled it to neighboring blacksmiths and to the more venturesome souls who used it for heating their homes. As a general rule, the early farmers would not follow a seam very far underground because of a superstitious fear. But they often leased their mineral right to others. As small companies were organized to mine the coal, the farmers and their farm hands frequently worked for them in winter months. The regular miners, jealous of their jobs, did not welcome them and there were physical clashes in consequence.

In the early 1830's numerous small mining companies sprang up like mushrooms in many parts of the country, notably in the Appalachian regions and along the Ohio, Illinois and Mississippi Rivers. The companies, as a rule, had little capital and few of them survived. It was a picturesque era when coal was transported by wagon over mountain roads or by barges and "arks" on canals and rivers.

It was not until 1840 that the bituminous industry mined its first million tons, but from then on its growth has been steady.

How Is Coal Mined?

In the United States, where coal mining has reached a higher stage of efficiency than in any other country, there are three general methods of extracting coal from the earth. These are governed by the nature of the terrain, the thickness of the seam or vein and the proximity to the surface.

By the shaft mine method, at least two vertical shafts are sunk into the earth. One brings the coal to the surface and transports the miners and their supplies. Fresh air for ventilation is commonly drawn down the hoist shaft and the foul air exhausted to atmosphere by a fan located at the top of the other shaft.

The depths of the mines vary greatly in different parts of the world, depending upon the richness of the deposits and the extent of the underground workings. The deepest shaft in the world is in Belgium, about 4,000 feet. In the bituminous fields in the Appalachians a shaft in Alabama exceeds 3,000 feet.

The opening in the slope type of mine is made by a bore that goes down to the coal seams on a gradual incline, or slope. These mines are not so deep as the shaft mine, but the underground workings extend horizontally for great distances, sometimes for many miles.

The drift, or outcrop, is reached either by a tunnel, or horizontal bore into the side of the hill.

Stripping, sometimes called open-pit mining, is a term used when the coal is taken from or near the surface. Some strip mines are only a few inches under the surface. They are rarely more than seventy-five feet below.

There are two general methods of underground mining— "room and pillar" and "long wall."

In the first, "rooms" are dug out adjacent to what is called the main gallery, or entry. Wooden props or pillars are erected to support the "roof."

The rooms, with ceilings so low that the miner often has to duck his head to avoid a hard knock, are dug systematically, something like blocks and alleys in a city. The tunnels leading to the rooms extend along the seam of coal.

After the coal has been dug out, the pillars are removed— the miners call the operation "pillar robbing"—and the roof is allowed to fall. In England and in this country pillar robbing has at times resulted in the sinking of streets above the mines. Even today this is occuring in some of the cities in the anthracite districts of Pennsylvania.

In the second method of mining, the long wall, the face or breast of the coal vein is cut in long straight faces. No pillars are

[494]

left, but the roof is supported by pack walls, made of refuse, located some distance behind the face. Generally, a larger percentage of coal can be obtained in this manner.

These underground "cities" are often very extensive. One mine that this writer visited had an underground area of more that ten square miles. The largest mine in the world is believed to be the New Orient Mine in southern Illinois, which is capable of turning out more than ten thousand tons in a single day.

One of the richest seams in the world, if not the richest, is known as "the Pittsburgh Coal Bed." This fabulous seam extends through western Pennsylvania, Ohio, Virginia, West Virginia and Maryland. Its thickness varies from five to nine feet.

In strip mining, gigantic mechanical shovels, weighing hundreds of tons, gouge the earth's surface like a plow to lay the coal bare from dirt and shale. One of these monster shovels, which picks up thirty-five cubic yards in one mighty gulp, operating in eastern Ohio, alone permitted the mining of one million

Fine coal dust which explodes easily usually accumulates after blasting and cutting. To prevent such explosions, a fine "rock dust," a whitish powder largely limestone, is blown against the walls by powerful electric blowers. This process dilutes the dust and cleans the air.

An electric cutting machine cuts into the face of a narrow coal seam. The coal is immediately loaded onto an endless belt conveyor. Note the wooden pit props that support the ceiling of the room and prevent it from collapsing on the miners.

tons in a single year. Used also are many smaller shovels like those for ordinary excavation work.

Bituminous mining, as might be expected from one of the great industries of the nation, represents an investment of billions of dollars by the owners, ranging from great modern corporations to small individuals. There are the same variations in the size and modern equipment of mines as there are in the great department stores in cities and the village stores at country crossroads.

In the early days of mining all the work was done by hand, and laborious work it was. In recent years, however, mining has been revolutionized by the steadily increasing use of specially designed machinery. Bituminous coal is now mined mechanically in ⅓ of the mines in America. In the last twenty years more than $400,000,000 has been invested by the operators in mining machinery, thus obviating the old pick-and-shovel work.

[496]

Why Is Coal So Important?

Coal has been called by various picturesque names to catch the public imagination. Some phrase-makers have called it "King Coal" because of its exalted position in industry. Others have called it "bottled" or "packaged sunshine," with the obvious reference to the millions of years that the sun provided the energy for growing the great forests in the carboniferous era. Still others have called it "black diamonds," which has perhaps become the most popular nickname. But the person unknown to posterity, who first coined this designation, did not go far enough. It might more properly be called "magic black diamonds" or "black magic," because of the miracles produced through the wonders of modern chemistry.

There are so many amazing and essential things in everyday life that have been developed in the laboratories from bituminous coal that it would take a whole chapter simply to enumerate them.

What Is Coke?

The first great magical step—which demonstrated that bituminous coal was a great deal more than a fuel and source of endless energy—is known as "carbonization" of coal. Stripped of technicalities, this is the decomposition process of heating bituminous coal to a high temperature, about 1800° Fahrenheit, in a closed chamber out of contact with air. The intense heat drives off all volatile matter, such as gas, tar, ammonia water and oils. The residue, or char, that remains is called coke.

The discovery of coke was the second great magical step in bituminous utilization. It opened up whole new industrial empires. The chemists of the world went to work to recapture all the volatile matter driven off from coal in the coke ovens. Step by step, with infinite patience in overcoming seemingly insurmountable obstacles, there were developed other such primary products as coal tar and light oils; ammoniacal liquor and coal gas. The by-products and derivatives of these are almost endless.

The principal industries using products from coal may be summarized as follows: iron and steel, gas manufacturing, road building, wood preserving, railroad building, dyestuff, plastic, chemical, paint, varnish and lacquer, explosive, fertilizer, photographic chemical, leather, perfumery, textile, medicinal and sanitation, drug, tire manufacturing, rubber.

A large percentage of all bituminous coal from American mines today is manufactured into coke for the smelting of iron and other branches of metallurgical work. In olden times, especially in England, charcoal was virtually the only fuel used for these purposes. But as the charcoal supply dwindled and its cost became correspondingly higher, experiments were undertaken to find substitute fuels.

How Was Coke Discovered?

An Englishman unknown to science, Abraham Darby, hit upon coke in 1735, little realizing that he had started an industrial revolution. The story of that epic event is worth retelling.

He built a fireproof hearth in the open, upon which he piled a considerable quantity of bituminous coal and covered it with layers of clay and cinders. He left a little opening for just enough air to cause the fire to burn slowly. After watching it many hours he took the cooled residue to a near-by smelting furnace and filled it with the new, then unnamed material, instead of the customary charcoal. Then for six consecutive days and nights he hovered over his experiment, like a mother watching a child. So intense was his interest that he never left the furnace for a moment during all this time. His meals were sent to him at the furnace top. He managed to get a "few winks" of sleep. At last, on the sixth night, when his hopes were at low ebb, the smelting began. As the first iron poured from the furnace and he realized, jubilantly, that his dream had come true, he dropped off at once into a sound slumber, utterly exhausted.

What Are the Modern Ways of Making Coke?

In general, there are three processes for coke-making: the beehive, the by-product and the gashouse. The beehive, the first used, is now nearly obsolete. It got its name from the long rows

Loaded coal cars returning from a room where coal has been blasted. The rod behind the driver is the trolley pole of the long, flat, electric locomotive that hauls the coal cars behind it. The overhead wire the trolley pole touches is the electric power line. This coal train is on its way to the hoisting machines which will bring the coal to the surface.

of conical brick ovens resembling beehives in shape. These ovens, which poured great volumes of black smoke over the countryside, were prodigiously wasteful of the by-products.

At one time it was estimated that there were about fifty thousand coke ovens in the United States, principally in western Pennsylvania. In Europe, meantime, retort ovens, which salvaged the precious by-products, had replaced the beehives, and it was not long before American plants were installing them.

The bulk of all metallurgical coke is now made by the by-product method. The modern regenerative oven, with its retorts heated by vertical flues, consists of three chambers—the coking, heating, and regenerative—laid out in many units, ranging

[499]

Here you see the coal which has just come to the surface from the mine, inside the "tipple" into which it is poured off conveyor-belts. It is being sorted according to size. Some of the finer screens are visible in the foreground. The men watch for pieces of slate, rock, or shale which they remove as the coal passes by.

from ten to ninety. The special "coking coal" is charged into the oven from the top and subjected to terrific heat. The oven is sealed and the volatile matter is drawn off through pipes into the by-product plants. Here the gases are separated and purified.

In the gashouse process, the coke, which is largely used for domestic heating, is the residue left in the retorts during the manufacture of illuminating gas.

One ton of good bituminous coking coal, when processed at a by-product plant, will produce from 1,400 to 1,500 pounds of coke; between 10,000 and 11,500 cubic feet of gas; from 9 to 10 gallons of coal tar; 20 or more pounds of ammonium sulphate and smaller percentages of benzol, toluol, xylol and crude naphthalene.

The exterior of a coal tipple. After being sorted, the different sizes of coal travel on conveyor belts, each size on its own belt, to the proper chute. The chutes are loading coal of different sizes into railroad cars.

What Is Coal Tar?

The coal heated in the by-product plant gives off a black, sticky, evil-smelling substance known as "coal tar." It is one of the most wondrous substances known to mankind. The chemists are always finding new uses for it.

The discovery of coal tar may be called the third great magical step in the utilization of coal through chemistry. The start of this great industry came in 1856 in England. A young chemist, William Perkin, working in the laboratories of the Royal College of Chemistry in London for a substitute for quinine, accidentally discovered aniline purple, from which now come the myriads of dyes used in the textile industry.

[501]

Not all coal mines are underground. There are many long narrow seams of coal close to the surface of the earth. Here you see one of the giant steam shovels used in strip mining digging a deep furrow into the earth to get at the coal. Strip mining destroys the top soil, which is needed for agriculture. Coal companies now reforest and rehabilitate all areas they have mined after the coal is removed.

The English, however, did not at first comprehend the magnitude and possibilities of Perkin's discovery, at least from an industrial standpoint. The Germans capitalized on it and for many years they were preëminent in the field. The rest of the world depended upon the German output.

The need for dyestuffs was so urgent in the United States during the early years of World War I that German submarines brought supplies to Baltimore and New London, Connecticut, running the risk of being sunk by the British Royal Navy. That was before America's entry into the war. Since then, however, America is no longer dependent upon Germany or anyone else for its dyestuffs. It has developed its own coal tar industry.

It seems well-nigh incredible that from this dirty liquid has emerged some of the daintiest of perfumes for milady, the pleasantest of flavors, the dyes, invaluable medicines, moth balls, phonograph records, cleaning fluids, the high-powered explosives so necessary in war, nylon stockings, lip rouge, naphtha soaps, printing inks, shoe polishes, disinfectants, and so on through a list of impressive proportions.

Of the more than 2,000 important commercial chemicals now made in the United States, 1,500 of them were never made commercially here until the growth of the modern coke ovens and the by-product plants.

What Are the By-Products of Coal?

As an illustration of some of the products derived from bituminous coal, walk into a drug store and you would find the following.

Antiseptics and germicides: hexylresorcinol, mercurochrome, gentian violet, chloramine.

Photographic chemicals: cathecol, amidol, hydroquinone, metol.

Artificial flavoring materials: for candy, chewing gum, pastry, etc., wintergreen, vanilla, almond, rose, peppermint.

Plastics: toothbrushes, combs and brushes, clock cases, picture frames, cigarette cases, cosmetic containers, phonograph records, costume jewelry.

Edible dyes (food colors): certified by the United States Food and Drug Administration, blue, green, orange, red, yellow, etc. for candy, medicines, pastry.

Food preservatives: sodium benzoate, sodium salicylate.

Internal medicines: aspirin, all sulpha drugs, anacin, salol, synthetic quinine, phenobarbital, acetanilide, phenacetin, phenolphthalein.

Sugar substitutes (for diabetics, etc.): saccharin.

Waterproof fabrics: shower caps, baby pants, bathing shoes.

A FEW OF THE 200,000 PRODUCTS
DERIVED
FROM

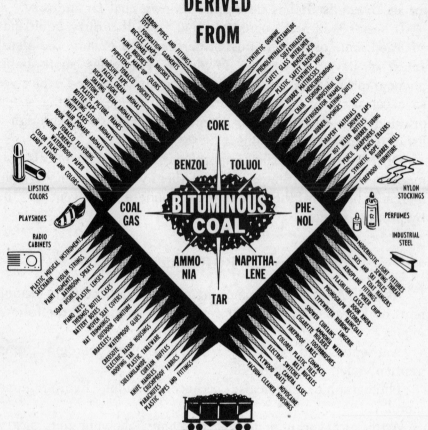

Perfumes: a wide variety of fragrant odors as well as fixatives, blends, and modifiers. Examples: synthetic musk, coumarin.

Writing inks: various colors.

Vitamins: nicotinic acid, B Complex, Vitamin K.

Moth repellents: moth balls (naphthalene), dichloride (para-dichlorobenzine).

The great research laboratories connected with the industry are busy with many projects looking to the more efficient use of coal in industry and in the home. In progress are such things as the development of handy "smokeless stoves," the improvements in stokers, the greater uses of pulverized coal.

Truly, coal may be called black magic!

What Is Cork?

Cork is the outer bark of a species of oak which grows in Spain, Portugal and other southern parts of Europe and in the north of Africa. The tree is distinguished by the great thickness and sponginess of its bark, and by the leaves being evergreen, oblong, somewhat oval, downy underneath, and waved.

The outer bark falls off of itself if let alone, but for commercial purposes it is stripped off when judged sufficiently matured, this being when the tree has reached the age of from fifteen to thirty years. In the course of eight or nine years, or even less, the same tree will yield another supply of cork of better quality, and the removal of this outer bark is said to be beneficial, the trees thus stripped reaching the age of 150 years or more.

The bark is removed with a kind of ax, parallel cuts being carried around the tree transversely and united by others in a longitudinal direction, so as to produce oblong sheets of bark. Care must be taken not to cut into the inner bark, or the tree would be killed. The pieces of cork are flattened out by heat or by weights, and are slightly charred on the surface to close the pores.

Cork is light, impervious to water, and by pressure can be greatly reduced in bulk, returning again to its original size. These qualities render it peculiarly serviceable for the stopping of vessels of different kinds, for floats, buoys, swimming belts or jackets, artificial limbs, etc.

Where Is the Pentagon Building?

The Pentagon Building is a five-sided, five-storied structure at Arlington, Va., across the Potomac from Washington. It was built during World War II to house some 30,000 War Department employees, and it became the nerve center of the nation's fighting forces. The central open space is surrounded on five sides by solid blocks of office buildings. Behind this first group are four more rings of buildings, actually twenty-five in all. The outer ring is almost a mile in perimeter. The Pentagon Building, a veritable labyrinth, has over sixteen miles of corridors. There is a huge bus concourse to accommodate the stream of buses connecting the building with the capital.

How High Is the Eiffel Tower?

This remarkable tower, which stands in the Champ de Mars, Paris, opposite the Trocadero, rises to a height of 984 feet. It was built of interlaced ironwork by Alexandre Gustave Eiffel (1832-1923) for the Paris Exposition of 1889, and was for many years the tallest building in the world. But today the famous Eiffel Tower is dwarfed by such structures as the Empire State Building (1,248 feet high) and the Chrysler Building (1,046 feet), in New York. The beautiful Washington Monument is 555 feet high, the world's tallest masonry building. The Great Pyramid in Egypt steps upward to a height of 450 feet.

[505]

THE STORY OF OIL

Huge storage tanks in an oil refinery.

Our complex industrial civilization is more dependent on oil than on any other product. Oil provides the gasoline that runs most of our motor cars, trucks, farm machinery. It provides the fuel oil that runs most of our warships, much of our industrial machinery, and many of the generators that produce electrical power. It provides most of the lubricants, without which no machinery can operate. It provides heat. It provides hundreds of medical and industrial by-products, and synthetic products such as rubber and other plastics.

It is only within the last hundred years that man has found so many uses for oil. In the thousands of years that this great gift from nature has lain in the earth and upon its surface, man had used it only occasionally, in building ships, making lamps, and for a few other purposes.

How Was Oil Made?

The deposits of oil we now find in the earth have been there for millions of years. We think they may have been formed like this:

The sun shone on the earth—just as it does now. The light and heat of the sun became part of plants—just as they do now. The plants grew in and around warm seas that covered much of the earth. Animals swam in these seas. The light and heat of the sun became part of the animals, too. This process went on for millions of years. The plants and animals lived and died. Their remains piled up on the sandy floor of the sea. Soft mud buried them. The weight of many layers of mud pressed them down.

Tremendous changes took place on earth. Parts of the sea became dry land. The mud and sand of the old sea floor turned to rock. The sunshine, which had been changed to plants and animals, turned to a dark, greasy liquid. This liquid was held in small spaces or pores in the rock as water is held in a sponge.

We call the dark liquid petroleum. The word "petroleum" comes from Latin words meaning "rock oil."

Centuries ago, some oil leaked from the rock. It came to the surface in puddles called oil seeps. The oil got into wells and spoiled the taste of drinking water. It made sticky pools of pitch, or asphalt. Here and there, fires blazed up and burned for days, even years. Natural gas, always found with oil, had been set aflame by lightning.

What Were the First Uses of Oil?

Early man looked on oil with curiosity. Then he began to find it useful. It would burn. When old walled cities were attacked,

[507]

the defenders sometimes poured burning pitch on the attackers. Kettles of burning pitch were the flame throwers of those days. Pitch was used also in time of peace. It bound bricks and stones together in buildings. Rubbed on baskets, pitch made them waterproof. Boats coated with pitch became more seaworthy. In such boats, men first dared to set sail on the Mediterranean.

Egyptians, Chinese, and the American Indians used oil as a medicine. They rubbed it on their bodies to relieve aches and pains. They swallowed it, in spite of the bad taste.

From early times, oil has lighted man's way in the dark. At first, reeds were dipped in oil to make torches. Later it was burned in lamps. But other kinds of oil were easier to find than petroleum. Ships sailed from New England to far seas in search of whales to supply fuel for whale oil lamps. Then whales became scarce. Some additional source of oil for illumination had to be found. About 1850, improved ways were discovered to refine petroleum, or crude oil. The result was a liquid later known as kerosene. It burned in lamps with a clear light.

At that time crude oil had to be soaked up in rags or sponges from the surface of ponds and streams. Only a little oil could be collected—not nearly enough for everyday use. Someone said, "Why not drill in the ground for oil, as we drill for water? We might get more oil for less work and less money." These words opened the way for a great new industry.

When Was the First Oil Well Drilled?

Colonel E. S. Drake, a retired railroad conductor, was the father of the modern petroleum industry. In 1859, with some partners, he leased land near Titusville, in western Pennsylvania, where he put up a wooden derrick 30 feet high. It stood near Oil Creek, where the Indians had skimmed off oil for many years. Farmers called the derrick "Drake's Folly." An iron pipe and an oak battering-ram were fastened to the derrick. A steam engine worked the battering-ram, which drove the pipe into the ground. At 69½ feet, oil was reached.

Drake's well produced only 15 barrels of oil a day. Now, about 4,800,000 barrels of oil pour daily from 400,000 wells in the

A forest of oil derricks grew up almost overnight on this Texas land when oil was discovered. The scene has been duplicated many times in Texas, Oklahoma, California, and other states. Under the law, a property owner is entitled to all the oil he can get from a well on his land, even though the subterranean oil pool may extend under adjacent properties. When a pool is discovered, all land owners in the vicinity hasten to build derricks and get their share before the oil is exhausted. This reckless exploitation has been curbed to some extent by regional agreements to limit the daily production per oil well.

Oil explorers set off miniature earthquakes to detect subterranean rock formations that may contain oil.

United States alone. In all, a million wells have been drilled for oil in our country. Some of them stab more than three miles into the earth. That is twice as far down as man has gone in search of any other of the earth's products.

How Is Oil Found?

Man uses much more oil than has come to the surface of the earth in seeps. He has to dig into the earth for it. But first he has to find out where to dig. He can never be sure, when he starts drilling in a certain spot, that he will find oil. But science has helped him to recognize certain telltale signs that show where oil *may* exist.

We know that oil was formed in rocks that used to be the bottoms of old seas. Finding the bed of a sea that may have existed many millions of years ago is not easy. Nature never seems satisfied with the earth. She is always making changes. The bed rocks of the old sea may have been buried and lifted to the surface a number of times. The rocks may have been uncovered and worn

[510]

away by wind and water. The layers of rocks may have been tilted, folded, or broken up.

Geologists find old seas by examining rocks. They look for the traces of ancient sea plants and animals that were buried when the rocks were mud. Some of these traces are so small they must be hunted with a microscope. But oil is not found everywhere a sea splashed once upon a time. It is found only in certain places. It collects only in porous rock, such as sandstone.

What Is an Oil Trap?

The underground oil-collecting places are called "traps." The oil in a trap may have traveled some distance to reach it, as water on the surface may travel before reaching its pond or lake trap. An oil trap is more like a crumpled sandwich than like an underground pool. It consists of porous rock between layers of nonporous rock. The layers are not usually flat; they are usually tilted or folded upward.

Gas, oil, and water are often found together in a trap. Gas, being lightest, is highest in the trap. Oil, being lighter than water, comes next. Lowest in the trap is water, usually salt water, for salt water exists in most porous rocks which formerly were sea bottoms. Oil formed in the rock rises over many thousands of years through the water to the upper parts of the traps. Of course, if it does not meet a trap, it may never collect in large quantity. It may remain spread out or perhaps escape and be lost.

There are three principal kinds of oil traps. One is at the top of an upward fold of rock. Geologists call such a fold an anticline. To get an idea of what an anticline is like, lay a magazine on a table. Put your hands at each edge and push them toward each other until the pages buckle upward. The upward bending pages are then like the layers of rock in an anticline. The porous rock folded between nonporous rock into an anticline is sometimes a trap for oil.

A second oil trap is a fault, or a break, in layers of rock. The rock on one side of the break has moved up or down, so that the layers on either side no longer match. You can see how this is by cutting a slice of layer cake, and then lifting the slice a little.

[511]

A fault may make an oil trap where rock that is porous is faced by rock that is not porous. Oil may collect where it is stopped by the nonporous rock.

A third type of oil trap is like a buried beach. There the porous sandstone that may once have been an old beach tapers off like a wedge, ending between layers of rock that are not porous. The oil moves through the sandstone until it can go no farther and it collects to form an oil field.

How Are Trap Formations Detected?

Drilling is expensive. Sometimes exploratory wells take a year to drill and cost over a half-million dollars. Drilling is usually the last step in hunting for oil, and it is done only after the earth has been felt scientifically and has had its pulse taken. The oil hunter can feel for an oil trap in several ways, by using scientific instruments and methods. The principle methods are as follows:

Measuring Gravity. Gravity is the pull of the earth upon an object. But the earth does not have the same pull in all places. Heavy rocks near the surface pull harder than light ones or than heavy rocks at greater depth. You will never notice that you weigh more when you stand on granite rocks than when you stand on sandstone, but you do. A delicate instrument called a gravity meter can measure very slight differences in pull. By measuring the pull of underground rocks, the gravity meter gives clues to the kind of rocks that are below the surface.

Measuring Magnetic Forces. A magnetometer may also be used to "feel" the rock below the surface. It works somewhat like the gravity meter but measures the variations in the magnetic field of the earth in different places. This is the same magnetic field that governs the magnetic compass.

Man-Made Earthquakes. The most widely used method so far discovered for feeling the earth is by making a small earthquake, and then timing and measuring the earth's shivers. The earthquake is made by setting off a charge of dynamite. Waves are set up in the surrounding earth like waves in a pond when a stone is thrown into it. A seismograph (siz' mo-graf) in a truck a short distance from the dynamite charge measures the earth's waves and times them. They travel faster through some kinds of rocks and are reflected better by some.

Electrical Methods. Another way of exploring the underground is to "feel" the rock layers by electricity. A special electric probe is lowered into a well during drilling. A current is passed through the rock layers. The rock's resistance to the current is measured. Different kinds of rock have different resistances to electricity. It passes easily through some rocks, not quite so easily through others. The resistance is affected also by the contents of the rock: oil, gas, or water.

How Are Oil Wells Drilled?

After the scientific findings have been checked and rechecked, there is just one job left: that of drilling in the most favorable place for the oil. There are two methods of drilling a well: cable tool drilling and rotary drilling. No matter which is used, all wells are started in the same way. A pit is dug for certain machinery and pipe connections, and over it is built a steel tower called a derrick. The derrick may be as tall as a 17-story building. Its purpose is to support the long drill that digs into the ground.

Cable Tool Drilling. Cable tool drilling is the older method. A hole is punched into the earth by lifting and dropping, over and over again, a heavy sharpened bit on the end of a cable. All earlier wells were drilled by this method.

Rotary Drilling. Over 90 per cent of all wells are now rotary drilled. Rotary drilling bores a hole into the earth, as a carpenter bores a hole with a brace and bit into a board. The brace, or turning machine, is a large wheel lying flat on the floor of the derrick. This wheel, or turntable, is turned by machinery. The bit is at the end of a hollow drill pipe, the upper end of which is attached to the center of the turntable. There are several kinds of bits. One looks like the drill a carpenter uses, but is much bigger. The commonest type has ridged rollers at the bottom. As the bit is turned, these rollers grind the rock into powder.

The drill or bit is hollow. A stream of "mud" is forced down through it constantly. This mud returns to the surface around the outside of the pipe. It is a mixture of water, special clays and

A modern steel derrick rising above an oil well in California.

chemicals. It keeps the bit cool, plasters the sides of the hole to prevent cave-ins, and carries rock-cuttings out to the surface. The mud also holds back the pressure of gas, oil, or water. If this pressure gets loose, there is a "blowout."

As the hole is deepened, it is lined at intervals with large steel pipe called casing. Each piece of pipe, or "string," as it is called, fits inside the previous one, and all extend up to the surface. The result is something like a telescope. As the drill grinds it way farther and farther down, more drill pipe is attached to it at the upper end. Samples of the rocks penetrated are taken from time to time for laboratory study with a special bit. These samples are called "cores."

What Is a Gusher?

Oil will not move anywhere by itself. The "mover" of oil is the pressure of water and gas. Most oil as found underground has gas dissolved in it under great pressure, as ginger ale or soda water has gas dissolved in it. Also, water is pushing up against the oil. The pressure usually is sufficient to force the oil up the well to the surface. This action is called "natural flow." Drilling the well opens a door through which the pressure of the gas and water can drive the oil out of the trap.

In the early days of the industry, little was known about the hidden oil reservoirs. Wells were allowed to flow at full capacity. These were the "gushers." Today, modern wells are carefully controlled. Gushers occur rarely and usually only by accident.

[514]

How Is Oil Flow Controlled?

Today, when the oil sand is reached, the drill is removed while the mud holds back the flow. A pipe, called tubing, is lowered into the well. This tubing is only two or two and one-half inches across. It becomes the channel through which the oil will flow.

The tubing is sealed into the casing, so that the oil can find no way out around it. If the oil goes out, it must go through the tubing. At its upper end, at ground level, the tubing blossoms out in a set of valves, dials, and pipes called a "Christmas tree." The valves of the Christmas tree control the flow of oil up the tubing and into the pipes leading away from the well.

Giant distilling units in a one hundred Octane gasoline plant.

In time the pressure may become reduced. Then natural forces are not enough to bring the oil up, and the man must give the oil a boost with a pump.

Oil, as we have seen, is moved through the sand to the wells by the pressure of water or gas, or both. Oil men learned through scientific studies that when the wells in an oil field are allowed to flow at very high rates, the pressure in the oil sand drops rapidly. They found that slow rates of flow allow the gas and water to do a much better job of moving the oil through the rock.

What Is Crude Oil?

Oil just as it comes from the ground is called *crude* oil. It varies widely in appearance. Most crudes are thick liquids that may be almost black in color, or dark green, although some are as light and clear as gasoline or kerosene.

[515]

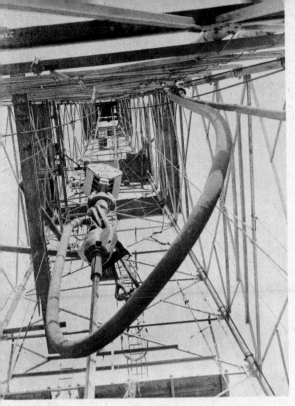
Looking up inside a derrick.

The reason for this great difference in crudes is that oil is not a single substance, like gold. It is a mixture of many substances, like gravy, and just as different gravies have different seasonings, so different crudes contain more of some substances. One crude contains more asphalt, another contains more wax, etc.

Crude oil, before it is refined, is hardly more useful than mud. It must be taken apart and worked upon before it can power an airplane or heat a home. Crude oil is the raw material from which are manufactured more than a thousand different liquid and solid products.

What Is a Refinery?

The factory in which crude oil is worked into useful products or materials is the refinery. A refinery is to crude oil what a lumber mill is to a log or a steel mill is to a pile of iron ore. There are many different kinds of refineries, according to the kind of crude they are intended to work with, and the products they are intended to make. They range in size from a refinery handling a few barrels a day to one handling more than 300,000 barrels a day.

A big refinery does not look much like a factory because it has little moving machinery. It looks more like a giant laboratory. There are tanks as tall as ten-story buildings. There are more pipes than many a large town has for its buildings. And there are fires making heat enough to cook dinner for an army.

How Is Crude Oil Taken Apart?

Distillation was the first refining process, and although many other processes are also used in refining now, it is still the beginning of nearly all refining. Distillation takes a crude oil mixture apart by boiling it. The different liquids in the mixture boil at different temperatures. When the crude oil is heated, the first substance to change to a gas and leave it is gasoline. When the oil is a little hotter, kerosene leaves in the same way. Then, as the temperature increases, we get gas oil, lubricating oils, fuel oil and asphalt. Each of the different substances, as it boils out of the crude oil, is led away and then cooled, changing it back to a liquid. Thus distillation takes crude oil apart in big "pieces," such as gasoline, fuel oil, and the others. Refinery men call these pieces *fractions* or *cuts*.

After many years of refining by distillation alone, oil scientists discovered how to put together certain fractions of petroleum in new ways, so as to make new and better products. Today many things are made from petroleum which are not in nature's oil at all. Synthetic rubber, made from oil, is one example.

What Is Cracking?

Another and very important refining process is called "cracking." It makes use of heat, pressure, and sometimes a "magic powder" called a catalyst. A catalyst is any substance that causes a chemical reaction between other substances, but comes out unchanged itself.

Cracking breaks up the heavier products of crude oil to make lighter ones. For example, when fuel oil is cracked it yields gasoline. Cracking thus makes it possible to produce more than twice as much gasoline from a barrel of crude oil as does simple distillation.

What Are Molecules?

To understand cracking and the other magiclike processes, we must know a little about the structure of matter. All substances on earth, including air and water, are built of tiny blocks called molecules. The building materials of the molecule blocks are what scientists call elements. Elements are the materials of molecules, just as sand and other things are the materials in a block of concrete. The nature of various substances depends on the number of elements and their arrangement in the molecules. For example, a water molecule contains hydrogen and oxygen. Both are gases. Yet, combined in certain proportions in molecules, they form water, a liquid. Combined in different proportions, they form hydrogen peroxide, another but much different liquid.

Petroleum is made of many different kinds of molecules, but they all contain the same elements of carbon and hydrogen. So scientists speak of oil and its various products as hydrocarbon compounds, meaning that they are combinations of hydrogen and carbon. The molecules of different parts of petroleum contain carbon and hydrogen and the way they are arranged in a molecule determine whether we have gasoline, kerosene, fuel oil, or something else.

Pulling up a drill that has cut thousands of feet into the earth in search of oil.

A big pump, called a "grasshopper pump," brings up oil from the underground pool.

With cracking and other processes, oil men change nature's product to suit man's needs by changing the molecular construction of petroleum. The names of some of these processes, like polymerization (pol' i-mer-i-za' shun) and hydrogenation (hi' dro-jen-a' shun), are longer than the magician's "abracadabra" and they bring about better and more certain results.

How Is Oil Transported?

Oil and oil products are some of the world's greatest travelers. Gasoline probably travels a hundred times farther to get *to* your family's auto than that gasoline travels *in* your auto.

Through big pipes, rivers of oil are flowing underground across the United States day and night, at all seasons. The pipes are like

[519]

giant steel veins and arteries. The fluid they carry is truly the blood of our modern way of life. If we think of oil as one kind of freight, then one-ninth of all the freight in the United States moves underground.

This great underground circulation system has big main arteries. There are smaller arteries leading into and away from them. The oil goes from the wells to storage tanks in the oil fields. Pipes called "gathering lines" carry the crude oil away from the storage tanks. The gathering lines run into larger pipes called "trunk lines." The oil from a number of oil fields may flow into a trunk line. Many trunk lines are about sixteen inches in diameter, about the size of an automobile wheel without its tire.

The trunk line may take the oil to storage tanks at a seaport. There the oil is pumped into a tanker, which carries the crude to a refinery. Or the trunk line may go directly to a refinery. There the crude oil is manufactured into useful products. The refinery may be near by, or it may be more than a thousand miles away.

The oil is kept flowing through the pipe lines' veins and arteries by many hearts, or pumps. If the pipes all ran downhill, the oil would flow by itself. But since they don't, the oil must be pushed along. In fairly level country there is a pumping station about every forty miles. In hilly country, the pumping stations are closer. Oil does not break any speed records on its underground journey. It hardly ever flows more than three or four miles an hour, or about as fast as a man walks.

An oil pipe line is usually placed one to three feet underground. It crosses under farmers' fields and under roads. It may be carried across a river on a small bridge, or trestle, or it may be sunk to the bottom of the river.

Whenever possible, machines are used to make the work of laying pipe easier. In most places, the ditch in which the pipe is buried is dug with a machine. It digs up the earth with scoops on a big wheel. Tractors with derricks lift sections of pipe 20 or 40 feet long. The sections are welded together into one long pipe. Before the pipe is laid into the ditch, it is painted and wrapped with heavy paper. A machine does the wrapping. Wrapping the pipe helps to protect it from chemicals in the soil.

There are 141,000 miles of oil pipe lines in the United States —enough to make almost six rings of pipe line around the earth. All but 10,000 miles of these pipe lines carry crude oil. The rest carry gasoline and other finished oil products.

What Is the Big Inch?

The pipe line called the Big Inch is 24 inches in diameter— big enough for a grown man to crawl through. If anyone tried it, however, he would wear out the knees of a good many pairs of pants. The Big Inch is 1,252 miles long. It was built to carry crude oil from Longview, Texas, to Phoenixville, Pennsylvania. It has an extension to refineries at Linden, New Jersey, and Philadelphia. The Big Inch carries a river of precious crude oil to the East, amounting to 310,000 barrels of oil a day. More than 1,400 tank cars, or a train of tank cars ten miles long, would have to arrive every day to carry that much oil.

Huge pipe lines carry petroleum products across the country.

THE STORY OF THE DIESEL ENGINE

The powerful engines in the Diesel locomotive turn generators that supply current for electric motors set in the wheel trucks. The electric motors turn the wheels.

THE POLICE, the newspapers and the public have long ago ceased to be interested in the fate of Dr. Diesel, who mysteriously disappeared in the fall of 1913. However, the present dramatic performances of the Diesel engine, which is playing such an important part in railroad, marine, bus, truck and power plant development, makes the story back of the early work on this engine again of interest.

Who Was Diesel?

Rudolph Diesel was born in 1858 of German parents living in Paris. He went to school in Paris until the war of 1870 between Germany and France forced his family to move to England. Later he went to the Munich Technical College, where he was graduated as an engineer when he was twenty-one.

The Diesel engine is preferred for large trucks and buses because of its economy and durability.

At college, his professor in thermodynamics was the famous von Linde, the first man to liquefy air. Hearing von Linde's description of the low efficiency of the steam engine, Diesel resolved to develop a better engine. After proving mathematically that such an engine was practical, he built the first engine in 1892. When he tried to start it, the first explosion wrecked the engine. The experiment did prove, however, that the compression-ignition engine would work. By 1897 he had constructed the first successful Diesel engine, which immediately attracted world-wide attention. Unlike many inventors, Dr. Diesel gained a fortune from his engine. Everywhere he went, he was honored and acclaimed.

On September 29, 1913, Dr. Diesel boarded the cross-channel steamer, *Dresden,* at Antwerp, bound for London. It was a clear evening and the water was calm. When the *Dresden*

[523]

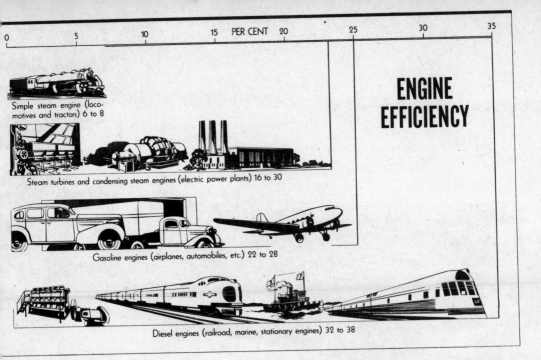

Simple steam engine (locomotives and tractors) 6 to 8

Steam turbines and condensing steam engines (electric power plants) 16 to 30

Gasoline engines (airplanes, automobiles, etc.) 22 to 28

Diesel engines (railroad, marine, stationary engines) 32 to 38

Diesels are the most efficient of all engines.

docked the next morning Dr. Diesel was missing. His bed had not been slept in. No one had seen him during the night. Passengers and crew could give no information.

Not until recently has any light been cast on the mystery. It has now been revealed that the fortune he had gained from his engine had been wiped out. In 1913, Dr. Diesel faced the prospect of bankruptcy; not only was he penniless, he owed large sums of money. He had discussed methods of suicide with his son, who mentioned leaping from a ship as his idea of the best method. This evidence of suicide, while circumstantial, is the most conclusive yet presented.

But regardless of the nature of his death, the future of his engine is assured. Capable minds have been steadily at work developing better Diesel engines and finding new uses for them.

Why Is the Diesel Engine Important?

The Diesel is inherently the most efficient type of engine built today. It converts several times as much of the energy in a fuel into work as does the ordinary steam engine. It is even better

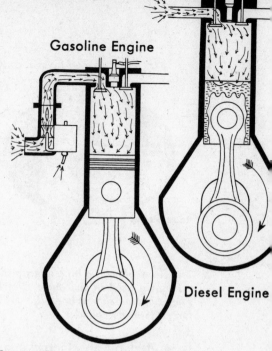

than our most highly developed gasoline automobile or airplane engines. The only power plant which approaches the Diesel in efficiency is the mercury-steam, but the weight of this type is excessive.

Efficiency is the measure of the percentage of heat in the fuel that an engine converts into useful work. All fuels are a storehouse of potential energy. The energy in gasoline, fuel oil and coal was obtained from the sun by prehistoric plants, and stored in the ground waiting for man to devise a way to reconvert the sun's heat energy into useful work. The potential energy of a fuel is measured in heat units per pound of fuel.

The gasoline engine requires a carburetor to mix air with gasoline vapor, and a spark plug to explode the mixture. The Diesel has an injector instead of a carburetor, and requires no electrical ignition system.

An engine is a machine for converting these stored heat units in the fuel into a form which can be used to do man's backbreaking tasks. The more of these heat units converted into work, the higher the efficiency. High efficiency means low fuel consumption.

What Is the Difference Between the Diesel and the Gasoline Engine?

Let us compare the Diesel and the gasoline engine, to see how the difference in efficiency comes about.

Both kinds of engines work by internal combustion, that is, by burning fuel inside a cylinder. The gases generated by this combustion drive a piston in the cylinder, thus converting heat energy into mechanical energy.

Burning requires air, so air as well as fuel is forced into the cylinder. This air is compressed before the fuel is ignited. A fact

[525]

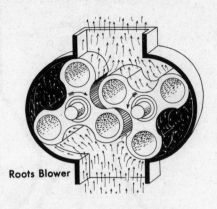

Roots Blower

The Roots blower, a type of air pump commonly used in two-cycle Diesels. The diagram shows how the air is forced into the cylinder.

of fundamental importance is that the higher the compression, the more efficient the engine.

In the gasoline engine, the air and the fuel are mixed together outside the cylinder, in a carburetor. The mixture is admitted to the cylinder and then compressed. The compression raises the temperature—indeed, that is its purpose. For the fuel burns more efficiently the higher its initial temperature.

When the piston is ready to start its down-stroke, the mixture is ignited by an electric spark. If it were to start burning before this time, during the up-stroke, there would be violent "knocking," and the engine might even start to run backwards. Therefore the mixture must not be heated so high that it starts burning spontaneously, without waiting for the correctly timed spark. The critical temperature is about 450° Fahrenheit.

The Diesel engine increases efficiency by raising the initial temperature before ignition to 1,000° Fahrenheit—about the temperature of red hot iron. To avoid premature ignition, the air

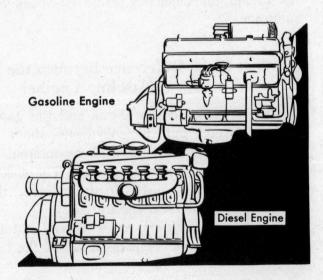

Gasoline Engine

Diesel Engine

Diesel engines weigh much more per horsepower than gasoline engines, and the latter accelerate more swiftly.

Great power is required to haul earth-moving machinery. Here a Diesel-driven wheeled tractor and a caterpillar tractor combine forces to operate an earth scraper.

alone is compressed in the cylinder. Then the fuel is injected and starts burning at once, without need for an electric spark.

Thus the Diesel engine does not have a carburetor nor spark plugs. Instead, it has a so-called fuel injector, which has the function of reducing the fuel to a spray and forcing it into the cylinder against the great pressure of the air, which may have been compressed by a ratio as much as 16 to 1.

Diesel engines, like gasoline engines, may be constructed to operate in four-stroke or two-stroke cycles.

What Is an Engine Cycle?

Let us see what happens inside the cylinder of a four-cycle Diesel engine. The piston head, a kind of plug, is free to move up and down in the cylinder. The piston is a swiveled rod connecting the head with a crank in the drive shaft, which turns as the piston moves.

The first stroke is the intake of fresh air. With the inlet valve open, the piston moving downward (away from the cylinder head) pumps air into the cylinder. As the piston passes the bottom of its stroke, the inlet valve closes.

The second stroke is the compression. The piston moving up compresses the air to 500 or 600 pounds per square inch, thereby raising its temperature to about 1,000° Fahrenheit.

A Diesel truck with the engine in the conventional place at the front. Diesels are often used in trucks that carry heavy loads because of their low fuel consumption and great power.

The third is the power stroke. As the piston reaches the top of its second stroke, the fuel injector commences to spray oil into the hot air. It starts to burn at once. The pressure rises to 800 or 850 pounds per square inch, and the piston is forced down.

The fourth is the exhaust stroke. The exhaust valve opens, and the piston, moving up, forces the burned gases out of the cylinder to make way for a new charge of fresh air.

Thus in the four-cycle engine every fourth stroke of the piston is a power stroke. In the two-cycle engine, every second stroke is a power stroke. But the same four operations still have to be performed. One of them, compression of the fresh air, is done by each up-stroke of the piston. The other three operations are combined in each down-stroke. First the fuel is injected and the piston starts down in a power stroke. When it reaches a certain point, the exhaust valve opens, releasing the pressure and allowing the burned gases to escape. At a lower point still, the piston clears intake ports in the bottom of the cylinder and admits a charge of fresh air, which helps to expel the burned gas. At the end of the stroke, all valves close and the piston commences the next compression stroke.

How Does the Injector Operate?

The heart of the Diesel engine is the fuel injection system. It is often stated that the Diesel engine is simpler than the gasoline engine because it eliminates the carburetor and ignition system. However, the fuel injection system on the Diesel, which must be substituted for these parts, brings up problems as highly involved as those in the carburetor and electric ignition system. The reasons will be obvious from the description of a typical injector used on a modern Diesel engine.

The first engines used compressed air to blow the fuel oil into the cylinder. Air at over 1,000 pounds per square inch pressure was necessary to inject and atomize the oil. This is just about the water pressure half a mile down in the sea.

Most Diesel engines built today use a pump to inject the fuel. "Solid injection" is the term applied to this system. There are many types of pumps designed for solid injection. They force the oil into the cylinder at the tremendous pressures of from 3,000 to 20,000 pounds per square inch. In comparison, a mile deep in the sea, the water pressure is about 3,000 pounds; it is 20,000 pounds at about 9 miles.

The Diesel engine of a large bus is placed across the rear end of the chassis and drives the rear wheels.

In any solid injection system it is necessary to have a pump that will force the oil into the cylinder against the compression pressure of 500 or 600 pounds per square inch. In the unit injection system there is a small pump for each cylinder, operated by a mechanism similar to that which operates the valves. The fuel must be split up into a fine fog as it enters the cylinder so it will burn rapidly and completely. A nozzle with a number of holes about the diameter of a small needle, breaks the oil into a fine spray. Its operation is similar to that of an atomizer. The unit injector has a pump and spray nozzle for each cylinder. The pump and nozzle are in one piece—hence the term, unit injector.

Why Are Air Pumps Used on Some Diesels?

In the four-stroke cycle engine the air is pulled into the cylinder by the downward movement of the piston on the intake

One of the engine rooms of a great Diesel freight locomotive. Individual engines in the locomotive can be stopped and repaired while the train is running.

A Diesel locomotive hauling freight along the Columbia River. This giant locomotive is made up of four parts, each carrying separate Diesel engines, and develops 5,400 horsepower.

stroke. The two-stroke cycle engine does not have a complete intake stroke, so an external method must be used to fill the cylinder with air. In other words, the four-stroke cycle engine uses the engine as an air pump half of the time; the two-stroke cycle engine uses an external air pump to fill the cylinder with a fresh charge of air. A number of methods are possible. Almost any type of air pump can be used. One type will serve as an example of the air pumps that are most successful. This pump also may be called a blower.

The blower is often of the Roots type. It has three lobes in each rotor, shaped something like giant gear teeth. The lobes in the two rotors mesh when they are rotated just as the teeth in two gears mesh. The blower is driven by the engine through a set of gears.

When the rotors revolve, air enters at the bottom opening and is trapped between the rotors and the case which surrounds them. The air is discharged at the top opening. This air is piped

The U. S. Submarine Skipjack. Like all submarines she is driven by Diesels while on the surface and electric motors while submerged. The Diesels give her a speed of twenty knots.

The seagoing tug Intent. Powered by a marine Diesel engine, this 102-foot craft made a historic run from Port Arthur, Texas, around the Cape of Good Hope to Massawa on the Red Sea.

to the intake ports surrounding the cylinder. The revolving door in many of our office buildings acts something like one side of the Roots blower. Each person who is trapped between the doors and the side represents a charge of air in the blower.

When the 1,200-horsepower, 16-cylinder engine is running full speed, the blower pumps over 6,000 cubic feet of air every minute. This is capacity enough to pump all the air out of two large-size living rooms every minute. And the blowers keep this up hour after hour as long as the engine runs.

What Fuel Do Diesels Use?

Diesel engines have been run on various types of fuels: powdered coal, tar, vegetable oils, animal fats and petroleum oils. However, it is not correct to say that any Diesel engine will run satisfactorily on all of these fuels.

The Diesel requires a petroleum fuel oil which is held to specifications as strict as those for the gasoline used in your car. First, it must be fluid enough so it can be pumped and injected into the cylinder. Second, it must be clean, or else the closely fitted parts of the fuel system will wear rapidly and the fine holes and passages will be plugged. Third, it must have the proper ignition properties so it will burn rapidly. Fourth, it should be reasonable in price.

This last factor, price, is often misunderstood. It is only partly true that the Diesel engine runs on cheaper fuel than the gasoline engine. At the present time the fuel oil used is much the same as the fuel oil used in household oil burners. The price per gallon of

A Diesel tractor uses its bulldozer to fill the 32-cubic-yard bucket of a great coal stripping shovel. Although dwarfed by this super steam shovel, the Diesel tractor here is very powerful.

Two Diesel engines are used to drive a mast type rotary drill rig. Operating 24 hours a day, each engine uses no more than 4½ gallons of fuel.

this oil and of gasoline is almost the same at the refinery. The big difference to the customer comes in the extra costs of distribution and especially the tax on gasoline. If we added these extras to fuel oil, the price would be nearly that of gasoline. If more processing of the fuel oil becomes necessary to suit the requirements mentioned in the preceding paragraph, the difference between the cost of Diesel fuel oil and gasoline may disappear entirely.

However, there are two factors which operate in favor of the Diesel in so far as fuel costs are concerned. First, the Diesel engine is more efficient than the gasoline engine, when running at full speed and developing full power. Second, the Diesel is very much better than the gasoline engine when developing only part of the full rated power.

The real reason for the lower fuel costs on a Diesel engine is that it obtains more useful work from the fuel.

To start a large Diesel engine all that is necessary is to start the flywheel turning with the throttle partly open. This initial movement can be obtained in a number of different ways. A common method in large engines is to inject compressed air into the cylinders. Air from a tank is connected to a valve in the top of the cylinder. When the valve is open, the highly compressed air forces the piston downward. After a few revolutions, the fuel will ignite and keep it going.

When the Diesel engine is connected to an electric generator, the generator is often used as a motor to turn the engine over. Smaller engines use an auxiliary electric starter.

Where Are Diesels Used?

The most spectacular application of Diesel power was the installation in the streamlined trains in 1934. Record speeds of 120 miles an hour were at once established. Within a few months, record long-distance runs were made. Denver to Chicago, a distance of over 1,000 miles, was made at an average speed of 77.6 miles per hour. The transcontinental run from Los Angeles to New York, over 3,000 miles, was made in 56 hours and 55 minutes, bettering the previous time by almost a day.

The first 3-car, streamlined train completed in 1934 was powered by one 600-horsepower, two-cycle Diesel engine. At present, Diesel locomotives with 10 times the power, 6,000-horsepower, are in regular service. These giant locomotives, the largest

A water pump driven by a Diesel engine provides water from the Trinity River, near Weaverville, California, for use in placer mining.

Diesel-powered ever built, are longer than the whole original streamlined Diesel train. They are made up of 3 power cars, each holding two 1,000-horsepower main Diesel engines. Speeds well over 100 miles an hour are easily attained.

The Diesel has invaded the last stronghold of the "Iron Horse"—freight service. Diesel freight locomotives, pulling heavier trains on long hauls in many hours less time and with lower operating costs than ever before possible with any type of locomotive, are now in service on leading railroads.

An automobile owner would feel quite at home in the cab of a Diesel locomotive. The comfortable, upholstered seat would do credit to any automobile. He would find that the windows are made of safety glass, and are equipped with windshield wiper, defroster, and sun glare shield similar to those on his car. There

A Diesel-driven electric generator used to provide electricity for a small plant when rains fail to provide enough water to run a water wheel which turns the generators.

Large caterpillar tractors driven by Diesel engines, with bulldozers mounted in front, move great quantities of earth.

is an instrument panel with many familiar dials—speedometer, oil and temperature gauges, and others. The controls are different but very simple—a throttle lever, brake lever and reverse lever, with the addition of a foot pedal which automatically stops the train if the operator's foot is removed.

In practically all Diesel locomotives, the Diesel engine drives powerful electric generators. The electric current they generate is used to operate large electric motors built into the axles of the driving wheels. This makes a flexible drive between the Diesel engine and the wheels, giving great pulling power to start and high maximum speeds.

To the railroads, the Diesel has meant lower operating costs, high fuel savings, and less time in the roundhouse. Schedules never before attempted have been made possible. In arid regions where water is difficult to obtain, the Diesel locomotive makes it unnecessary to maintain an expensive water supply.

A Diesel motor grader with a snow plow and wing keeps the roads open to the world's highest oil field near Craig, Colorado. The Diesel works well despite the temperature of twenty-five degrees below zero.

Because it is available more of the time, one Diesel locomotive can often be substituted for several steam locomotives. To cities and land owners along the railroad, the Diesel means freedom from smoke and cinders, with the resulting cleanliness.

Two-cycle Diesel engines are now built in a wide range of sizes for almost any purpose where a low cost, dependable source of power is required. The smallest engine is a one-cylinder unit developing 15 horsepower. The largest develops 1,500 horsepower and is a 16 cylinder, Vee type engine. Many intermediate sizes with 1, 2, 3, 4, and 6 cylinders are built for developing the proper amount of power for the particular application the engine is required to fit.

[538]

The Diesel cannot be surpassed for marine power. It has been used for everything from small pleasure craft to large freighters. The engines may be directly connected to the propeller, or drive may be through a reduction gear, depending upon the size of the boat and the installation. In some installations a Diesel electric drive, similar to that in the locomotives, is used. Many vessels in the United States Navy and Coast Guard are powered with this engine, which proved to be an important factor during World War II.

In the motor vehicle field, the two-cycle Diesel engine has been applied to buses and large trucks. For commercial vehicles, the economy and reliability of the Diesel engine results in large savings in operating costs. The Diesel obtains almost twice the fuel mileage of the conventional gasoline power commercial vehicle.

The two-cycle Diesel is particularly suited to a wide variety of uses isolated from the usual power sources. Small factories, mills, oil pipe lines, pumping stations, mines, quarries, canneries, and refrigeration plants find sizes suited to their needs.

The application of the Diesel engine is in its infancy. At present it is a sizable industry and growing rapidly. The present engines are not at all like the first heavy engines of forty years ago.

With the light-weight Diesel of the present, the Diesel engine can be used in hundreds of places never before practical. In many fields it is already powering the machinery and transportation of the world of tomorrow. A new industry has been born— Diesel, the modern power.

Why Is the South Called "Dixie"?

By some it is supposed that the term "Dixie" is derived from "Dixon" in the phrase "Mason and Dixon's line." By others it is said to be derived from a slaveholder of Manhattan Island who was called Dixie or Dixy. The immensely popular song of the Southland, "I Wish I Was in Dixie," is generally attributed to Daniel Emmett (1815–1905), the famous minstrel man. "Dixie" is believed to be a transcription of an old German song, and it is said to have been originally worked into a popular air by Prof. Herman F. Arnold, who, at Montgomery, Ala., discussed the music with Emmett, with the result that Emmett wrote the words and adapted the air as we have it today. Prof. Arnold died at Memphis, Tenn., in April, 1927.

THE STORY OF LUMBER

The storage yard of a big pulp mill. When needed, these logs will be fed onto the chain conveyor at the right and started on their journey to the mill.

LUMBER is one of the most important products of our natural resources. Almost every state produces lumber, but the biggest producers are located in the Pacific Northwest. By far the largest in the United States, the state of Oregon contributes about six and one-half million board feet a year to America's lumber supply. Washington is second with an average of four and one-half million board feet yearly, while California ranks third. Several Southern states have considerable lumbering industries. They produce mostly soft pine, which is a cheap and abundant material used in many building industries. The biggest producer in the South is Alabama, which markets more than two million board feet a year.

[540]

America's forests are one of our richest resources. This is a Douglas fir forest in the Pacific Northwest. The protection of our forests is the duty of every citizen, since nine out of ten forest fires are caused by humans.

Giant Douglas fir trees in a northern California forest. These are mature trees, ready for the logger's ax. When mature, trees must be used or they soon die and fall to the forest floor to rot or become fire hazards.

[541]

With ax and saw, the logger ends
the forest life of a giant California
pine. First the wedge cut is made
with a long-handled ax, then a two-
man ripsaw is used. The tree falls
in the direction of the wedge cut.

With a roar like thunder a giant of
the forest crashes to the earth.

Bucked into short lengths, the tree leaves the forest. Here a puffing donkey engine loads the logs onto railroad cars.

Where highways are available, logs are trucked to the sawmills on giant trailers.

Although logging railroads and trucks are the chief means of transporting timber from the forests, river drives are still used in some parts of the country. Here is a great log jam in the Clearwater River in Idaho.

Hauled to the sawmill by railroad, by truck, or by railroad, the logs are dumped into the mill pond, where they are stored until they are ready to be cut. "Boom men" move the logs about the pond, keeping a line of logs ready to feed the whirring saws.

On the way up the conveyor or "jack ladder" the logs are washed clean of stones or metal that cling to the bark and endanger the saws.

Once in the mill, the logs are placed on moving carriages and the sharp saws slice the timbers, which fall onto the rapidly turning "lively rolls."

Giant trimmer saws cut the green timber to length, and square up the ends.

Logging operations do not stop in the winter. Here, logs are stacked ready to be transported from the forest.

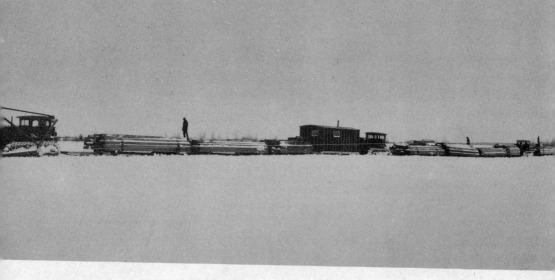

Sawmills are sometimes set up in northern forests and the logs are cut into lumber on the spot. The lumber is loaded on sleds and hauled by tractors. Even the small shack of the lumbering crew is mounted on runners and hauled as part of the tractor train. As many as five or six tractors help move the sleds.

Smaller logs are piled on crude sleds and hauled through the snow by caterpillar tractors.

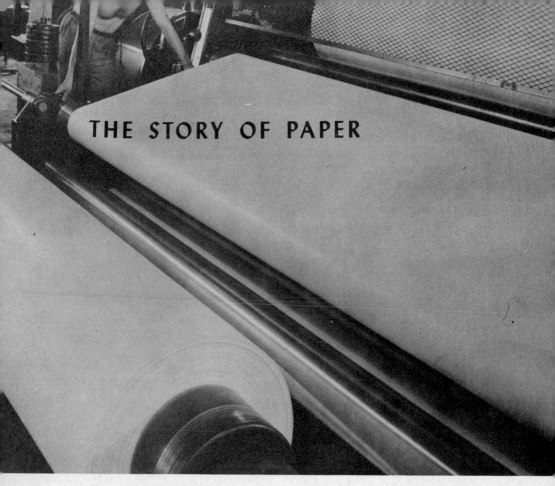

THE STORY OF PAPER

Wood pulp, fed into the machine with a constantly running stream of water, is transformed by heat and pressure into paper. Here the new paper comes off a paper machine in an endless roll.

THE first known writing was done on stones, ivory, bark and almost any substance that had a flat surface. In ancient Babylonia an immense commerce was carried on in which all transactions were recorded by indenting characters on clay bricks which were afterwards baked.

For filing and reference these records proved far from practical, but it was not until between 2500 and 2000 B.C. that the ancient Egyptians learned how to make an easily handled writing material from the papyrus plant which grew along the river Nile. It is from this that we get our word "paper."

The stalk of papyrus was split into thin strips, which were laid flat with edges touching. Another layer was placed at right angles over the first, both were pounded together, then smoothed with a stone. This made a coarse but serviceable surface. Thousands of papyrus manuscripts have been preserved in the equable climate of Egypt, and give us much of our knowledge of ancient cultures.

The first real paper, that is, a sheet composed of fibers "felted" together, was made by the Chinese about A.D. 100.

This process was kept secret for nearly six hundred years; it was not until the Mohammedan Arabs conquered Samarkand (western Asia) in 704 that it became known in the Western world. The Moors carried the process into Spain; by the end of the twelfth century paper-makers were active there and in Italy, and from these countries knowledge of paper-making spread to the rest of Europe. The first mill in America was built in 1690, near Philadelphia.

How Is Paper Made by Hand?

All paper at that time was made by hand, and hemp, linen and cotton rags formed the only raw material available. The rags were reduced to pulp by the action of a stamping mill, usually driven by a water wheel. The pulp was then placed in a vat and highly diluted with water. A skilled workman dipped a quantity of pulp and water out of the vat by means of a form with a wire screen bottom and a removable frame, or deckle, around it. With an expert twist or shake, the workman felted the fibers as the water drained through the wire screen, leaving the fibers matted on top of the screen.

The deckle frame was next removed, the screen with the wet fibers turned upside down, and the sheet of fibers pulled off onto a piece of felt. Another felt was placed on top and the performance repeated. When the pile of felts and paper was about a foot high, as much water as possible was removed by pressure. The separate sheets of paper were then hung over poles to dry.

Naturally, paper production under this process was limited, and it was also very expensive, so that writing materials and books were scarce and, because of their cost, out of the reach of the average person.

Who Invented the Paper Machine?

In 1799 a Frenchman, Louis Roberts, conceived the notion of making paper on a movable, endless wire screen. He sold his patents in England to Henry and Sealy Fourdrinier who developed the principle, and in 1804 constructed the first practical paper-making machine.

With the invention of the paper machine, paper production was very materially increased, and many new uses were found for it which heretofore had been prohibited by its high price. Soon, however, the supply of rags became very scarce, and appeals were made to the inventors of all countries to find a substitute raw material.

In 1841 Gottfried Keller of Saxony invented the process of making paper from a pulp made by mechanically grinding wood

A continuous flow of logs moves to the chipper, a revolving steel disk with four sharp knives in its surface. Logs are held against the disk and quickly reduced to chips.

against a revolving stone. Today, newsprint is made largely from fibers in this way. The chemical composition of the wood is not changed in the grinding process, and as a result, paper made from this mechanical pulp is subject to the same decomposition as the wood itself.

What Processes Are Used in Making Pulp?

In 1867 Benjamin Tilghman of Philadelphia invented and patented a chemical process of separating the fibers of wood from the other products of the growth of the tree. Though it was many years before the imperfections of this process were overcome and it became commercially practical, toward the end of the nineteenth century chemical wood pulp began to be used extensively in the paper industry.

There are a number of chemical methods of producing wood pulp. These are: the sulphate process, which produces pulp suitable for wrapping papers; the soda process, used extensively for book papers; and the sulphite process. The sulphite process (named after calcium bisulphite, the cooking liquor used) is an elaborate treatment by which the resinous and ligneous substances in the wood are dissolved, leaving the pure cellulose fibers for paper-making. It is this process that has been developed to a high degree assuring uniform papers of the highest order.

How Are Spruce Trees Made Into Paper?

Selected spruce trees furnish the fiber material for paper. These are cut into logs four feet long, and are shipped by boat from the woodlands to the mill.

The spruce logs are carefully barked by being rolled over each other while streams of water play on them to loosen the bark and wash it away. Inspectors watch for logs not completely barked and return them through the barking process. After barking, the logs are washed free of dirt and remaining pieces of bark. At this stage, any knots are removed by special boring machines.

The logs are then reduced to chips, which are screened to free them of chip dust. The larger chips are broken up, with the

[551]

Chips are reduced to even size by repeated beating and are sent on a conveyor belt to the pulp cooker.

result that chips of very uniform size are used. These are stored until ready to be "digested."

Acid-resisting, brick-lined tanks, fifty feet high, called "digesters," are filled with the chips. Then the cooking liquor, calcium bisulphite, is pumped in and, under controlled temperature and pressure, is circulated through the mass of chips by means of a pump.

At the expiration of about twelve hours, the incrusting substances have been freed from the fibers, leaving pure cellulose. From the time the cellulose leaves the cooking or digesting stage, until it reaches the bleaching process, it is subjected to one cleaning after another to remove the cooking acid, in which are the suspended impurities, and all undigested particles of wood and dirt.

This series of cleaning steps is closely supervised and the degree of cleanliness is determined by laboratory tests. The laboratory is in constant touch with every step throughout the entire process. It tests the different elements entering into each operation, as well as the pulp and paper at every stage during their manufacture.

After having been thoroughly cleaned, the fibers are subjected to the bleaching action of chloride of lime, which turns the pulp to a beautiful shade of white.

The pulp is now placed in "beaters" for treatment essential to the character of paper to be made. A beater consists of a tub partly divided by a partition, on one side of which a large roll revolves rapidly. The outside of the beater roll has bars of bronze spaced at regular intervals. The "roll" rotates above a "bed

Immense digesters, over fifty feet high and lined with acid-proof brick, are filled with chips uniformly by a distributor. Preheated acid cooking liquor, under automatically controlled temperature and pressure, circulates through the chips. After twelve to thirteen hours these chips are reduced to pulpy cellulose fibers which are blown into the blow pit, where they are washed and made ready for purifying operations that follow.

After being cooked and bleached the wood pulp is conveyed to the beaters, large tubs with revolving drums (see inset at left), which reduce the fibers in length and fray them so they will lock together or "felt" in the sheet of paper.

plate" of similar bars. As the roll turns, the fibers are brushed between the blades and reduced in length. The sides and ends of the minute fibers become frayed so that they will lock together or "felt" more strongly in the paper.

Certain essentials, such as the necessary colors, are added to the pulp while being beaten. A gluelike substance called "size" is also added to close up the hollow strawlike fibers, so that when the sheet is written upon, the ink will not penetrate, but will dry on the surface of the paper.

After beating, the "stock" is passed through Jordan refining engines, which have bronze blades somewhat similar in action to the beater.

Then the pulp passes through a "stock chest" or storage vat to the paper-making machine called the "Fourdrinier" after the two men who developed it over a century ago.

Cooked and beaten, the wood pulp is washed clean with pure filtered water. After further processing it is ready for the giant paper machine.

How Does the Modern Paper Machine Work?

On the Fourdrinier machine the stock, diluted to between 97½ to 99½ per cent water, is allowed to flow onto a continuous belt of bronze screen of very fine mesh. As this screen, or "wire" as it is called, moves along, the water drains away. A sidewise shaking of the wire lays part of the fibers crosswise to give the paper strength in both directions, otherwise it would tear apart easily.

As the water drains out, the pulp forms a wet thin sheet composed of millions of fibers adhering to each other. A series of felt blankets and heavy rolls remove more of the water. Then the paper travels over and under a long series of huge steam-heated cylinders that dry out most of the remaining water. Sprays of sizing material close the surface pores, then another series of electrically controlled dryer rolls bring the sheet to the desired degree of dryness.

The proper finish is given the surface of the paper by "iron-ing" between steel calendar rolls at the end of the paper machine. The paper is then wound in large rolls.

From the machine, the paper is taken to the final process, called "finishing." In the finishing room the rolls are cut into sheets, then inspected and counted. Defective paper is removed by hand sorting, sheet by sheet. Great care and the closest inspec-tion of the paper during each step in the finishing process result in a very uniform product of high quality leaving the mill.

After having been counted into reams of five hundred sheets and given a final examination, the paper is cut to exact size, wrapped, labeled and sent to the packing department to be packed into cartons for shipment to every part of the United States and to most of the countries of the world.

(Copyright by Hammermill Paper Company. Reprinted by permission.)

What Were the Seven Wonders of the World?

As understood by the peoples of ancient days, the Seven Wonders of the World were: (1) the Pyramids of Egypt; (2) the Hanging Gardens of Baby-lon; (3) the Temple of Diana, at Ephesus in Asia Minor; (4) the statue of Jupiter, in the valley of Olympia, in Greece; (5) the Mausoleum at Halicar-nassus, on the east side of the Ægean Sea, opposite Greece; (6) the Pharos, or lighthouse, at Alexandria, Egypt; and (7) the Colossus of Rhodes, on the island of Rhodes in the Mediterranean.

What Is a Siren Horn?

There are a great many different kinds of signals for the guidance of ves-sels during fogs, when lights or other visible signals cannot be perceived.

One of the most powerful signals is the siren foghorn, the sound of which is produced by means of a disk perforated by radial slits made to rotate in front of a fixed disk exactly similar, which is set in the small end of an iron megaphone. The disks may each contain say twelve slits, and the moving disk may revolve 2,800 times a minute; in each revolution there are, of course, twelve coincidences between the slits in the two disks; through the openings thus made steam or air at a high pressure is caused to pass, so that there are actually 33,600 puffs of steam or compressed air every minute. This causes a sound of very great power, which the trumpet collects and compresses, and the blast goes out as a sort of sound beam in the direction required. Under favorable circumstances this instrument can be heard from twenty to thirty miles out at sea.

THE STORY OF FARM MACHINERY

A self-propelled combine which harvests all threshable crops in one operation. Only one man is required to operate it.

OVER one hundred years ago a Virginia farm boy of twenty-two, after a few weeks of concentrated thought and toil, solved a problem that had baffled the minds of men and blocked the progress of civilization for nearly two thousand years—perhaps longer.

That midsummer day of 1831, when Cyrus Hall McCormick publicly proved the success of his reaper, marked the beginning of the new agriculture that was soon to change farming from the sheerest drudgery, with the poorest of results, into a business calling for mind as much as muscle and yielding substantial results for reasonable labor.

That day, too, marked the beginning of a new epoch in civilization, in which mankind was to be freed forever from the presence of hunger and the dread of famine; in which millions

Rear view of the world's first reaper, invented by Cyrus Hall McCormick in 1831.

of men, emancipated from universal enslavement to the soil, could give their time and strength for the development of the industries, the arts, the sciences, the research, and the culture of modern life.

Who Was Cyrus McCormick?

Cyrus Hall McCormick was of Scotch-Irish ancestry. His father, Robert McCormick, was an educated, prosperous landowner who, besides his farms, operated grist mills, sawmills, a smelter, and a blacksmith shop. He was a reader and a student, gentle but energetic, an active churchman, and had wide interests. His mechanical ingenuity, interest, and imagination made him an inventor of rare ability.

Cyrus Hall McCormick was born on February 15, 1809, on the family farm, Walnut Grove, in Rockbridge County, Virginia. As a boy Cyrus went to the Old Field School. When he was fifteen he found that his boyish physique was insufficient to swing a heavy cradle in the harvest grain; so he made a smaller implement to suit his slight muscles. At eighteen he made himself some needed surveying instruments. Of greater importance was the

Hand reaping with cradles was laborious and slow work. Based on the scythe, the cradle was developed in America between 1776 and 1800.

invention of a hillside plow, which was his first major contribution to modern agriculture.

How Did Cyrus McCormick Become Interested in Farm Machinery?

In 1816, Robert McCormick made the first of his several attempts to build a mechanical reaper. Like the devices of others who had interested themselves in the problem, his machine was pushed ahead into the grain by two horses, and the wheat was to be pressed against stationary convex sickles by rapidly revolving beaters. This machine utterly failed to cut the grain. At various times during the next fifteen years he made other fruitless attempts to revive his scheme. His oldest son was informed as to his ideas and may have helped him prepare his last machine for its unsuccessful trial in May, 1831.

Cyrus must have started on his own machine as soon as he saw the admitted evidence of his father's failure. Between May and July he conceived his own new principles, built one or more models, and developed a machine that cut grain successfully.

[559]

McCormick's first reaper in action. Crude as it was, it could cut as much grain in a day as five men with cradle scythes.

He did not know that for years many men had been toiling to solve the problem of the reaper or that before his time many futile reaper patents had been issued in England and America. He had never heard of Pitts' work nearly fifty years before, nor of Bell and Ogle, nor did he know of Manning, who had already patented several of the features he was to incorporate in his own machine. McCormick's sole experience was with his father's unsuccessful attempts.

When Was the First Successful Reaper Built?

Cyrus McCormick set to work in the old log blacksmith shop cutting and fashioning wood and bending into shape the few iron pieces of the machine. His first reaper was built in about six weeks. He tried it out privately in an adjacent wheat field on

The early reaper could cut six to eight acres a day and required a man to rake the grain from its platform.

the farm with none but the members of his family for spectators. Convinced that he was on the right road, he set to work feverishly to remodel it for a public test. The initial machine of early July had a straight-edged reciprocating knife, actuated by gears from the main wheel, a platform extending sideways from the wheel, shafts for a single horse, an outside divider to separate the standing grain from that to be held against the cutter bar, and fingers to project in front of the blade. The late July machine had the improved divider, a better cutter bar, provided with saw-toothed incised serrations along its leading edge and a reel to hold the grain against the knife.

There is no record of the exact day of the first public trial in July, 1831. The reaper worked in a small field near Steele's Tavern, Virginia. Neighbors assembled from the vicinity. Cyrus' family had driven down the valley from their farm. The young

A small tractor and combine for medium-sized farms. The combine threshes and bags the grain after it has been cut.

inventor walked behind the machine. Jo Anderson, the Negro servant who had toiled with him to build the reaper, walked, rake in hand, beside him to keep the platform clear from severed grain. Certain farm hands were also there, men carrying sickles and scythes which, with the cradle, were the only instruments of harvest. They may not have understood what they were seeing, but the reaper was, nevertheless, laying the foundation for their future emancipation.

What Are the Essential Features of the Reaper?

Whatever the present world has since added to the science of agricultural equipment, all modern grain-cutting machines contain the essential elements that Cyrus Hall McCormick put into his reaper. These essential features were seven:

1. The straight knife with serrated edge and reciprocal or vibrating motion that cuts the grain.
2. Fingers or guards extending from the platform to prevent the grain from slipping sideways while being cut.
3. The revolving reel that holds the grain against the knife and lays the cut stalks on the platform.
4. A platform behind the knife for receiving the cut grain and holding it until raked off.
5. The master wheel that carries most of the weight of the machine and, through ground traction, furnishes power to operate the reel and the knife.
6. Forward draft from the right or stubble side by means of shafts attached in front of the master wheel.
7. A divider on the left side to separate the grain to be cut from that to be left standing.

A powerful caterpillar tractor pulling a giant combine which cuts, threshes and bags the grain as it moves along.

Small farms require small tractors. Here a light tractor operates a cultivator on a small vegetable farm.

In 1831, and for several years thereafter, Cyrus had not the slightest idea that he was not the sole and original discoverer of each one of these cardinal elements. Actually he originated them all independently and alone, but in the case of six of them he was duplicating prior discoveries of other inventors. Only the main wheel was original with him. Even so, he is honored as the first inventor of the reaper because an invention need actually be no more than a new combination of known features producing a novel result.

The reaper was patented in 1834. McCormick saw in a magazine the picture of a reaper patented the previous autumn by Obed Hussey. He did not necessarily feel that his own machine was a finished product, but he felt the necessity of protecting his interests and so secured a patent of his own. In later years Hussey admitted the priority of McCormick's reaper.

Modern farm machinery has relieved the farmer of his backbreaking work. A light tractor pulling a small plow which can be raised or lowered at the touch of a knob.

When Were Reapers First Manufactured for Sale?

In 1840 McCormick made his first real reaper sales. He sold one reaper to a farmer who rode in from the northwestern part of the state and one to a man from the James River district. These two machines did not work well; so he spent the harvest period of 1841 in private experimentation. By the next year he had so improved the cutting ability of the knife, by changing the angle of the serrations, that he was able to sell seven reapers in 1842. The volume of sales rose to twenty-nine in 1843 and to fifty in 1844. The price of the reaper was $100. All the early machines were made in the blacksmith shop on the Walnut Grove

Farm. In 1844 he sold reapers in New York, Tennessee, Ohio, Indiana, Illinois, Wisconsin, and Missouri, as well as in his home country.

In 1847 McCormick moved to Chicago. Among the several firms that he had licensed to build reapers was Gray & Warner of Chicago, manufacturers of cradles. For a time Gray became his partner and together they built 500 machines for the harvest of 1848. Then Gray sold out to William B. Ogden, the great pioneer of early Chicago, and W. E. Jones. The firm name was McCormick, Ogden & Company. By 1849 they agreed amicably to disagree, and McCormick bought the Ogden and Jones half of the business for $65,000. Fifteen hundred machines had been sold that year (and he had made enough money); this enabled McCormick to pay so large a price. Already, at forty years of age, the Virginia farmer boy had become a captain of young industry.

Deep plowing with a caterpillar tractor. A 22-inch breaker plow turning over virgin marsh soil in Indiana.

The factory of 1848 was remarkable in the eyes of those who saw in it the beginning of Chicago's industry. Growth began immediately. By the end of 1849 the main building had been extended to a length of 190 feet. One hundred and twenty men were at work. There were river side docks for unloading materials from lake schooners and for shipping finished reapers. In 1859, when it had passed its tenth birthday, there was a total floor area of 100,000 square feet and a working force of 300 men. By 1856 there were McCormick agents all over the wheat-growing sections of the United States.

How Did Europe Receive the Reaper?

Ever since 1849, when McCormick built a special machine designed for presentation to Prince Albert's Royal Agricultural Society, he had been turning his eyes toward the English market. The Crystal Palace exhibition of industries of all nations in the summer of 1851 furnished the suitable occasion. He sent a special reaper across the Atlantic in the spring and himself followed in August. Hussey sent a machine of his own. They met on the farm of J. J. Mechi, a rich manufacturer, where, before 200 spectators including the jury from the exhibition, Hussey's machine failed miserably because of the operator's lack of skill. A second trial confirmed the result of the first, and the Virginia reaper was awarded the Council Medal, the highest prize of the fair. McCormick made arrangements with a British firm to manufacture his reaper, and went home.

France clung to hand-reaping methods until 1855, when there was an international exposition in Paris. A great field trial for reapers was organized in LaTrappe. The McCormick machine won and received the grand gold medal of honor.

Use of the reaper began early and spread rapidly throughout Europe. A McCormick machine was sold in Austria in 1850. In 1856 the reaper was introduced into Prussia and Poland. In 1858 the first McCormick machine reached Russia. In 1878 McCormick was made a member of the Legion of Honor and a member of the French Academy for having done more than any living man for the cause of agriculture.

Cultivating the soil between rows of walnut trees with a tractor-drawn basin lister.

How Did the Reaper Aid the North During the War Between the States?

The War Between the States furnished the supreme test of the worth of the reaper. The United States Commissioner of Agriculture said in 1862 that it would have been impossible to harvest the wheat crop if it had not been for the reapers in use in the West, each of which released five men for service in the army. The *Scientific American* declared that without "horse rakes, mowers, and reaping machines, one-half the farmers' crops would have been left standing on the fields." Secretary of War Stanton said: "The reaper is to the North what slavery is to the South. By taking the place of regiments of young men in Western harvest fields, it released them to do battle for the Union at the front and at the same time kept up the supply of bread for the nation and the nation's armies. Thus, without McCormick's in-

A spring-tooth harrow drawn by a caterpillar tractor harrows the soil before it is seeded with spring wheat.

vention, I feel the North could not win, and the Union would have been dismembered."

Although it was the war that first brought to public notice the great value of the reaper, its importance proved no less in peacetime. The reaper enabled farmers to plant and harvest thousands of acres more than they could before. In fact, the rise of the United States as a foremost wheat-growing country can be traced directly to the introduction of farm machinery.

What Improvements Were Made in the Reaper?

McCormick's interest and activity in improving his machine never waned. He secured two other patents in addition to his original patent of 1834—one in 1845 and one in 1847—and thus the original implement of the thirties became "Cyrus McCormick's Patent Virginia Reaper," a two-horse machine with a wider cut and a seat on the side whereon the raker sat as he worked. Before 1855 the weight of the machine had increased from 800

Tractors are replacing horses even on small farms. A side delivery rake arranging hay in rows.

to 1,200 pounds. The main wheel was enlarged; the reel was further improved; the wood platform was covered with sheet zinc to make it more durable and easier to rake clean; malleable iron guards were substituted for cast iron. Most important of all, the modern form of knife with riveted-on cutting sections was devised in 1851.

Many men had for a long time been trying to build a self-rake reaper, and invariably they tried to sell their ideas to McCormick, but he was never satisfied. McCormick stood his ground and refused to desert his original type of reaper until something better appeared. His own self-rake machine was produced in 1862. This was the regular reaper equipped with a rake arm pivoting near the axis of the reel which swept grain off the platform and to the side of the machine. It eliminated the time and work of one man.

The next important forward step in grain-cutting machinery was the Marsh harvester, patented in 1858, but not in general use

A hay-chopping machine drawn and powered by a tractor delivers chopped hay to a wagon behind it.

for some years after that. This machine raised the grain by means of continuous canvas aprons from the reaper platform over the top of the main wheel, where it fell neatly on a table. Two men rode the machine, standing before this table on a footboard. They bound the grain as fast as it fell over to them and then tossed the bundles to the ground. One by one the reaper manufacturers, including McCormick, began the manufacture of Marsh-type harvesters.

Then, in 1874, Charles B. Withington sought out McCormick and showed him a model of a wire binder. The reaper inventor immediately bought the Withington device, made a few machines experimentally, and in 1877 was ready to produce the wire binder in quantities. Fifty thousand of the new machines were sold

A small, automatic, tractor-drawn and tractor-operated hay baler, designed for the farmer's own use.

during the next few years. Hand labor had now been practically eliminated from cutting and binding. A boy old enough to drive a team could reap and bind the crop.

William Deering entered the reaper business as a silent partner of E. H. Gammon in 1870. In 1879 Deering, then in sole control of the business, decided to move away from Plano and build a new factory in Chicago's northern suburbs. At the same time he bought shop rights under the patents of John F. Appleby and prepared to build himself a twine binder. In the first season, 1880, he made and sold 3,000 of the new machines. The wire binder's brief day of supremacy was over. Appleby, one of the great names in the history of American invention, hit upon the combination of successful units that had barred the access of all other men to the secret of a successful twine binder.

Thus, fifty years after the test of his reaper at Steele's Tavern, McCormick found his leadership challenged by competition far more serious than the Marsh harvester of a few years before. With lightning rapidity he adapted himself to the new circum-

Tractor-operated loader lightens farm work. It can be used as a fork for manure or as a scoop when the tines are covered.

stances, arranged for a license to manufacture Appleby binders, and entered the 1881 harvest ready to do battle as before.

How Did the Reaper Improve Farming?

Before 1831 farmers relied almost entirely on human labor to cultivate and gather crops. It is true that horses and oxen were utilized for plowing, for hauling, and for transporting the families when they moved on in search of new lands; but the majority of operations on the farm were slow, tedious handwork. Almost 90 per cent of the population lived on farms, and to eke out an existence they labored from sunup until long after dark. It was a life of drudgery, privation, and heart-breaking toil.

Conserving American soil. Depleted soil is restored with the aid of a solid and fluid manure spreader.

For fifty years after McCormick's reaper became popular—the period up to 1900—farmers relied entirely on animal power. The reaper was gradually but consistently improved until it evolved into the twine binder. Machines for harvesting corn and cutting and curing hay followed the development of the grain machines, all with the same objective in mind—to lift the work from human shoulders and place it on the stronger muscles of animals. Oxen, horses, and mules relieved the farmer of the heavier power tasks and served agriculture faithfully and well. But, like man, they were only bone and muscle power—subject to the same fatigue and similarly affected by climatic conditions. The present eclipse of animal power is no indication of its failure in the past. Relying solely on animals for power, agriculture was able to triple the output of every worker in a brief fifty years.

When Did the Tractor Replace the Horse?

The twenty years from 1890 to 1910 were America's best years of horse farming. Undoubtedly this period marked the peak of efficiency of animal power and horse-drawn equipment. In the

A two-row cut-off corn harvester which cuts the stalks, snaps and husks the ears, delivers them to the wagon behind and shreds the cut stalks.

wake of the reaper and its successors for harvesting grain, hay, and corn, all kinds and types of machines for utilizing animal power had been developed and agriculture prospered.

During this twenty-year period a new power was being born —the internal-combustion tractor. By 1910 it had become a formidable competitor of the horse. The more adventurous farmers—the same type of hardy pioneers who were first to turn to the reaper—invested in tractors to help them in the hardest of all farm power jobs—the job of plowing. The motor truck for farm transportation was already on the horizon. Along came World War I, and tractor popularity mounted.

The war created an unusual demand for animals for military purposes and thus again, spurred by necessity, farmers sought

The mechanical picker may change the economy of the South. Barbed spindles pick the cotton from the plant and pass it to a vacuum conveyor which carries it to a cage behind the driver.

more efficient power to meet the requirements of increased production. This time the tractor stepped into the breach and replaced the horses and mules that were shipped to the front.

The end of the war saw the beginning of the end for animal power. In commercial work, keyed to an automotive age, muscle and bone could not stand the strain. In recent years the horse has all but disappeared, as a beast of burden, from city streets, During the same period, horses and mules have been decreasing on the farms at the rate of nearly a million animals a year. By now, mechanical farm power has made its way into every section of the country, and the transformation of agricultural power from an animal to a mechanical basis is almost complete.

THE STORY OF ICE REFRIGERATION

Blocks of ice are placed in a grinder and pulverized until the ice looks like fine snow. A blower, attached to the grinder, forces the pulverized snow through a giant hose and sprays it into the perishable loads of refrigerator cars and trucks.

WHEN and where ice was first used to keep food fresh, nobody knows. Many thousands of years ago when our ancestors lived in caves and existed largely on the wild game they killed, someone made a great discovery. He found that meat which was kept in the coolest part of the cave stayed fresh much longer than meat that was left in the heat. Later another member of this prehistoric race found that in winter time he could do still better with his meat. He could bury it in snow or surround it with ice and keep it for weeks. So began the history of ice refrigeration.

[577]

Primitive man found that hanging the carcasses of freshly killed animals in the cold air of natural caves, and suspending goatskin bags filled with milk in deep holes in the ground, kept these foods edible for a longer time.

How Was Food Preserved in Ancient Times?

Long before the birth of Christ, Egypt was a great nation. The rulers and nobility of that land lived in great luxury and among other comforts they had ice. To get it they had their servants set out hundreds of shallow, clay pans of water each night. During the night a thin covering of ice formed and this was harvested before sunrise the next morning and used for cooling foods and beverages.

In Macedonia another method of chilling foods was discovered and written about. Alexander the Great, then conqueror of India, was fond of good living. During his Indian campaign he demanded that a way be found to chill his wine. One of his officers, eager to please the general, sent hundreds of soldiers in to the mountains to gather snow. They rushed back and packed it into deep trenches where it kept long enough to cool the wine. Three hundred years later the Romans were sending slaves to dig snow on Mount Albanus and bring it into Rome. There it was packed into pits and caves and covered with branches of trees to keep it from melting. The Portuguese, too, valued ice and when water froze in depressions and caves during the winter it was covered with moss and sod to keep it for use months later in hot weather.

Fifteen hundred years later the Italians discovered a way to cool liquids artificially. They poured wine into long-necked

The ancient Egyptians made ice by filling shallow porous clay pans with water in the early evening. In the morning thin layers of ice would be harvested for the day's supply. These ice-making fields were about 4 acres in size.

The ancient Greeks also used the principle of rapid evaporation of water through porous vessels to produce refrigeration. They placed huge clay vessels on the rooftops and all night long slaves sprinkled water on the jars.

bottles, which were suspended in containers of water, to which saltpeter was added.

But so long as these expensive methods for cooling or refrigerating foods were used, only the very wealthy could afford iced drinks or the milk and water ices (which Marco Polo had discovered in his journey to China). Even for the wealthy, foods were very limited in variety, and there were few fresh fruits or vegetables in the winter season. Even in Revolutionary times little was known about refrigeration, and the only preserving of foods was with salt and spices. In fact, this limited preserving made spices in such demand that men travelled to the ends of the known world to procure them. Of course, without refrigeration vegetables and fruits could never be shipped from one part of the world to another and even kings had a very limited diet. For an Englishman to enjoy an orange in the sixteenth century he had to travel to Spain where oranges grew, and people that lived inland never knew the taste of delicacies found in the sea, such as lobsters and oysters.

When Did Ice Harvesting Begin?

Meanwhile, winter after winter, millions of streams and lakes the world over were coated with ice. Finally men began to cut this ice into blocks and to pack it away in store houses where a covering of sawdust and straw kept it from melting so it could be used when summer came. Some time in the sixteenth century

The Romans, about 50 B. C., dug snow on Mt. Albanus and packed it into pits 50 feet deep and 25 feet wide and covered them with straw and tree prunings. The stored snow was later cut out with picks and used for refrigeration purposes.

During the latter part of the 13th century, Marco Polo, the famed traveler and navigator, while on one of his Asiatic journeys, learned the secrets of making water and milk ices and brought back the methods with him to Italy.

an enterprising man started selling ice to neighbors who had not stored any for their own use. After that ice rapidly became a big business.

Yet even then no one dreamed of the vital part ice, made by man instead of Nature, would play in our modern, mechanical world where it is used in manufacturing processes and surgery as well as for the preservation of food. Today ice refrigerators keep foods fresh in millions of homes. Ice refrigerator cars, loaded with perishable foods, roll along the railways bringing fruits, vegetables and other foods to market. All this has resulted from the discovery of a method for manufacturing ice.

When Did Ice Become a Business in America?

By the seventeenth century, dealers in ice and snow were fairly common in France, and frozen lemonade and other ices were sold on the streets of Paris during warm weather. A hundred years later, in 1799, a shipment of ice, cut from a pond near what is now Canal Street in New York City, was taken to Charleston, South Carolina and the ice business in America had its start. Before that many families built their own ice houses to store ice they cut during the winter from nearby ponds or lakes, but no one sold ice in any quantity. The first big ice storehouse in the United States was built in 1805, and ice was soon a part of the cargo carried by Yankee Clippers to the West Indies. Loads of ice also went to England and for many years most of the ice used

On a hot day in August, 1774, the Duc de Chartres was greatly delighted when the proprietor of a Parisian coffee house (known for its iced liqueurs) placed before him his coat-of-arms moulded in a "frozen milk mixture." (Ice cream.)

In 1550, Italians cooled liquids in long-necked globular vessels which they immersed in a large container filled with water. As the bottle was driven around with a quick motion, saltpeter was gradually added to the outer vessel.

there was shipped across the ocean from Wenham Lake near Boston.

In those days, ships depended on the winds for power, and sailing vessels were sometimes on the high seas for months. Lack of fresh foods often made the sailors ill, and ships would put into port with many of the crew incapacitated. Then ice chests were built into these sailing vessels, making it possible to carry fresh foods. The diet of the sailors was thus improved and illness aboard ship was greatly reduced. In the middle of the 1800's an Englishman built the first home container for ice. It was called an "ice preserver" and the forerunner of today's efficient ice refrigerators. Some of those early refrigerators were fancy pieces of furniture, combining a china cabinet with an ice box and were built for use in dining rooms.

How Was Ice Cream Made Known in America?

By this time people in the United States were hearing about ice cream, the wonderful frozen dessert served in Paris. Today ice cream is considered an American food and is sold in every city and village in this country! Dolly Madison, wife of our fourth president, was the first American housewife to make ice cream known. She often served it at the White House, and guests went home talking about this delicious dessert. Soon ice cream freezers were put on the market, and ice cream was being made everywhere.

In 1820, ice cutting, because it was done by hand, occupied the entire winter months. Areas were cleared of snow and with specially designed tools the ice was cut and afterward stored in ice houses located on the near-by shore.

In 1834, Jacob Perkins, an engineer, secured the first patent on an ice machine using ether as refrigerant to cool brine circulating around receptacles filled with water. The brine at low temperature froze the water into ice.

Ice was especially in demand by people in the warm South. During the Civil War, blockade runners often took daring chances with Union warships in order to deliver ice into New Orleans, where it sometimes sold for as much as a dollar a pound!

When Was Artificial Ice First Made?

As cities grew and the use of ice in homes, hotels and hospitals increased, not enough ice could be cut from lakes and rivers to supply the demand. Men began to seek a way to manufacture ice instead of having to depend entirely on what would be harvested in the winter and stored for summer use.

As early as 1755 a Scotchman, Dr. William Cullen, invented a machine for making ice. But it was not until 1850 that a really practical machine was produced. This, too, was developed by a physician, Dr. John Gorrie of Florida, who realized the importance of ice in medical care as well as in preserving foods. However, this doctor had difficulty with his machine. It would freeze ice well, but then the doctor couldn't get the ice blocks out of the containers! A number of other ice-making machines were tried, but it was a Frenchmen, Ferdinand P. E. Carré, who first introduced the use of ammonia for evaporation. Modern ice manufacturing plants even today use a method similar to the one he invented.

Even after a practical method of manufacturing ice was known, people for many years continued to harvest ice from lakes

Thomas Masters invented one of the first hand-operated ice cream freezers. Dolly Madison, wife of the fourth president of the United States, was credited with being the first to popularize the use of ice cream in America.

One of the first containers used for natural ice appeared in London in the middle 1800's. Invented by Thomas Masters, this equipment was given the name "Ice Preserver" and was used to cool beverages and foods.

and rivers in the winter. Then, an unusually warm winter resulted in such a light harvest that there was a serious ice shortage. After that, ice manufacturing began in earnest and has been enlarged over the years. During World War II, the manufacture of ice increased rapidly to meet the need for ice to preserve foods for the armed forces, for shipping whole blood to the fighting forces, and for providing for the needs of civilians. In 1945 more than 51 billion tons of ice were manufactured in America.

Today the largest users of ice in the United States are public institutions—hospitals, hotels, restaurants, drug stores and markets. These places have to keep quantities of food in prime condition, and in 1945 it took more than 15,270,000 tons of ice to supply them. This same year the homes of the country used another 15 million tons of ice, for there are more than 11 million ice refrigerators in this country today. Railroads and trucking companies used another 13½ million tons of ice. It is in such use that ice performs one of its greatest services.

How Does Ice Permit Us a Varied Diet?

Without ice we would be limited largely to local produce instead of enjoying the fruits and vegetables of other climates. Without ice refrigeration to transport foods from harvest field to markets, the present exportation of foods to the hungry people of other lands would be impossible.

In Civil War times, attempts were made to refrigerate cars of produce by setting chunks of ice every few feet throughout a car.

Ferdinand P. E. Carré of Paris developed the first ice machine using the principle of ammonia absorption that is in general use today. In 1863 one of these machines was run through the blockade and later was set up at Gretna, Louisiana.

But the melting ice damaged the equipment as well as much of the food. Engineers worked to solve this problem and by 1872 the first refrigerator car was developed. It had bunkers, "miniature ice refrigerator spaces," at each end. Floor racks were installed to permit the circulation of air around the freight, thus keeping the temperature the same throughout the car.

How Do Modern Railway Refrigerators Work?

Today the quantity of ice and method of filling the bunkers is determined by the cargo. For shipments of meat, frozen foods and similar perishables that require low temperatures, 300- to 400-pound blocks of ice are broken into smaller pieces and mixed with salt. This ice and salt mixture is fed into the bunkers through giant funnels, or this mixing of salt and ice is done right on top of the car as the bunkers are filled. For some cargoes, the blocks of ice are broken into pieces and slid into the bunkers from the top of the car, and no salt is added. Each car, when iced, is equipped with icing directions. The railroad orders these cars iced and passes these directions along to an ice company at each re-icing stop until that shipment reaches market.

There are several systems for loading the refrigerator bunkers. At important shipping terminals where icing or re-icing of refrigerator cars is on an around-the-clock schedule, icing is done from platforms built along the tracks at a height above the trains. An ice plant is often located near by. The manufacture of ice and the refrigerating of the cars becomes a continuous

Icing refrigerator cars is called "bunker icing" because these cars are built with spaces, or bunkers, at each end, which are filled with ice or ice and salt, according to requirements for each shipment. Each bunker holds 10,000 to 15,000 pounds of ice.

process, with conveyor belts carrying the ice from the factory to the loading platform.

At other points, the icing is handled from trucks. Some depots are equipped with ice escalators, which carry the ice from the loaded trucks to the top of the trains. Others have loading elevators which are raised to lift the load of ice from truck level to the top of the refrigerator cars. Ninety-nine per cent of the perishable foods shipped by train move under ice protection, in either bunker-iced refrigerator cars, or under a mountain of snow-ice in the body of the car to seal in the garden-freshness and vitamin content. Sometimes both methods of icing are used in the same car.

Hauling 300-pound blocks of ice to the top of railroad cars for loading the refrigerator bunkers. This escalator is mounted on a special type of truck.

Icing refrigerator cars is referred to as "bunker icing" because of the spaces, or bunkers, at each end, which are filled with ice or ice and salt, according to requirements for each shipment. Ten thousand to fifteen thousand pounds of ice are needed for loading each of these bunkers. More than this is required for initial icing, where melting is needed to cool the car to a suitable shipping temperature.

What Is "Snow-Icing"?

But for some foods even more ice protection is needed than is given by the refrigerator cars. By 1925 men who ship fruit and vegetables across the continent had discovered that blowing finely pulverized ice through a tube over boxes of lettuce and other vegetables would form a blanket of snow-ice. Giant blowers, attached to the ice grinders, blow 2,000 pounds of the pulverized ice into a refrigerator car or truck in 14 minutes time. This blanket shuts out air as well as heat and brings such produce to market practically garden fresh. Snow-icing, used first for lettuce, was soon adopted for shipments of carrots, celery and most leafy green vegetables.

Now, vine-ripened honey dew melons, picked in California one day before full ripeness, are brought in this way safely to markets one to three thousand miles away. Sweet corn also has been added to the foods that travel from farm to market "sealed in ice." Experiments are under way to extend this protective snow-ice shipping to other products. Today the finest fruits and vegetables are ice protected not only on their journey to the market, but at the wholesalers and in the retail stores as well. Research carried on in 16 university and college laboratories has proved that some fresh produce loses up to 40% of its vitamin C content in the first 24 to 36 hours after it is harvested, unless it is protected by ice. The tests show that these vitamin losses are greatly reduced when the produce is protected with ice. Losses in vitamin A and B_2 are also serious unless these foods are kept in ice from harvest time until they are eaten.

Despite our vast knowledge of science and our ingenious machines, ice remains the best preservative for perishable foods and for many other uses. This simple product, which Nature taught us to make, is still the last word in protection for the fruits of the gardens, orchards and fields.

What Is "Dry Ice"?

What we call "dry ice" is solidified carbon dioxide. At all ordinary temperatures, carbon dioxide is a gas. It is the gas that humans exhale after breathing air into the lungs, and which plants inhale to extract the carbon which is the chief constituent of plants.

To make dry ice, carbon dioxide gas is scrubbed with water to remove alcohol and other impurities and passed through charcoal to remove odors. It is then cooled, compressed, and bottled in steel cylinders while in liquid state. If allowed to expand suddenly from the cylinders, it solidifies into granules of "snow." This snow is used extensively in refrigerator railroad cars. It can be pressed into solid cakes.

Dry ice is much colder than ordinary water ice, and care must be taken not to let it touch the skin. Its freezing effect is not unlike that of a severe burn.

THE STORY OF THE OCEAN

Information recorded by instruments about the ocean bottom is translated into charts and maps in the drafting room of the United States Coast and Geodetic Survey ship Explorer.

A T ONE time in the long history of the world there was only one ocean, a gigantic body of water that covered the whole globe except for a huge rocky continent at the South Pole. The spinning of the globe caused this barren block of a continent to pulse rhythmically with ever-increasing force until finally it broke to pieces. Giant fragments began to move slowly to other parts of the world, making new continents and dividing the huge ocean into separate seas.

How Solid Is "Solid Land"?

Geologists tell us that the surface of our earth has never ceased to change. The ocean basins that now cover two-thirds of this surface have continually risen and sunk. Many places that are dry

[587]

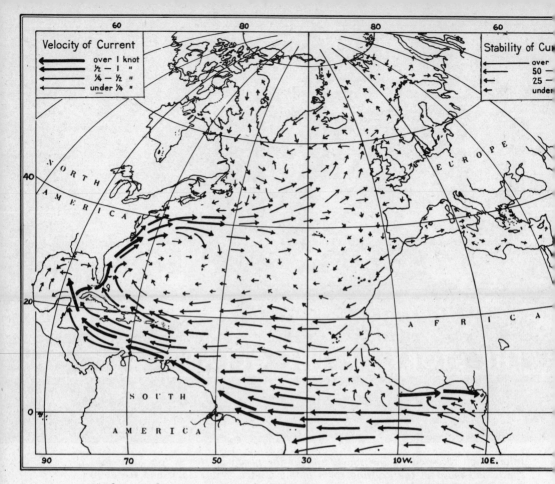

A chart of the major currents in the North Atlantic Ocean. These currents do not vary and a knowledge of their speed and location are essential to navigation on the North Atlantic.

land today were once on the ocean floor, and many places which were once dry land have now sunk beneath the sea. For thousands of years the Pacific coast of the United States has been rising, and we believe that in time there will be much more of California, Oregon, Washington and western Canada than there is today. At the same time, the Atlantic coast has been sinking, and in time the ocean will cover much of New England.

The ancient Greeks and Romans knew about only one ocean, the Atlantic. Apparently even their most learned scientists did not think much of this body of water, because Pliny, the great Roman naturalist, wrote, some two thousand years ago, "In the sea and in the ocean, there exists nothing that is unknown to us." Few scientists have ever been as wrong as Pliny was!

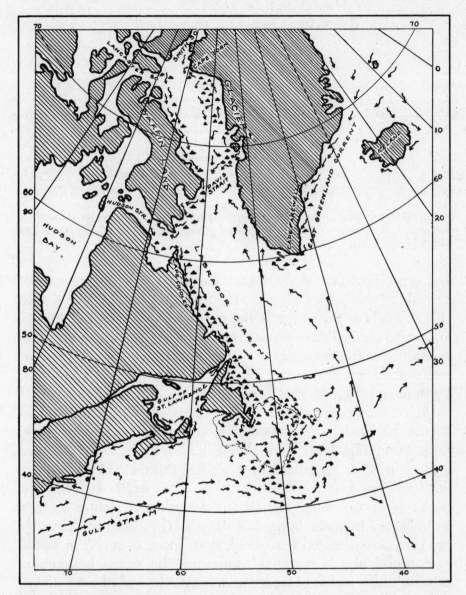

The warm Gulf Stream meets the icy-cold Labrador current off the coast of New-foundland, causing heavy fogs.

How Is the Ocean Explored?

Studying the ocean has been one of the hardest jobs that adventurous scientists have ever tackled. A man equipped with a diving suit can go down no farther than 360 feet into the ocean

[589]

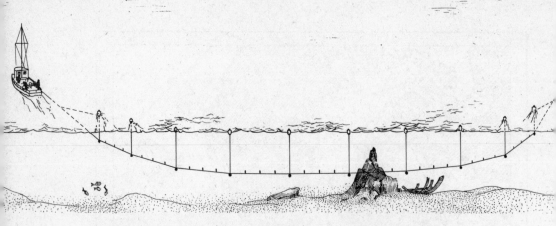

A *diagrammatic view of how a wire drag is used to locate underwater menaces to navigation. It consists of a cable supported at an adjustable depth by buoys and towed by two boats.*

and come up again alive. Submarines of the latest type cannot descend to much more than one thousand feet. Before World War II, Dr. William Beebe made the most daring attempt in history to unravel some of the ocean's mysteries when he climbed into his specially constructed steel ball—his "bathysphere"—and was lowered ½ mile into the ocean. This is the greatest depth to which any human being has ever penetrated.

Since direct exploration of the watery abysses is so difficult, science has had to rely mainly upon deep-sea soundings from ships. Soundings with lines having lead weights attached were made as early as Magellan's time. Today, this method of "heaving the lead" has been replaced by the "sonic depth finder." This device sends out sound signals and records their echoes as they are reflected from the bottom of the sea. The depth of the water can then be calculated from the known speed of sound in water.

Samples of the material composing the ocean bottom are brought up by means of waxed weights on the end of long chains, and also by means of dredges. Another contrivance recently perfected shoots a hollow cylinder deep into the ocean floor. The cylinder is hauled back to the ship from whence it was fired, the core of material is removed and studied by the oceanographers.

Taking all of the information that has been obtained in these and other ways over a period of centuries and putting it together, we have been able to get a fairly good picture of what the bottom of the ocean is like. We have also been able to find out what forms of life exist at various levels of the ocean.

What Is the Bottom of the Ocean Like?

Like the land that lies above the water, the ocean floor has its high mountains, its valleys, abysmal gorges and rolling plains. If we could pump all the water out of the oceans, we would then be able to see old land-bridges between the continents, river beds and mountain chains of ancient days, enormous rock masses, reefs built up entirely from the skeletons of microscopic animals, and canyons larger than our own Grand Canyon of the Colorado. Yet not so many years ago, it was believed that the bottom of the sea was just a gently rolling plain without any distinguishing landmarks at all!

Have you ever heard the old song, "There's a hole in the bottom of the sea"? There actually are holes in the bottom of the sea! Oceanographers call them "deeps." Several of these deeps have been measured to depths of over five thousand fathoms. In the North Pacific there is a large area that is more than six miles deep in all locations sounded. You could drop Mount Everest— the tallest mountain peak above sea level—into this chasm and it would be completely submerged. Elsewhere, the ocean floor is covered with a slimy ooze rich in oil and such minerals as radium. The bottom of these deeps, however, is covered with red clay. Some scientists believe that the clay came from meteors at some time in the earth's past.

Most famous, perhaps, of all the "submarine valleys" of the ocean is the one off the harbor of New York. In ages past, this gorge was a river bed. Today it measures twenty-five miles long, three miles wide and half a mile deep. There are probably many more such canyons scattered over the ocean bottoms.

What Causes Ocean Currents?

You may be surprised to learn that rivers can exist in the ocean as well as on dry land. Yet it is so. The seas contain vast bodies of water constantly in motion, always moving in certain well-defined directions. Oceanographers call them "currents."

No one knows for certain just what causes these currents. Many explanations have been offered. The pull of the moon has been suggested, as has also the difference in temperature and weight of the water at the North and South Poles and at the equator. Old time sailors believed that the winds cause the currents. Most oceanographers today believe that currents are not caused by any one particular force, but are the result of many forces, all acting together. The various factors are the sun, the winds, the amount of water evaporated from the ocean, the amount of salt in the water, the melting of polar ice, and the contour of the bottom of the sea.

How Do Ocean Currents Affect Us?

Ocean currents are important to man as well as to the creatures that live in the sea. If there were no currents, western Europe would have a climate as cold and disagreeable as that of Newfoundland. If there were no currents, the whole history of the world might have been different. It was the Labrador Current that carried Leif Ericson to the shores of North America—Vinland the Good, as Leif named it. The Equatorial Drift of the Atlantic caused the Portuguese to discover Brazil, where they settled in great numbers. Pacific Ocean currents carry part of their tropic warmth to Eastern China and to Japan. Then, curving down from the north after striking America, these same currents warm our west coast and give California its famous climate. There are huge eddies of water in the North and South Atlantic, the North and South Pacific, and in the Indian Ocean. Warm currents, deflected towards the poles by continents and islands, sweep up the coast lines. West winds push them out to sea again in what sailors call "drifts." They are at last caught up by the trade winds and pulled again towards the equator. North of the equator, all currents rotate in a clockwise direction; south of the equator, they rotate counterclockwise.

Most widely known of all currents, perhaps, is the Gulf Stream. This warm ocean-river flows from the tropics all the way up into the North Atlantic, where it curves, and sweeps south by way of England. The Gulf Stream brings balmy weather to our

The submerged "Washington Monument," a rock pinnacle reaching up 650 feet which was found in Alaskan waters by a wire drag. Only 17 feet of water covers this pinnacle. The real Washington Monument is 555 feet in height.

own Southern states and makes the climate of the British Isles much warmer than it would be otherwise. If the course of the Gulf Stream should shift a few miles to the west—nearer to the continent of North America—the great fisheries on the Georges Banks would be wiped out. This is not mere speculation. Not many years ago there was a sudden, extreme chilling of the Atlantic Ocean

water in the region where the "tile" fish live. A few days later the ocean off the coasts of New Jersey and Long Island was covered for many square miles with dead tile fish.

What Causes Ocean Tides?

Those other regular movements of the ocean, known to everyone as "tides," have proved fascinating to people of all ages and all countries. According to an ancient legend, tides are caused by a large hole or cavern, located somewhere near the "end" of the ocean. Twice a day water spurts forth from this hole in such vast quantity as to cause the ocean to rise and flood the beaches. Six hours later, this excess water rushes back into the hole and beaches become dry.

By use of a machine called a fathometer, ocean depths can now be recorded without dropping weighted cables to the ocean floor. The fathometer works by sound echo.

The Greeks actually knew what causes tides. A famous sailor, Pytheas, who lived about two thousand years ago, discovered that the tides are somehow related to the moon and its motions. If Pytheas had been able to carry out his work with modern precision instruments, he would have learned that the dry surface of the earth as well as the waters of the ocean respond to this tidal movement. Pytheas never learned the whole truth of the matter—that the entire earth pulses twice a day, just as if it were breathing!

The old Greek sailor never discovered, either, that the tides are more regular and certain than any clock. The tides are just as likely to change their rhythm as the moon is to change its course. Only when the moon starts to travel a different path will the tides change their schedule. With this certain knowledge, huge machines—often called "brains of brass"—have been constructed which will calculate the exact time and height of a tide at any spot in the world for any desired hour. This "brain" will tell what a tide was a thousand years ago, or it will predict a tide a thousand years in the future.

Tides are caused mainly by the pull of the moon. To a lesser extent, they are due to the pull that the sun also exerts upon our globe. As the moon revolves about the earth, its gravitational pull actually makes our world bulge. It is really a "two way stretch" because the earth bulges on the side facing the moon and on the side directly opposite. Thus, there are two high tides each twenty-four hours and fifty-two minutes.

Recording tide predictions from the dials of a tide-predicting machine. Sometimes called "brass brains," this machine can predict tides for years in advance.

How High Are Tides?

When the sun chances to be in direct line with the moon and the earth, there is more of a pull than usual on the earth and so the tides are noticeably higher. These are called the "spring" tides. When the sun is at a right angle to the line made by the earth and the moon, smaller tides known as "neap" tides are formed.

Not all the waters of the world have a great variation between high and low tides. The tides at the mouth of the Hudson River, for instance, are only a little more than five feet high on an average. In the Gulf of Mexico, the tides are even smaller. In the Mediterranean Sea, the tides are so small as to be scarcely noticeable. And Lake Michigan has a tide which measures just two inches!

On the other hand, certain localities are famous for the way in which the ocean rushes landward twice a day. In the Bay of

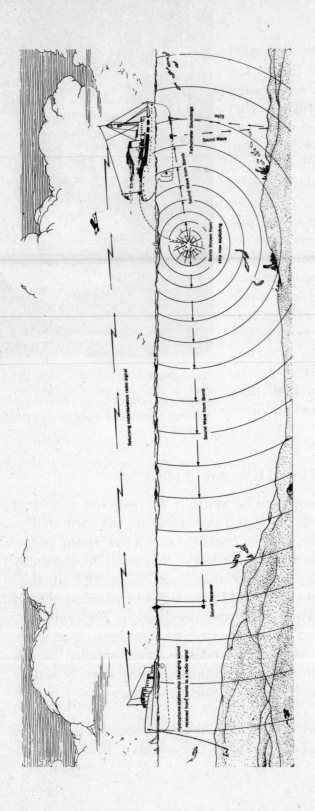

A diagrammatic view of sounding by use of the fathometer. A small bomb is exploded under water near the sounding ship. The fathometer measures the time it takes the echo of the explosion to return from the ocean bottom. From the known speed of sound in water, this interval gives the depth, which is calculated automatically by the fathometer. The exact position of the sounding ship is at the same time plotted by reference to its distance from two or more fixed ships. The sound of the explosion is picked up by microphones in the water near these ships and radioed instantaneously back to the sounding ship. Again, the distance of the ship from each microphone is reported automatically by the fathometer.

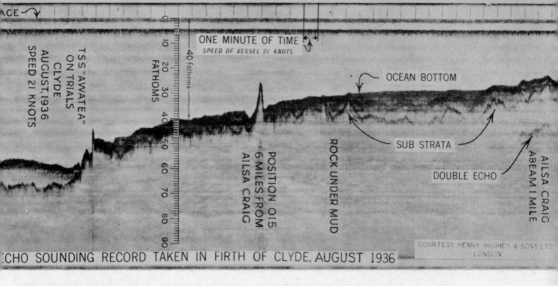

ECHO SOUNDING RECORD TAKEN IN FIRTH OF CLYDE, AUGUST 1936

As the ship moves along, the fathometer automatically records on a paper tape the depth of the ocean under the ship. This produces the profile view of the sea bottom shown above.

Fundy, the low water level in some places is fifty feet below the level reached at high tide. Long, flat beaches extending a full mile back from the low-water shore line are completely flooded at high tide. Here the tides come rolling in with such appalling swiftness that the whole beach is flooded in a matter of minutes. Beaches on the Bay of Biscay in France are also covered with water at the same speed.

A peculiar form of tide is experienced sometimes in wide rivers that have funnel-shaped mouths. This form of tide is known as a "bore." The bore, or wave, sweeps up the river with considerable force. At the mouth of the Amazon River, bores are often twelve feet high and travel at a speed of twenty miles an hour. The greatest bore of all occurs in the Chinese River of Tsien-Tang-Kiang. Here, the tidal bore is a huge wall of water that towers to four times the height of a tall man, rushes upstream at a speed of twenty miles an hour, and makes a roaring sound louder than that of Niagara Falls.

What Is a Tidal Wave?

The "tidal waves" which prove so destructive from time to time are not really tides at all since they are not caused by the pull of the sun and moon. Neither do they occur with periodic regularity.

[597]

They could better be called "solitary waves" or "surges." They are caused by various forces—earthquakes on the ocean floor, sudden changes in air pressure, and sometimes by winds.

Many tidal waves have been reported to have reached the astounding height of one hundred feet. A wave like this will overwhelm practically anything that lies in its path. The most destructive of all tidal waves occurred during the earthquake which shattered Lisbon, Portugal, in 1755. The bed of the ocean near the shore line of the town suddenly sank six hundred feet straight down. The water was at first sucked away from the shore. Then it returned with such terrible speed and power that it deluged the city, killing one hundred thousand people and destroying an enormous amount of property.

What Is a Guyot?

A new kind of mountain has been discovered as a result of a geologist's work in the United States Navy during World War II. It isn't possible to see these mountains, however, because they sit on the bottom of the Pacific Ocean, and, while their tops tower to heights of two and three miles above the ocean's floor, at least half a mile of water covers their summits.

Professor Harry H. Hess, of Princeton University, the man who made these discoveries, has named these new mountain forms "guyots," in honor of Arnold Guyot, the famous Swiss-born geologist and geographer who died about sixty years ago. These mountains may prove to be important laboratory specimens to tell us more than we now know of the past development of the features of the earth's surface.

How Were the Guyots Formed?

Actually, these guyots may tell us what other structures in the Pacific are worth investigating for the purpose of tracing the history of the earth. Dr. Hess believes that the guyots are very ancient, probably dating from at least 600,000,000 years ago— before there were any living things capable of leaving fossil remains.

Rushing tides off Dinagat Island in the Philippines are eroding this rock with such rapidity that it will topple over in a few years.

The other mountains that stretch their bulks from the floor to the surface of the Pacific have coral growths on them, proving that they became and remained islands since corals first came into existence.

A guyot is a flat-topped mountain with a gently sloping shoulder that turns downward sharply and falls abruptly to the ocean bottom. Guyots in the same neighborhood do not have the same heights, which is, as yet, a somewhat puzzling feature, if they were formed as Dr. Hess suggests.

Dr. Hess's picture is of volcanic mountains which were submerged and planed off by the action of surface water; as the continents rose, the bottom of the sea sank, carrying with it these leveled-off ancient volcanoes. Because there were, in those days, no reef-building animals to keep the limestone level near the surface level, these mountains now stand with their table tops from three thousand to six thousand feet below the surface.

Dr. Hess discovered twenty-five guyots from his own soundings in the stretch of the Pacific between Johnston Island, southwest of Hawaii, and the Marianas, north of Guam. Later, in the Hydrographic Office in Washington, he located 140 more, from

[599]

charts and records of earlier soundings. Some of them lie near well-known islands. Eniwetok Atoll in the Marshall Islands seems to sit between two guyots that crowd it closely on either side.

What Will the Coral Reefs Tell Us?

If, as Hess believes, the guyot type of mountain antedates corals and other reef-forming organisms, the coral reefs themselves should then provide us with complete cross sections of the marine life of the past half-billion or more years. The guyots represent the stage of the earth's history immediately before the coming of the fossil-leaving creatures. Consequently, boring down all the way through coral reefs to depths of five thousand feet or more should carry us all the way down through the period during which these creatures have existed and have been working to keep their heads at or above the level of the water. This will tell us an untold number of new facts about the earth on which we live and the seas covering and surrounding it.

What Causes Floating Islands?

A floating island consists generally of a mass of earth held together by interlacing roots. Sometimes such islands are large enough to serve as pasture grounds. They occur on the Mississippi and other rivers, being portions of the banks detached by the force of the current and carried down the stream, often bearing trees.

Artificial floating islands have been formed by placing lake mud on rafts of wicker-work covered with reeds. They were formerly used in the waters around Mexico and may be seen in Persia, India and on the borders of Tibet. On these the natives raise melons, cucumbers and other vegetables that need much water.

What Makes a Stick Seem to Bend in Water?

When we hold a stick partly in the water, it looks as though the stick bends just where it enters the water. That is due to the change of the direction of the light after it enters the water. This change in the direction of the light rays is called refraction. Glass, water and other solids and fluids each have different powers of refraction.

The law of refraction comes into operation when a ray of light passes through a smooth surface bounding two media not homogeneous, such as air and water, or when rays traverse a medium the density of which is not uniform, such as the atmosphere.

How Deep Is the Ocean?

The Murray-Challenger expedition reported that the greatest depth found in the Atlantic Ocean is 27,366 feet, in the Pacific Ocean 30,000 feet, in the Indian Ocean 18,582 feet, in the Southern Ocean 25,200 feet and in the Arctic Ocean 9,000 feet. They also stated that the Atlantic Ocean has an area in square miles of 24,536,000; the Pacific Ocean, 50,309,000; the Indian Ocean, 17,084,000; the Southern Ocean, 30,592,000, and the Arctic Ocean, 4,781,000.

Where Do Pearls Come From?*

Below the surface of the ocean, there's a strange, enchanted world. Living in the midst of its grandeur are most marvelous and delicate creatures that ceaselessly toil to strew the ocean's bed with lustrous gems—pearls.

Nature provides for the denizens of the deep that make these beautiful gems. The ocean pearl oyster or bivalve (*avicula margaritifera*) and fresh water mussel (*unio margaritifera*) have wonderful homes — their shells. Coarse, rough, rugged, often distorted on the outside, within they are lined with smooth, softly glowing, iridescent "mother of pearl." The membrane, attaching the bivalve to its shell, extracts lime from the water, building the shell from the inside outward in successive layers, preserving the finest nacreous secretions for the smooth inside lining, thus protecting its delicate body.

In this comfortable home the mollusk is contented, but an enemy sometimes attacks it by boring through its hard shell. Leucodore, clione and other borers, parasitic or domiciliary worms work into the shell, and instinctively the protecting nacreous fluid envelops the intruder. This is the birth of the pearl. The intruder, now covered entirely with the pearl-nacre, is constantly rolled and lapped about, and successive layers of nacre are applied until in a few years a pearl of great size and value is formed and awaits the hardy, daring pearl fisher.

Pearls were the first gems discovered and used as ornaments in prehistoric ages. Found in their natural state in utmost perfection, needing no cutting or polishing, these glowing beads of the sea were the first baubles of savages, tribes and nations. Today the pearl is the favored gem of those who are surfeited with valuable jewels. It is essentially a gem for the wealthy. The connoisseur, accustomed to the possession of jewels, finds in its soft luster a grandeur above that of all the sparkling stones.

Fancy pearls include all those of decided color, having a rare and beautiful tint. "White pearls" include pure white and white slightly tinted with pink, blue, green or yellow. Of these colored white pearls, the delicate, lightly tinted, pink pearl of fine color and luster known as "rose" is the most beautiful. Every white pearl is classified according to its respective tint and thus its price is determined, the values ranging in the order named above, from highest for pure white, to lowest for yellowish-white.

* Courtesy of Mr. Charles L. Trout.

THE STORY OF STEEL

This giant bucket suspended from an overhead traveling crane has just brought a load of molten iron from the storage mixer to the furnace where it is to be converted into steel. The iron is flowing into the furnace through a portable funnel. The furnace is of the so-called "open hearth" type. It is a square room of fire-resisting brick, where flames lick across the face of the iron and other materials dumped on its floor. Gas, coal, or oil, burned in a forced draft of hot air, raise the temperature to 3,000 degrees Fahrenheit.

STEEL is the sinews of our modern civilization. Everywhere we turn, we see structures of steel—buildings, bridges, railroads, factories, machinery, as well as many smaller things, tools, household appliances, furniture. In fact, some scientists who have traced the history of man through the Stone Age, the Bronze Age, call the present the Steel Age.

Steel is made from iron by the removal of impurities and the addition of small amounts of other substances. Iron is one of the most plentiful of elements on our earth. Dig a spadeful of earth anywhere and you are practically sure to find some iron in it.

Some iron ore mines are underground and some are on the surface. Here is a view of the Hull-Rust open-pit mine at Hibbing, Minnesota. The largest man-made hole on the face of the earth, it is 2½ miles long and one mile wide, with an area of 1,100 acres. In its lifetime it has yielded a greater quantity of overburden and iron ore than the amount of material excavated for the Panama Canal (232,000,000 cubic yards).

The earth in which there is a proportion of iron high enough to make its extraction commercially profitable is called "ore." The United States is rich in iron ore; there are especially large deposits in Minnesota and Pennsylvania.

Iron rarely occurs in pure form; it is almost always found in chemical combination with other elements, such as oxygen, sulphur, silica. The process of extracting pure iron from the ore is called "smelting." This process consists essentially of heating the ore so as to liquefy it. The iron, being the heaviest ingredient, sinks to the bottom and so can be drawn off the bottom of the smelting furnace, while the lighter materials float to the top as "slag." Iron is turned into steel by further heating and purification, plus the addition of manganese and other elements to give the desired qualities of hardness, ductility, and so on.

[603]

A miner of bituminous coal tests the security of his roof. He strikes the wooden beams with his pick and feels the vibrations with the open palm of his other hand.

Steel production and coal go hand in hand, for huge quantities of fuel are needed to smelt iron and convert it to steel. The chief fuel is coke, which is made by heating coal so as to drive off the more volatile impurities. Coke burns with a hotter flame per unit of volume than does coal. The best coke is made from bituminous or "soft" coal.

Here you see a battery of coke ovens, where coal is baked to remove its impurities. The oven at the right is discharging hot coke into a hopper car, which will carry it to a quenching house where streams of cold water will cool it.

Blast furnaces for the smelting of iron ore. The furnace itself is the conical structure rising from the octagonal shed, at the right of the picture. It is about 100 feet high and is lined with fire-resisting brick. The cylindrical structures to the left of the furnace are its hot-air stoves. Iron ore, limestone, and coke are poured into the furnace from the top, in measured proportions. Then hot air from the adjoining stoves is forced through the bottom of the furnace by high-pressure pumps. Under the extreme heat of the burning coke, metallic iron sinks to the bottom of the furnace. The limestone combines with nonmetallic impurities to form a slag that floats to the top of the molten mass.

Every four or five hours, the bottom of the blast furnace is tapped and molten iron flows out through channels into these huge iron buckets. The buckets are mounted on trunnions in a wheeled cradle, so that they can be moved quickly to the storage mixer, tilted and emptied. The mixer is a huge cauldron that keeps the metal in a molten state until it is ready to be converted into steel or cast into ingots of "pig iron."

A charging machine dumps a load of limestone into an open-hearth furnace. The limestone helps to carry away impurities left in the pig iron. A certain amount of scrap steel must also be put into the furnace to convert the iron into steel. That is why the demand for scrap steel is so great when the need for new steel rises.

Workmen shoveling other essential materials into the open-hearth furnace. Ferric oxide in the form of ore is added to burn out part of the carbon in the steel. Later, ferro-manganese is put in, to remove excess oxygen and also to help harden the steel.

Although 90 per cent of American steel is produced by the open-hearth process, some is produced by the Bessemer process. The pear-shaped steel vessel seen at the left in this picture is a Bessemer converter. Lined with heat-resisting brick and clay, it holds about 15 tons of molten iron. The bottom of the vessel is perforated with hundreds of holes, through which a blast of air is periodically forced. Streaming through the liquid metal at the rate of 20,000 cubic feet per minute, the air causes a sudden sharp increase in temperature that burns out the impurities. The "blowing off" of a Bessemer converter, as seen in the background of the picture, produces a brilliant shower of sparks and white-hot particles.

Molten steel being poured from a giant bucket into ingot molds. The molds are the cylinders on the flatcars below the bucket. The ingots will be carried away, cooled, and stored until ready for fabrication, when they will be reheated.

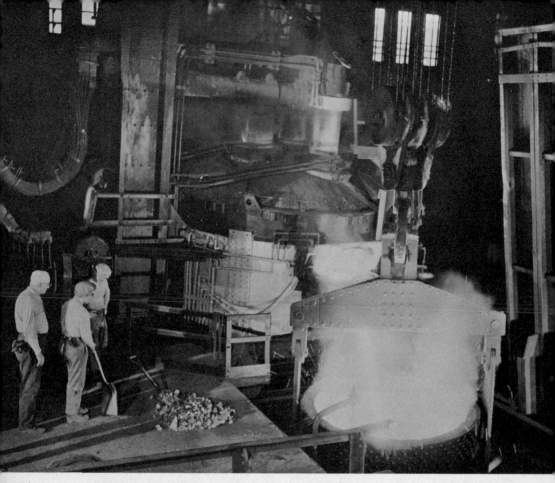

Another method of purifying steel is by means of the electric furnace. This is the method usually used to make high-quality alloy steel and stainless steel. The electric furnace is a steel shell lined with fire-resisting brick. Large sticks of carbon, called electrodes, extend through the roof to within a few inches of the metal. When the current is turned on, electric arcs are struck between the electrodes, generating enough heat to melt the metal and burn out impurities. In this picture, an electric furnace has been tilted so as to discharge a load of refined steel into a bucket.

When a steel ingot is to be fabricated, it is first put into a furnace called a soaking pit. After about six hours of heating, when it has reached a white-hot temperature of 2,200 degrees Fahrenheit, it is lifted from the pit by huge crablike tongs and quickly transferred to the rolling mill.

Most steel products are fabricated by "rolling." The steel ingot is squeezed through heavy rollers that knead it just as a rolling pin flattens a mass of dough. Here you see an ingot, still white hot, that has been squeezed between power-driven rollers into a flat slab.

Rollers of various shapes squeeze the ingots into different structural forms, such as rails, beams, plates. Here is depicted a stage in the fabrication of an "I" beam. Of course, the original ingot had to pass through many sets of rollers, each differing from the next only a little, before it reached this form.

Although steel is kept hot for malleability during all early stages of fabrication, some finishing operations are performed with the steel cold. Sheet steel, for example, is cold-rolled. Here you see fine-gauge sheet steel being rolled from sheets of coarser gauge. Cold rolling produces a brighter, cleaner finish than does hot rolling. Most automobile bodies are made from cold-rolled steel sheets.

Steel is also fabricated by "forging." The ingot is pounded into shape by repeated blows, much as a primitive blacksmith fashions a horseshoe from a red-hot iron bar. But the blacksmith's small hand hammer is replaced by a massive steam hammer. Here you see a powerful steam hammer with rounded jaws pounding hot steel to make an axle.

Drawing extremely fine stainless steel wire. Wire is made by drawing the metal through a fine hole in a die. In the picture, the dies are locked in the projecting box between the two rows of wheels. The strands of wire extend from one set of wheels to the other. Jets spurt from a pipe down upon the wire at the rear row of wheels, cooling the wire after it has been heated by the friction of drawing. Most wire is drawn cold from wire of heavier gauge.

Rolling and forging produce rough shapes which are then tooled into final form. Steel rails, for examples, after leaving the rollers, must be straightened and the ends must be trimmed. Axles and similar forgings must be turned down to precise size in lathes. Compare the finished railroad car axles in this storage shed with the previous photograph of an axle being forged by a steam hammer.

[611]

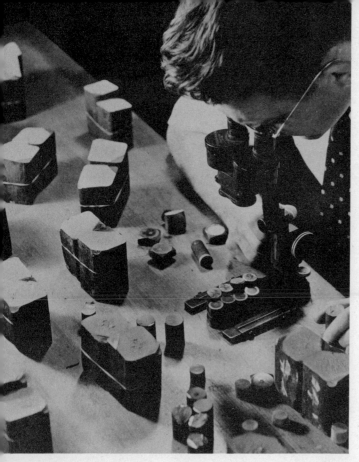

In the metallurgical laboratory of a steel plant, a research worker examines a broken piece of steel through a binocular microscope to determine whether the grain structure is coarse or fine. From this information the effects of certain kinds of heat treatment can be discovered. Chemical and microscopic research have aided the steel industry to produce new and superior kinds of steel.

Studying a specimen of steel through a metallurgical microscope with a photographic attachment. Microphotography is one of the most important tools in the study of the internal structure of steel, which is of course the chief clue to how the steel will behave under various types of stress.

THE STORY OF SKYSCRAPERS

New York skyscrapers seen from the observation roof of the RCA Building.

AMERICA has given the world a new kind of architecture in the lofty steel-frame building that we call the "skyscraper." Chicago is credited with having produced the first such structure. Today there are many splendid examples of skyscraper construction, not only in Chicago, but also in many other cities of the United States. Indeed, there is scarcely a city of any size in the country that does not boast at least one skyscraper.

How Long Will a Steel Building Last?

Opinions differ as to the lasting qualities of the steel building. So far as construction is concerned, a skyscraper may be in excellent condition at the end of fifty or even a hundred years. But this is a fast-moving age, and age of constant change, and, according to the opinion of the National Association of Real Estate Boards, "It is unlikely that the period of economic usefulness of a skyscraper can be much longer than forty years."

Chicago's oldest skyscraper, the 14-story Tacoma Building, was razed in 1929. At the end of twoscore years it had outlived its usefulness and had to give way to a new 49-story structure. Examination of the old building, however, proved it to be as sound structurally on the day of its wreckage as it was on the day of its completion. There were no traces of rust or crystallization in the huge columns, and the steel framework was in perfect condition.

Why Are Skyscrapers Built?

The heart of New York City is an island—Manhattan Island. The city expanded in population faster than new bridges, tunnels, and rapid transit lines could be built to connect Manhattan with Westchester, New Jersey, and Long Island. When all building

space on Manhattan was exhausted, the city had to reach into the clouds, and so it adopted the skyscraper. Today New York has many more skyscrapers than any other city in the world. But the same limitation of space in the commercial districts of many other cities has led to the erection of thousands of steel towers throughout the country. Boston, Philadelphia, St. Louis, San Francisco, and hundreds of others have not been slow to follow this lead of Chicago and New York.

The 70-story RCA Building in New York City, the largest privately-owned office building in the world.

Although brought into use first for office buildings, the steel-construction principle has also been applied on a large scale to apartment houses. Near the center of many a city the older 6-story "walkup" apartments are rapidly being replaced by apartment skyscrapers from 12 to 20 stories high. Even the suburbs have been invaded by this type of building.

What Are the Highest Skyscrapers?

For many years, the tallest office building in the world was the Woolworth Tower in New York—that amazing monument to the business enterprise of the founder of the five- and ten-cent stores. This mammoth creation is 792 feet high, with 60 stories. Other notable skyscrapers in the famous skyline of Manhattan are the Singer Building (612 feet high, with 41 stories) and the Metropolitan Life Building (700 feet high, with 50 stories). Farther north, another group of even taller buildings has grown up, including the Chrysler building and Radio City. At present, the

Manhattan's tallest tower, the Empire State Building, has 102 stories and soars to a height of 1,248 feet.

The skyscrapers of lower Manhattan, looking across the East River from the Brooklyn shore.

highest of all is the Empire State Building (1,248 feet high, with 102 stories). A massive mooring mast atop this monster was designed to be used by dirigibles, but early experiments in steering a lighter-than-air ship close enough for the transfer of mooring lines proved the undertaking too hazardous.

Why Is Building a Skyscraper Such a Complex Task?

The same considerations that prompt the erection of a skyscraper usually mean that there is little "elbow room" around the site. The huge building operation has to be conducted in an extremely limited space. Therefore every stage of construction has to be carefully planned so that steelworkers, masons, carpenters, plumbers, and all the rest of the trades will find room to work and store materials. Then, too, the costs of the operation, running into millions of dollars, will be increased even more if the work becomes clogged and delayed. Once started, the work must be finished as expeditiously as possible. An all-important preliminary is the planning of a time schedule—the dates for the arrival and departure of each individual trade, the dates for the deliveries of material, the dates for the production of detail designs and plans for each stage of the work.

In a broad sense the various building operations may be grouped in three categories: (1) Foundation and walls to street level; (2) superstructure without finishing trades; (3) finishing trades.

How Is the Foundation Laid?

The first step is preparing the site. This includes measurements of the location, siting of levels, razing of existing structures, removal of pipes and wires, laying of driveways for the passage of trucks. The next step is the installation of stationary equipment for excavation and pile driving—engines and cranes. Then the power shovels can go to work.

At the outset, the material excavated by the steam shovels can be loaded into trucks at street level. As the work progresses and the shovel goes lower, a bridge or inclined way has to be built so that the trucks can reach it. Often a "booster engine" is installed to pull the loaded trucks up to street level.

Shoring is put in place to keep the banks of the excavation from sliding in. If there are any buildings adjacent, they must be reënforced by underpinning. If quicksands or springs are encountered, pumps must be installed and trenches dug to con-

Philadelphia's tallest skyscraper, the PSFS (Philadelphia Savings Fund Society) Building is one of the most modern in the world.

Steel framework of a skyscraper. This is the University of Pittsburgh, one of the first universities to be housed in a skyscraper.

trol the flow of water. It is frequently necessary to put up sheeting —a system of compacted or interlocked piles forming a wall to hold back the soil and seepage of water.

The excavation of rock is carried out with drills (steam, electric, or pneumatic) and dynamite cartridges. In difficult ground, caisson excavation may be necessary. A caisson is a heavy steel structure, usually cylindrical, of diameter from four to forty feet. It is a kind of mobile retaining wall that sinks into the earth as a hole is excavated beneath it. The excavation is often done by "sandhogs" working inside the caisson under heavy air pressure. The excavated material is lifted to the surface by suspended buckets and lowered by means of a "niggerhead," its cable leading from a hoisting engine. At each five-foot depth, four metal rings of rolled flat bars are inserted, two sections to the ring; then further excavation continues another five feet. The caisson may be carried down to bed rock, or may be stopped and belled out on a hardpan stratum. In either case, it is finally filled with concrete and forms the base for foundation piles.

So complex and costly is this excavation work, so likely is it to encounter unexpected engineering difficulties, that it has become a specialized business, and the general contractor for the erection of a skyscraper usually hands the job of building the foundation over to a "foundation" corporation.

How Is the Steel Frame Erected?

The first operation in preparing to build the superstructure is the erection of derricks. The kind and number of derricks depends in part on how much space is available for guy lines to support them. Of the three common types, the guy derrick, the stiff leg, and the "Chicago boom," the last is used only in very close quarters. Power may be supplied by steam or gas engines, but for very high buildings electric power is preferred.

Derricks must be hoisted from time to time to the upper part of the framework as it is built up. The steel members that support the derrick must be completely bolted or riveted up, but other members are bolted loosely in place by connectors until a whole section is ready for riveting. Under favorable working conditions of the fabricating shop, driving rivets on the floor panels may be started as soon as the beams are raised to position.

Concrete flooring requires the use of forms or "centering"; the forms are removed about ten days after the concrete is poured. The floor arch system calls for embedding of horizontal pipe runs and other conduits.

The patent swinging scaffold is indispensable on steel-frame buildings. This scaffold is suspended from projecting outriggers at the highest point available on the frame. The wire cables carrying the scaffold lead to cast-iron drums, which are controlled by a trailing hand rope through the medium of worm gear and sheave. Brick, mortar, and other materials are raised to the floors by elevators running through open hatchways.

What Are the Jobs of the Plumber and Electrician?

Piping operations are most economically carried out at the earliest possible stage of the building's erection. Plumbing, steam, electric, and ventilating work follow the erection of the supporting framework as closely as permitted. The same may be said of horizontal lines and branches, such as suspended sewers, soil lines, and steam mains. Vertical lines, such as soil, down spouts, sprinkler risers, steam and return lines, electric-

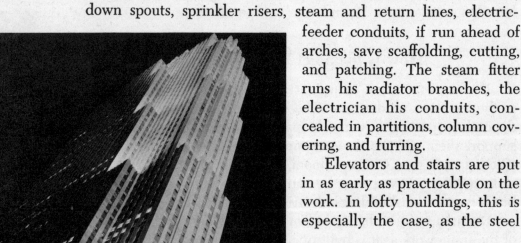

feeder conduits, if run ahead of arches, save scaffolding, cutting, and patching. The steam fitter runs his radiator branches, the electrician his conduits, concealed in partitions, column covering, and furring.

Elevators and stairs are put in as early as practicable on the work. In lofty buildings, this is especially the case, as the steel

The floodlighted shaft of the RCA Building in Rockefeller Plaza, seen as the cameraman tilts his lens toward the top of the great structure.

A view of the headquarters building of the New York Telephone Company in lower Manhattan. It is 490 feet high and has 31 stories.

erector's derricks can then hoist the elevator machines, already prepared, and, with machines in place and guides erected, temporary cars for freight and passengers can be called into service as soon as the roof is enclosed.

The installation of ornamental ironwork is carried on at the same time. This prepares the way for "finishing" trades. The exterior window sash is first to be installed. Plaster and marble work often proceed together. Interior wood trim, the setting of radiators, plumbing and lighting fixtures, are now installed, and painting of exterior and interior wood and metal surfaces is begun. On account of the immensity of the outer surface, all former art motifs used in exterior wall decoration have had to be discarded as having a "spotty effect." Taking their place, we have enrichment of the surface by shafts affording fine displays of light and shadow. This completes the basic construction of the modern skyscraper.

At night the great buildings of Manhattan with their glowing yellow lights give an unreal fairyland effect. Seen in the foreground is the roof of Pennsylvania station.

THE STORY OF STEEL SHIPS

Launching a great ship of the United States Navy. The U.S.S. North Carolina *goes down the ways at Brooklyn, New York.*

THE building of a modern steel ship is a very complicated engineering accomplishment. It requires the skill of scientists, engineers, designers, and workers in dozens of trades to create even the smallest ship.

Long before actual construction can begin, hundreds of plans must be drawn up. There must be a blue print for every unit that goes into the ship. It takes a large staff of draftsmen several months just to turn out these detailed blue prints from the general designs furnished by the engineers.

Curiously enough, the advance planning must be much more complete and detailed for a steel ship than for a wooden ship. The reason is that wooden parts are often cut only to approximate size and then are trimmed to fit in the actual process of assembly. But steel parts must be cast and machined to fit accurately before they reach the hands of the assembly gangs.

[623]

How Are the Parts Fabricated?

The blue prints go first to a unique room called a "mold loft." A typical loft is over 700 feet long and 200 feet wide—bigger than two football fields laid end to end. In this great room are made the "templates," which are flat wooden patterns of the steel plates and all the other parts of the hull. The large floor space is needed because some of the parts are very large. Working from the blue prints laid out on the floor, expert woodworkers cut out the templates to the actual size and shape of the steel plates. Each template is then marked with a curious jargon of symbols, which indicate the kind of steel to be used, the thickness of the plate, and where the part is to go in assembling the ship.

Laying out the hull plates for a merchant ship in the mold loft. Using blue prints that have been drawn to the exact size of the desired plate, the loftsmen trace the design of the plate on wood to make templates. From the templates the final steel shape is cut.

Fitting the keel blocks for the laying of a new keel.

The templates are sent to the fabricating shop, where the steel parts are cut out. The template is laid on a sheet of the specified metal and the steel part is cut to exactly the same shape. The template also shows where to make the rivet holes and whatever other fabrication is necessary.

What Is Meant by "Laying the Keel"?

We all know that the first step in the actual building of a ship is "laying the keel." Just what does this mean?

The keel is the long fore-and-aft member at the bottom of the hull, to which the side plating is attached, and which is the most important part in holding the whole ship together. Because

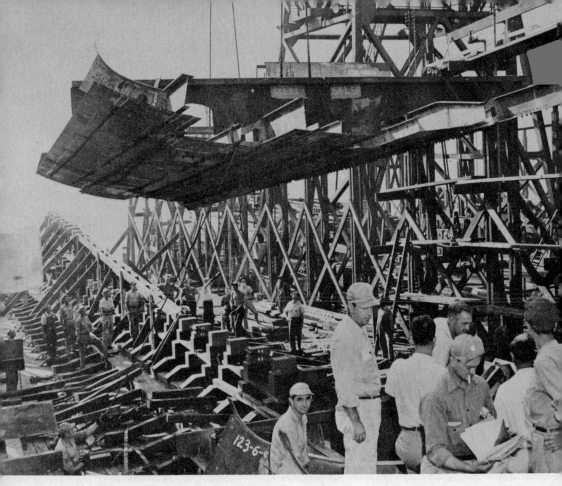

A section of bottom being lowered into place in a shipyard at Port Newark, New Jersey. The center beam that runs along the bottom of the ship is the keel. The bottom plates of the ship have already been riveted on either side of the keel in a prefabricated assembly. This type of prefabrication allows for greater speed of construction than the old method of riveting the ship together plate by plate.

of its size, the keel is built up of many pieces scarfed together. In steel construction, the first side plates are often attached to a section of the keel before it is set in its place along the "backbone."

While the ship is under construction, it rests on its keel, but in preparation for launching the weight must be transferred to the "ways" on each side of the ship. The keel is therefore "laid" on piles of blocks, called keel blocks, which can later be knocked away. If the ship is to be launched endwise, as most ships are, the keel is not laid level, but with the end toward the water lower than the other end. The launching ways also slant down toward the water, so that the main force in moving the ship into the water is gravity.

The keel of a steel ship is made in the form of an "I-beam." The horizontal plate at the bottom is the keel proper. The so-called vertical keel is a plate set vertically on edge on the keel proper. On top of it is laid another horizontal plate, the keelson.

How Is the Hull Built?

At the ends of the keel, upright girders are riveted in place to form the "stempost" and "sternpost." On each side of the keel, down its whole length, are riveted curved girders, the "ribs." To

Building a cargo vessel at the United States Steel Corporation's shipyard at Kearny, New Jersey. Many modern ships are welded together instead of riveted. The man on the left is using an electric welding arc which fuses the edges of the ship's plates together into one solid piece. The two men on the right are using acetylene torches to cut steel plates to the proper shape.

hold the ribs securely and keep them from spreading, "beams" are stretched between each pair of ribs at the top, extending transversely across the keel. These beams provide support for the decks, just as beams under the floor of a house provide support for the flooring. The beams themselves are given support by vertical steel pillars extending upward from the keel and the lower parts of the ribs.

The keel, ribs, and beams together form the framework of the ship. Now the skeleton must be covered. On the ribs, steel plates are set in place to make the "skin" of the ship. On big ships, these outer plates may be an inch thick.

The usual method in steel construction is to overlap the plates and rivet them together. With thousands of riveting machines hammering away at once, a steel shipyard is one of the noisiest places on earth. However, welding has been tried and proved satisfactory in place of riveting, and an increasing number of steel ships are being built in this way.

What Other Parts Are Built Into the Hull?

Besides the outer skin, a second skin is fastened to the ribs inside the hull, thus creating a "double bottom." The primary purpose of making a double skin is to increase the strength and safety of the ship. If the outer skin is broken by collision or shipwreck, the ship will still float if the inner skin is whole. The space between the skins is utilized for many practical purposes— to carry ballast, to store fuel oil and water. The ballast is sea water, taken aboard when necessary to make the ship sink low enough in the sea so that its propellers can operate efficiently.

After the double bottom is completed, there remains much construction to be done inside the hull. Heavy steel platforms must be put in place to support the engines. The "thrust block" and other strong supports must be installed to hold the long, heavy propeller shafts. Important to safety at sea, "bulkheads" must be built.

A bulkhead is a partition inside the hull, crosswise to the keel. In modern practice, the whole is partitioned into a series of water-tight compartments by bulkheads that extend from side

to side and from the keel to well
above the water line. This practice is credited with having saved
thousands of lives and many
ships. If the inner skin as well as
the outer is torn open by an accident at sea, the water can fill up
only the space between the
neighboring bulkheads. These
partitions keep the water from
filling the entire hull.

Many special bulkheads are
built for particular jobs. A bulkhead near the stern is designed
to keep the water out in case the
tubes housing the propeller shaft
are damaged. Bulkheads built
around the engines and boilers
give extra protection. Some ships
have no doorways at all through

The giant bow of a United States
cruiser being lowered into place. Prefabricated sections of the ship are
dropped into place by overhead cranes
and welded or riveted together.

the bulkheads, while other ships have water-tight doors that shut
automatically or are operated by electricity from the decks above.

After the hull is completed to the point where it can bear the
load, the engines are installed. Masts are put in place, stepped
directly to the keel. As in building a house, it is not feasible to
wait until the structure is complete before calling in the elec-
tricians, steam engineers, and members of the many other trades
whose services will be required. Many of their installations—
wiring, steam pipe lines, and the like—must be put in place before
bulkheads are built or the main deck laid. While the hull is
under construction, a maze of scaffolding covers it both inside
and out, on which swarm workers of thirty-six different trades,
besides the riveters or welders.

In a busy shipyard, a ship is not wholly completed before it
is launched, but is pushed off the "ways" as soon as possible to
make room for the laying of the next keel. In point of time, there
may be more work to be done on a ship after it is launched than
before.

How Is a Ship Launched?

The "ways" are two giant timbers, one under each side of the hull, extending in the same direction as the keel and slanting down toward the water. These timbers may be a permanent installation in the shipyard or may be put in place after the hull is built. Around the bottom of the hull is built a "cradle," which rests on the ways. Before the ship can be launched, the keel blocks must be knocked out from under the ship, so that its entire weight will fall upon the cradle supported by the ways.

One method of making the transfer is to drive big wedges into the keel blocks, build up the cradle under the ship, then knock out the wedges. The ship settles into the cradle and the keel blocks can now be removed. Another method is to raise the

A three-bladed manganese bronze propeller being polished at the Federal shipyard in Kearny, New Jersey. Weighing 30,000 pounds, the giant propeller is one of the twin screws of a United States merchant ship.

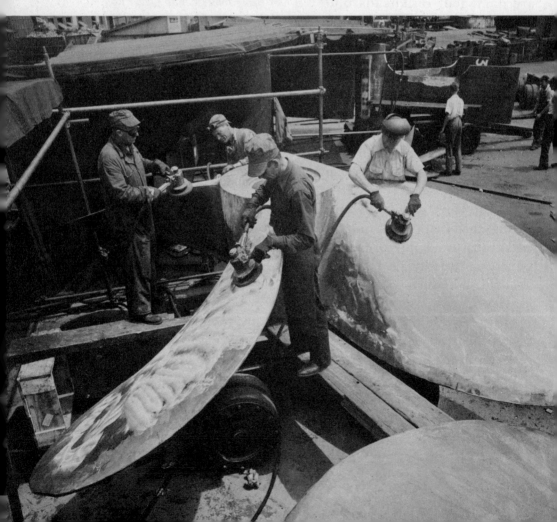

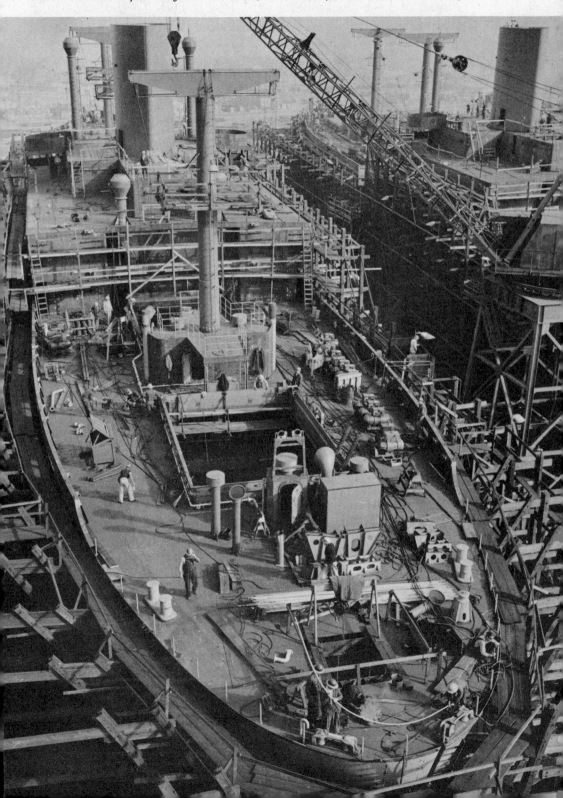

The wooden framework surrounding the ship goes up with each succeeding step in the ship's construction. Note the pathway of planks that goes around the ship's sides. When the ship is ready to be launched, the wooden framework is cleared away.

hull by powerful hydraulic jacks. A third method is the use of "cushion boxes." These are boxes of sand, placed on top of each column of keel blocks before the keel is laid. To settle the hull into the cradle, the boxes are opened and the sand is allowed to flow out.

The cradle is equipped with "sliding ways," heavy timbers resting on top of the "ground ways." While the keel blocks are being removed, the sliding ways remain bolted to the ground ways. For the launching, the ways are heavily greased, and finally the bolted ends of the sliding ways are sawed through. If necessary, the cradle is given an initial jolt with a hydraulic ram. Then gravity comes into play, and the cradle slips down the greased ground ways like a railroad car down a tilted track. Soon there is a tremendous splash as the ship, cradle, sliding ways and all, hit the water. Another ship rides the sea!

How Are Harbors Dredged Out?

There are several forms of mechanical, power-operated dredges. One of the most common is the "clamshell" dredge, consisting of a pair of large, heavy iron jaws, hinged at the back, in general form resembling a pair of huge clam shells. This with its attachments is called the grapple. In operation it is lowered with open jaws, and by its own weight digs into the ground that is to be excavated. Traction is then made on the chains controlling the jaws, which close; the grapple is hoisted to the surface and its contents discharged into scows alongside the dredge.

The dipper dredge, an exclusively American type, has a bucket rigidly attached to a projecting timber arm. In operation the bucket is lowered and made to take a curving upward cut, thus dipping up the bottom material, which is discharged through the hinged bottom of the bucket. The pump or suction dredge operates by means of a flexible pipe connected with a powerful centrifugal pump. The pipe is lowered into contact with the bottom to be excavated and the material is pumped into hopper barges or into a hopper-well in the dredge itself.

The center ladder bucket dredge operates by means of an endless chain of buckets moving over an inclined plane, which in structure is a strong iron ladder, one end of which is lowered to the sea bottom. The steel buckets scoop up the material at the bottom of the ladder, which they then ascend, and are discharged by becoming inverted at the upper end of the ladder. This dredge is the only one found satisfactory in excavating rock.

The U.S.S. Jack. Like all American submarines, she is able to cruise long distances. She is armed with one 5-inch dual purpose gun, and ten 21-inch torpedo tubes. Her length is 311 feet and she carries a crew of 85 men and officers.

THE story of the submarine takes us back three hundred years, to the reign of James I, of England, when a crude submarine boat was built, to be moved by oars, but one of no value other than as a curiosity. At a later date a man named Day built a similar boat, wagering that he would go down one hundred yards and remain there twenty-four hours. So far as is known, he still remains there, winning the wager which he has not come up to claim.

Who Built the First Practical Submarine?

Other such boats were constructed at intervals, but the first undersea boat of any historical importance was the *American Turtle*, built by a Yankee named David Bushnell during the time the British held New York during the Revolutionary War. He sought to blow up the British frigate *Eagle* with the aid of a torpedo, and nearly succeeded in doing so, seriously scaring the British shippers by the explosion of his torpedo.

[633]

A United States submarine submerging off the Eastern coast.

Who Showed How Submarines Could Be Used in Warfare?

The next to build a successful undersea craft was Robert Fulton, the inventor of the first practical steamboat. He, like Bushnell, was an American, but his early experiments were made in France, where Napoleon patronized him. With his boat the *Nautilus* he made numerous descents, going down twenty-five feet in the harbor of Brest and remaining there an hour. Fulton averred that he could build a submarine that could swim under water and destroy any war vessel afloat. But the French Admiralty refused to finance further experiment, one old admiral saying, "Thank God, France still fights her battles on the surface, not beneath it."

[634]

Fulton went to England and there built a boat with which he attached a torpedo to a condemned brig, set aside for that purpose. The brig was blown up in the presence of an immense throng, and Fulton finally sold his invention to the British Government for seventy-five thousand dollars.

When Were Submarines Actually First Used in Warfare?

During the American Civil War the Confederate Government built several submarines of a type known as "Davids," from the name of its inventor. Now, for the first time, the submarine demonstrated its powers. On the night of February 17, 1864, one of the "Davids," the *Hunley,* blew up the steamship *Housatonic* in Charleston Harbor. The wave caused by the explosion swamped the submarine, and carried the *Hunley* and its crew to a watery grave.

What Inventors Have Improved Submarine Design?

Other submarines were built and experimented with, not only in the United States but also in European countries. One of the later inventors was an Irish-American named John P. Holland, who, in 1876, built a submarine called the *Fenian Ram.* The *Ram* collapsed with the collapse of the Fenian movement.

In 1893 the United States Congress appropriated two hundred thousand dollars to encourage improvements in the submarine and invited inventors to submit designs. This, and a similar action in France, formed the first official recognition of the value of undersea boats. The prize offered by Congress brought out three designs, one by John Holland, the *Ram* inventor, one by George C. Barker, and a third by Simon Lake. The names of Holland and Lake have since been closely associated with the history of the submarine. Mr. Holland's design obtained approval, and in 1894 he received a contract to build a submarine vessel. This, named the *Plunger,* was begun in 1895, but was finally abandoned and a vessel of different type, the *Holland,* was built in its place. It was accepted by the government in 1900. Several other boats similar to the *Holland* were subsequently built.

[635]

The Holland boats were of the type now known as "diving." They were controlled by a rudder placed at the stern of the vessel and acting in both a horizontal and vertical direction. The force of the screw propeller driving the boat forward caused the boat to submerge. In 1904 the Navy of the United States possessed eight Holland boats, and the British Navy also had several.

Simon Lake's design, offered in 1893 but not accepted, had as its novel feature a door in the bottom of the ship. The crew could leave and enter in diving suits, the water being kept out by the force of compressed air. To maintain the vessel on an even keel, Lake introduced four vanes, called "hydroplanes," for regulating the depth of descent. By means of these and the horizontal rudder, it was found that the vessel would run for hours at a constant depth and on a level keel. There were other devices for diving and rising to the surface.

Both the bow and the stern of the submarine have horizontal fins called diving-planes. Moving these up or down makes the submarine move up or down when under way. Here two seamen are operating the diving planes.

In 1901, Lake built a large vessel of this type that was sold to the Russian Government and was in commission at Vladivostok during the Russian-Japanese War. He afterwards received orders from the Russian and other governments for a number of vessels of the even-keel type. His principles of control have since been generally adopted as the safest and most reliable controlling agency for undersea craft.

An important addition was made in 1901 in a French boat, the *Morse*, built at Cherbourg. The difficulty of navigators in determining the boat's position when under water, and of changing course safely without coming to the surface to reconnoiter, was in a large measure overcome by the addition of a periscope. This was a tube, rising above the water, and provided with reflecting lenses. It enabled the steersman to discover the surface conditions and see any near vessel or other object. The *Morse* was able to sink in seventy seconds, and her crew could remain under water for sixteen hours without strain.

During the early years of the century the submarine made great progress. Holland and Lake may be looked upon as the parents of the modern development of the submergible boat, their designs being at the base of the great European progress. France took up the work actively, its most successful early vessel being the *Narval*, built in 1899. This was 118 feet long by 8 feet 3 inches beam, 106 tons surface, and 168 submerged displacement. She was a double-deck vessel controlled by Lake

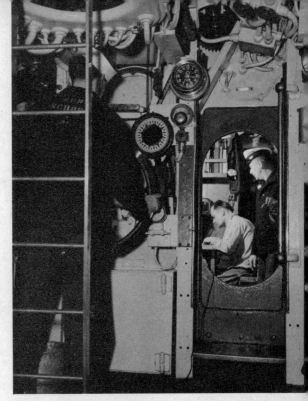

The captain's quarters, with an apprentice seaman at the controls, steering the ship by hand. Note the compass that guides the steersman. Space is scarce on even the most modern submarines; so the men must bend to go through steel partitions.

hydroplanes and had installed steam power for surface travel and electric power for undersea work. The French at this time kept their methods secret, and no useful type had been developed in England. The result was that a plant was provided for the building of Holland boats in England. Germany used the Lake devices, which had not been patented in that country and were applied by the Krupps.

How Are Submarines Powered?

The internal-combustion engine is the heart of the submarine. Steam, with its heavy engine, has been long set aside, and electricity, derived from the storage battery, yet awaits sufficient development. Gasoline succeeded them. The internal-combustion

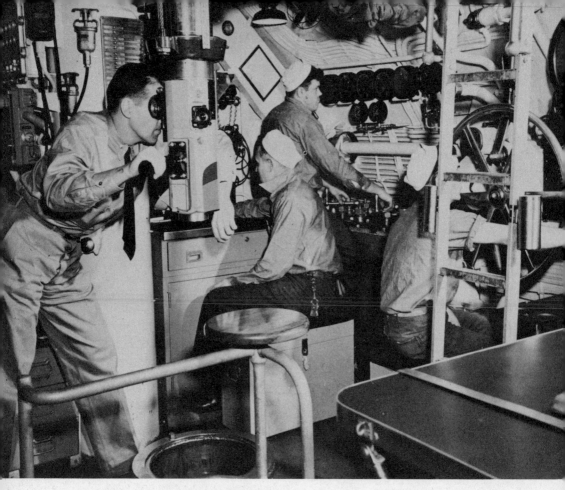

While the commander peers through the periscope, crew members man their battle stations in the control room. At the right behind the ladder a seaman regulates the depth according to order by moving the diving planes or elevators.

engine became essential because of its light weight and the fact that it could be started and shut down instantly. This is of prime importance, as it permits quick submergence or emergence, either to escape from a high-speed destroyer or to capture a merchantman. The gas engine weighs less per horsepower, takes up less room and requires less fuel per hour, than any other reliable motor. It was early used in both the Holland and Lake boats and is still the chief prime motor.

The difficulty with the early boats was that they were slow in speed, making only from eight to nine knots. Governments demanded increased speed and more powerful engines, within a fixed limit of weight. In early experiments to meet these require-

Powerful Diesel engines drive the submarine at 20 knots when it is on the surface of the water. The Diesel engines turn generators which charge electric batteries. These electric batteries run the submarine when under water.

ments, engines were built of such flimsy construction that they soon went to pieces. The gasoline used also gave off a gas of highly explosive character and one very likely to escape from leaky tanks or joints. Several explosions took place in consequence, in one of which twenty-three men were killed. As a result, all the nation demanded that a nonexplosive fuel should be used, and builders turned to the Diesel engine as offering a solution to the difficulty.

This heavy oil engine, weighing about five hundred pounds per horsepower, was not adapted to the submarine, and efforts have been made to decrease the weight. These have not as yet had a satisfactory result and experiments are still going on.

What Is a Periscope?

As the engine is the heart of the submarine, the periscope is its eye. The simplest form is a stiff, detachable tube from fifteen to twenty feet long and about four inches in diameter. On its top is an object glass which takes in all objects within its range and transmits an image of them through a right-angled prism and down the tube. By means of other lenses and prisms, an image of the external object is thus made visible to those within the submarine. In this process of transmission there is a certain loss of light; to allow for that the image is magnified to about one-quarter above its natural size.

With the simple periscope, it is difficult to gauge the distance of the object from the boat. Continued experiment has overcome

Crewmen have their bunks above and below torpedoes which are fastened in special racks. Torpedoes are lifted out of racks by chain hoists hanging from ceiling. Here the men are having coffee while off duty.

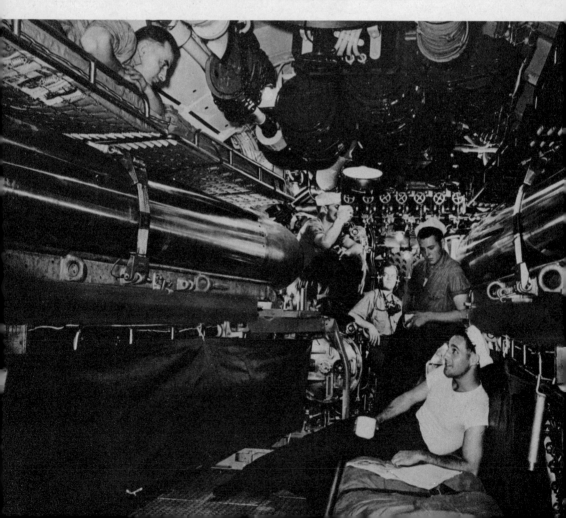

this difficulty. Simon Lake developed a satisfactory instrument and one which gave a simultaneous view of the entire horizon.

There is one shortcoming in the periscope not easy to obviate. The periscope is an instrument for day use only. When dark comes on, it becomes useless; this does away with the possibility of a successful submarine attack by night.

How Effective Is Submarine Warfare?

The submarine is the guerrilla of the sea. Its tactics are like those of the Indian who fights under cover or lies in ambush for his enemy. It is the weaker party and can hope for success only through strategy. Its invisibility makes the U-boat the terror of the seas. This was well proved in World War I. The North Sea and

The quartermaster in the conning tower sets the ship's course. Here the steersman follows the course, keeping an eye on the compass to the right of his wheel. Framed picture of a fish shows a cero for which this submarine (U.S.S. Cero) is named. All United States submarines are named for fish.

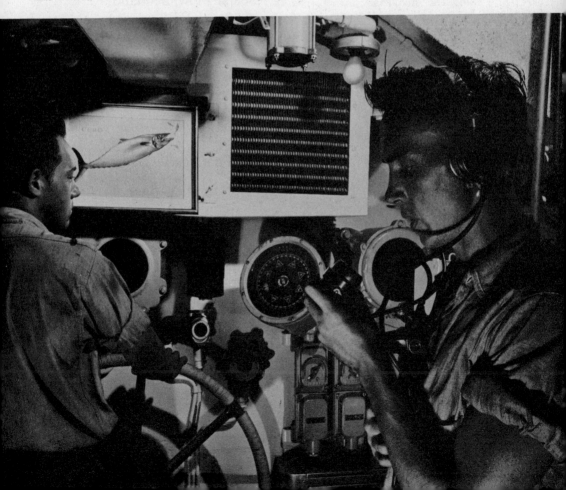

Deadly weapon of the submarine is the torpedo. Carrying several hundred pounds of explosives in its warhead, the modern torpedo is powered by electric motors. Note the contrarotating 4-bladed propellers in the tail behind the stabilizing fins. Torpedoes have speeds up to 45 knots.

the English Channel were invaded by German submarines, which played great havoc among merchant ships. This undersea warfare took a heavy toll of life, as in the signal instance of the *Lusitania.*

Twenty years later, when World War II began (1939), Germany resumed her submarine warfare, but with more regard for the lives of the seagoers. One notable feat, on October 14, 1939, was the destruction of the *Royal Oak,* one of England's great battleships, sunk by torpedo from a U-boat that had managed to get into the Bay of Scapa Flow, Scotland.

Strangely enough, submarines are safe from each other. Only one instance has been reported in which a submarine actually sank an enemy sub. In this case the enemy sub was on the surface and so was at the time a surface ship.

Do Submarines Have Peacetime Uses?

The great mission of the submarine in wartime has been as a commerce destroyer. But in the summer of 1916, in the midst of the war, the submarine appeared in a new rôle, that of commerce carrier. On July 9 of that year the people of Baltimore were astounded by the appearance in their port of a submarine vessel of unusual size and novel errand. This new craft was an unarmed carrier of merchandise. It had crossed the Atlantic, a voyage of 4,000 miles, laden with dyestuffs to supply the needs of American weavers. This new type of vessel, the *Deutschland,* was an undersea craft 315 feet in length, with a cargo capacity of more than

1,000 tons. The *Deutschland* managed to return to Germany in safety, and it made a second round trip.

Commerce is not the only peaceful mission of the submarine. In 1895 an association known as the Lake Submarine Company was organized. Its purpose was to use the Lake type of submarine boat for the recovery of lost treasures from the sea bottom and for other undersea work. The company was frequently called upon for aid in recovering sunken ships and their cargoes, building breakwaters and tunnels, dredging for gold, fishing for pearls and sponges, and similar operations.

The first vessel adapted to these purposes was the *Argonaut,* built by Simon Lake in 1894. Its important feature was a diver's compartment, by means of which divers could leave the vessel

The tiny galley or kitchen where food for the crew is prepared. All equipment is stainless steel. Stove and refrigerator are electrically operated. Two cooks work in this galley.

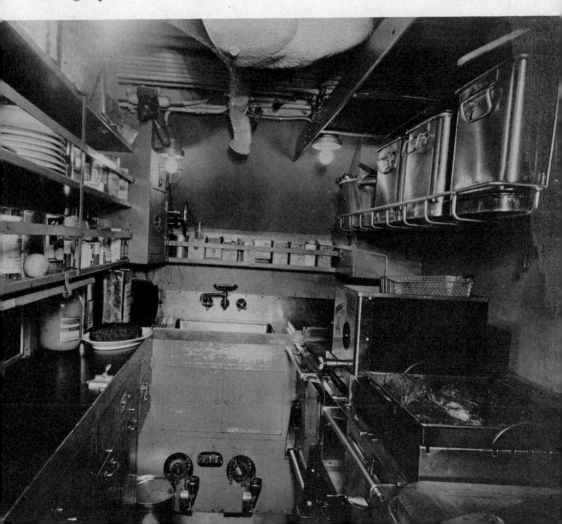

Space on a submarine is very cramped. Crew members sit very close to each other during mealtimes.

when submerged. The *Argonaut* and its successors have doors in the bottom of the hull. Deep-sea diving from such a submarine is much more practical than the old system of surface diving, the sea bottom being under direct observation and within immediate reach.

The sea bottom, in localities near land, is abundantly sown with wrecks, which in many cases contain permanently valuable cargoes, such as gold and coal. The Lake system greatly simplifies the work of search for sunken ships. The vessels are able in a few hours' time to search over regions that would have taken months by the old method. Many wrecks have been found by these bottom-prowling scouts and much valuable material recovered.

Gold-bearing sands are found at the mouth of certain rivers in Alaska and South America. With the Lake system it is possible to gather material from such localities to a depth of 150 or more feet, the material being drawn up by suction pumps into the vessel, and its gold recovered. Places on the Alaskan coast, laid bare at high tide, are said to have yielded as much as $12,000 per cubic yard.

Another important application is that of fishing for pearl shells, sponges, and coral. This is blind work when done by divers from the surface, the returns being largely a matter of chance. By aid of submerged boats, with their powerful electric lights, the work becomes a matter of certainty. The recovery of the oyster, clam and other edible shellfish is also a feature of the work which the Lake Company has in view. The present method of dredging is of the hit-or-miss character, while the submarine method is capable of thorough work. Vessels have been designed with a capacity of gathering oysters from good ground at the rate of five thousand bushels per hour.

These particulars are given to show that the submarine vessel is not wholly an instrument of war, but that it is capable of being made useful for many purposes in peace. With continued practice the utility of the submarine will grow, and by its aid the sea bottom, up to a certain depth, may become as open to varied operations as is the land surface.

The U. S. Navy's first submarine, U.S.S. Holland.

How Fast Does Sound Travel?

The experienced fisherman who smiles at the amateur's restless fidgeting and complaining has discovered by careful observation that the fish who swims around in such an exasperating manner just a foot or so away from the temptingly baited hook has had an advance tip that something out of the ordinary is going on up above him. For sound, whether it be the noise of an oarlock or a companion's casual remark, can be heard more than four times as easily by the fish in the water beneath than it can up above in the air. Sound travels very quickly through the air, traversing ten hundred and ninety feet in a second, but it reaches forty-seven hundred feet away under water in the same time.

When the crowd on the other side of the baseball grounds yells across the field it seems as though we have heard their cheers as soon as they have been given, and so we have for all practical purposes, although in reality half a second has elapsed while the sound has been coming across the field. The time taken by sound in traveling is more apparent when the volume is sufficient to carry it a long distance. The sound of an explosion of a large quantity of dynamite and ammunition in Jersey City was not heard in Philadelphia, ninety miles away, for over seven minutes after it occurred.

What Is Denatured Alcohol?

Under a law passed by the United States Congress in 1907, the internal tax need not be paid on alcohol intended for use as fuel or for illuminating purposes, or other mechanical employment. But to avoid taxation it must be rendered unfit for drinking by the addition of such unpalatable substances as wood alcohol, pyridin, benzola, sulphuric ether or animal oil. Thus treated, it is spoken of as denatured.

How Fast Can a Bird Fly?

Undoubtedly the wing power of most birds is very great, but it is difficult to make calculations of the speed attained, for we must remember that there is a difference between air speed and ground speed; wind pressure must be taken into consideration. The duck hawk is one of the fastest birds; so also is the carrier pigeon, which can keep up for hours an average of fifty-five miles an hour. Professor J. A. Thomson quotes the case of a flock of swifts flying 6,000 feet above Mosul, in Iraq, which, as paced by an airplane, were doing sixty-eight miles an hour, and were probably capable of making over a hundred miles an hour. The eagle, soaring to a vast height in the sky, can rise out of sight in less than three minutes, thus attaining a speed of not less than sixty miles an hour. The small song birds fly at from twenty to thirty-five miles an hour.

THE STORY OF DEEP-SEA DIVING

A diver comes up from the ocean bottom in the South Pacific after locating some lost gun barrels. A crane is hoisting one of the gun barrels up as the diver ascends. At the right is an air compressor which supplies air to the diver while he is under water.

DEEP-SEA diving has a long history. The ancient Greek poet Homer, in his *Iliad*, mentions the action of a diver diving for oysters. Thucydides, the Athenian historian, who lived during the fifth century B. C., tells of the use of divers during the siege of Syracuse to saw down the barriers that had been built below the surface of the water to obstruct and damage any Greek vessels trying to enter the harbor. Alexander the Great, at the siege of Tyre, ordered divers to destroy the submarine defenses of the besieged. Livy, the early Roman historian, writes that much treasure was recovered by divers from the sea in the reign of Perseus.

What Were the First Diving Devices?

Aristotle, Greek philosopher of the fourth century B. C., was the first writer to mention any appliance for aiding divers. Divers, he wrote, were sometimes supplied with instruments for drawing air from above the water so that they could remain a long time under the sea. He said that divers breathe by means of a metallic vessel, which does not get filled with water but retains the air in it. Alexander the Great himself was recorded to have descended into the sea in a machine called a *colimpha*, which kept a man dry and admitted light. The Roman Pliny wrote of divers engaged in war who drew air through a tube, one end of which was in their mouths, while the other floated on the surface of the water.

In 1240 Roger Bacon was said to have invented a device to enable men to work under water. Books published in the sixteenth century show engravings of a diver wearing a tight-fitting helmet, with a long leather tube leading to the surface, where the tube is kept afloat by a buoy. In the years that followed, other experiments were made with underwater suits, but it was not until 1830 that Augustus Siebe invented the diving suit that was to become the ancestor of today's modern diving garb. Siebe's helmet was fitted with air inlet and regulating outlet valves. Since Siebe's death in 1872, many important improvements have been made; nevertheless, his basic principle is the foundation of the deep-sea diving gear of today. His invention, with its improvements, opened up the whole modern era of efficient underwater work.

What Is the Modern Diving Suit?

Diving apparatus in use today consists essentially of seven parts: a helmet with breastplate, a waterproof diving dress, a length of flexible air tube with metal couplings, a pair of weighted boots, a pair of lead weights for breast and back, a life line and an air pump.

The helmet, of which there are several patterns, is secured to the breastplate by rings, the plate being clamped to the vulcanized rubber collar of the diving dress. This dress is a combination suit covering the whole body except the hands, which project through elastic cuffs. Air is supplied to the diver through a non-return valve at the back of the helmet by means of a flexible tube connected with the air pump. The air escapes through a spring valve at the side of the helmet, this valve being adjustable by the diver. With this arrangement the pressure of the air in the helmet is always equal to, or slightly greater than, the water pressure at the outlet valve. It is absolutely necessary that the diver should breathe compressed air, otherwise his breathing would be instantly stopped and blood would flow from his nose and mouth. The greatest hazard in diving is fouling, or rupture of the air hose.

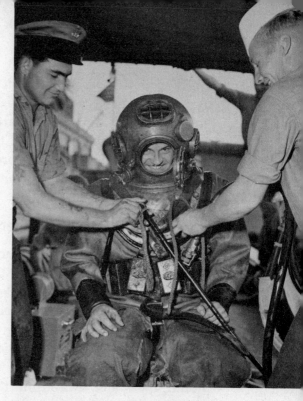

Two crewmen help a Navy diver into his heavy rubberized suit. The helmet locks into the metal breastplate and collar.

In order to enable him to sink and to stand firmly on the bottom, he carries a forty-pound weight on his chest and a similar weight on his back, and sixteen pounds of lead on each boot. Altogether the weight of the equipment is 175 pounds.

Besides the air pipe, the diver is usually connected with the surface by a signal or life line, in which are embedded telephone wires. He usually descends by a rope (shot-rope) attached to a heavy weight which has been previously lowered to the bottom, and on reaching bottom the diver takes with him a line (distance-line) attached to this weight, so that he can always find the shot-rope again.

As a diver enters the water the superfluous air in his dress is driven through the outlet valve by the pressure of the water on his legs and body. The water seems to grip all around. If the valve is freely open, he will feel his breathing rather labored by the time he gets his valve just under water. The reason for this is that the pressure in his lungs is that of the water at the valve outlet, whereas the pressure on his chest and abdomen is greater by something like a foot of water. He is thus breathing against pressure, and if he has to breathe deeply, as during exertion, the effect becomes serious. One of the first things a diver has to learn is to avoid this adverse pressure by adjusting the outlet valve so that the breathing may be quite free and easy.

How Does the Diver Work Under Water?

With all the apparatus which is at his disposal, the diver is a veritable submarine machine shop. He has air-driven wood- and metal-working tools of every description. The employment of one device used in an atmosphere of water is startling to the layman—this is the oxyacetylene cutter. The nozzle of an ordinary blow-pipe is surrounded by another nozzle, leaving a ring-shaped space between the two, and through this space air is forced, pulling the water away from the cutting jet.

Having inspected the bottom of a Navy warship, the diver laboriously climbs up diving barge next to the warship. Here a seaman assists the diver.

Each submarine disaster has emphasized anew the need of trained divers. When the S-4 went down in 1927, with the loss of forty men, this need was emphasized more forcefully than ever, so a school to train deep-sea divers was established in the Washington Navy Yard. The course of instruction lasts six months and is very thorough. Instruction is given in the actual technique of diving, in underwater cutting, in the structure of submarines, in the physics of diving, and in the physiology and chemistry of decompression.

What Are the Dangers Faced by Divers?

The most ever-present danger to the deep-sea diver is the pressure of the water in which he works. Water weighs 64 pounds per cubic foot. For every foot a diver descends he has to withstand a further pressure of 64 pounds on each square foot of his body. At a depth of 22 fathoms, or 132 feet, a diver is under pressure of 4¼ tons a square foot or a total load of 5 atmospheres—5 times as much as man was designed to stand. Air must be supplied the diver at slightly greater pressure than that of the water surrounding him to prevent his chest from being crushed by the colossal load of deep water. If through any accident the diver loses the air pressure in his suit, the weight of the sea crushes him.

Breathing under such unnatural conditions leads to the worst hazard a diver meets, that of "the bends." When deep-sea diving was just beginning, divers found that if they went much below a depth of sixty feet and stayed down much over an hour, they

A deep-sea diver prepares to descend from a Navy diving barge at sea. An assistant holds the airlines as the diver goes down. Officer raps helmet to tell diver all is ready.

Underwater view of a diver descending to the floor of the ocean. Heavy metal shoes and lead weights strapped around his waist keep the diver from bobbing up to the surface.

were subject, on returning to the surface, to a strange illness. The diver suffered terribly and doubled up in strange convulsions. Because of contorted movements, the malady was called the bends.

Often the bends took a more serious form. The victim was paralyzed for life or else died quickly after emerging from the

[652]

sea. Sandhogs working under air pressure, as when tunnels are constructed under rivers or providing deep foundations along river banks for huge bridges, also incurred the same disease.

In 1878 a French scientist, Paul Bert, demonstrated that the disease was caused by bubbles of nitrogen gas which got into the blood and tissues of a diver emerging from the sea. Bert concluded from his experiments that if the diver were to rise slowly but steadily to the surface, the nitrogen dissolved in his body would slowly come out of solution in amounts insufficient to cause sizable bubbles and would escape continuously through the lungs. This process is now known as decompression.

In 1906, J. S. Haldane, a British scientist, found it was safer to decompress in stages, coming up sharply part way to cut the pressure on the diver in half, permitting considerable nitrogen to escape, but with pressure still sufficient to prevent the formation of any large bubbles. Again and again the pressure was to be halved until all pressure was eliminated. Professor Haldane worked out a series of tables for times of decompression for different depths.

Another hazard of deep-sea diving is oxygen intoxication. At about 160 feet down, for instance, a diver breathes five times as much oxygen as he normally does. Reeling below the sea, a diver susceptible to this intoxication is completely helpless. Such divers have to be stricken from the lists for their own safety. Other divers show the effects of oxygen intoxication only upon returning to the surface, when they laugh and sing gaily.

The "squeeze" is another danger. The diving rig must be supplied with air pressure to counteract the sea pressure. But only the helmet and a little space in the suit just below the breastplate actually contain any air, to avoid too much buoyancy. The pressure of the air in the lungs of the diver, transmitted to every part of his body, inflates him to balance off the sea pressure. But a slight decrease in the pressure of his helmet results in a strange sensation of being hugged chokingly by the sea. With a little more air released, the embrace of the sea forces the blood out of the legs and then out of the lower abdomen, a condition at once painful and dangerous.

THE STORY OF PRINTING

An offset printing press. Most of the rollers at the left have the function of spreading the ink evenly before it is applied to the plate. The plate does not print directly upon the paper, but upon a rubber mat, which then transfers the ink to the paper.

THE DEBT that civilization owes to the art of printing is beyond calculation. Books keep the records of our history, the data of our sciences; books are the medium of education, of the exchange of ideas. Until the fifteenth century, books were written by hand—and there were not many books in the whole world. The ability to read and write was the privilege of a few people, and knowledge in a broad sense was confined to the few who had access to the libraries of hand-written books. The invention of printing made it possible to produce books by hundreds and thousands, in less time than is required to copy a single book by hand. It put books within the reach of everybody, enormously stimulated popular education, and put new tools in the hands of philosophers and scientists.

Who Invented Printing?

The use of carved wooden blocks for printing on paper, vellum and silk is very ancient. It is known that in A.D. 175 some of the Chinese classics were cut on tablets for reproduction. The Chinese used wood blocks to make prints of pictures, to decorate cloth, to stamp seals and signatures. It is not known how early wood blocks were used to print whole books, but the art is mentioned in Chinese literature of the tenth century. A printed Korean book that still exists bears the date 1337.

In Europe, references to block printing have been traced back to the twelfth century. A surviving woodcut of the Virgin Mary is dated 1418.

Despite the antiquity of printing from wood blocks, virtually all books prior to the fifteenth century were copied by hand, for the reason that more labor was involved in making woodcuts. The modern art of printing was inaugurated by the revolutionary invention of movable type—separate blocks for separate letters— and the use of metal instead of wood. Many more impressions can be taken from metal type than from wood before the type wears out, an important point in reducing the cost of printing. With separate movable type, the same blocks can be used to print page after page and book after book—a huge saving of time and labor over the older methods.

The invention of movable metal type is variously attributed to Johan Gutenberg of Mainz and Lourens Janszoon Coster of Haarlem. The earliest known document so printed is dated 1454.

The first English printer was William Caxton (1422?-1491). His book *The Game and Play of Chesse,* translated from a work of Jacobus de Cassolis, is said by some scholars to be the first book printed in English. The date was about 1475.

What Is Type?

The movable blocks used in printing are now called *type.* Modern metal type is made of an alloy of lead and antimony. The *face* of the letter or character lies in raised relief on one end of the rectangular block; this end is called the *shoulder.* On one

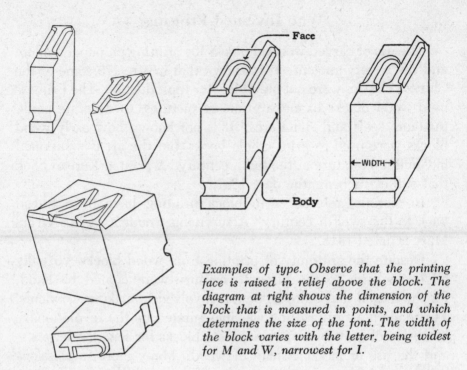

Examples of type. Observe that the printing face is raised in relief above the block. The diagram at right shows the dimension of the block that is measured in points, and which determines the size of the font. The width of the block varies with the letter, being widest for M and W, narrowest for I.

side of the body is a groove called the *nick,* which tells the typesetter through sense of touch how to place the type so that it will print right side up.

The height from base to face is the same for all type, a trifle over an inch. When a quantity of type is assembled on a plane surface, the faces of all the letters thus lie in one plane. An inked roller is passed across the top, and the ink adheres to the face of the type. Then a sheet of paper is pressed down on it, and the ink is transferred to the paper. The type faces are cut in mirror reversal of the printed letters, so that when printed the letters will be normal.

How Is Type Measured?

The smallest printed letters that can be read by average vision are about 1/12 of an inch high. Type sizes extend from this dimension up to several inches in height. Over one inch, sizes are expressed in inches and the type is made of wood, for metal would be excessively heavy. This very large type is of course used only for display purposes, on posters and some newspaper headlines.

All "body" type—used for text written in sentences and paragraphs—is less than an inch high. Here the size is expressed in *points*, a point being 1/72 of an inch. The sizes in common use are, in points: 6, 8, 10, 12, 14, 18, 24, 30, 36. Body type in newspapers is usually 8-point; in books, 10- or 12-point. This book is printed in 12-point type. There are also some odd sizes, 5, 7, 9, 11. The use of 9-point for body type in books is fairly common.

The point measurement refers to the shoulder on which the letter is mounted, not to the letter itself. Capital letters may be as high as the shoulder, but small letters never are. Some small letters are of "mean" size, such as *o, r, s, x;* others rise above the mean, such as *b, h, l, t;* others go below the mean, as *g, y;* but no letter goes both above and below. Consequently the apparent size of printed small letters may vary considerably in different fonts of the same point size. What makes the difference is the arbitrary size of mean letters relative to the shoulder.

Diagram of two different type faces of the same point size. The style at the left assigns a larger proportion of the body to the "mean" letter, such as x, so that all the letters are larger than those on the right. The style on the right accentuates the projection of "ascenders" and "descenders" above and below the mean letters.

A type block that is just as wide as it is high is called an *em*, for the reason that the letter *m* in most fonts is mounted on such a block. Similarly, a block half as wide as it is high is an *en*. The width of type varies with the letter, being smallest for the letter *i*. To make spaces between words, the typesetter is equipped with *spaces*, type blocks without letters. The minimum assortment in a font is usually ems, ens, and spaces of one-third of an em (usually called "three to em").

Larger distances, especially the lengths of type lines, are measured in *picas,* a pica being 1/6 of an inch. The standard newspaper column is 12 picas wide (2 inches), with one pica between columns. The type page in this book is 28 picas wide. (If all letters were an em wide, there would be 28 letters to the line, since the type is 12-point. Actually, there are about 60 characters to the line.)

What Are the Basic Type Faces?

An assemblage of type including the 26 letters, the numerals, punctuation, symbols, etc., all in the same design of face, is called a *font.* Hundreds of different fonts have been devised, but all may be classed in a few basic categories.

When metal type was first invented, the design of printed letters was patterned after the styles of script then in use. Four basic styles were developed: Text, Roman, Italic, Script.

| *Text* | *Roman* | *Italic* | *Script* |

Text is very ornate; it may be familiar to you as "Old English" or "German" or "Gothic." Its modern use is largely limited to short passages of an ecclesiastical character.

Roman, patterned after the severe simplicity of classic architectural inscriptions, is the standard for body text in all modern printing. Its vertical lines make for condensation and ease of reading.

Italic, originally an imitation of longhand script, has now become formalized as Roman with sloping strokes. Modern Italic is designed to be used in conjunction with Roman.

Script is a more genuine imitation of longhand, having all small letters connected. Its use is restricted to formal announcements and the like.

What Are the Parts of the Printed Letter?

Look at a capital *T* or *H* in this book. You will notice that the vertical strokes are heavier than the horizontal. The difference in weight is also visible in many of the small letters; look at a *w*, and compare the sides of an *o* to the top and bottom. This difference imitates the tendency in longhand writing to bear down more heavily on vertical strokes than on horizontal. In a compact body of letters, it makes for greater readability than is achieved by uniform strokes.

This is called the HAIRLINE or light element of the letter

This curved tip →
is called a serif

These serifs, in this form
of letter, point slightly outward
and rise *slightly above the hairline

This is called the STEM→
or heavy element of the letter

The bottom serifs are

bracketed or rounded into the letter

The heavy strokes are called *stems* and the lighter are *hairlines*. You will notice also that long straight strokes have a kind of crossbar at the end; this is called a *serif*. The purpose of the serif is not solely ornamental. It aids the eye in rapid identification of letters, being especially necessary in the small letters.

What Are the Basic Roman Variations?

Hundreds of different fonts, we said before, have been designed. Most of them are variations of the Roman style. They may be classified in six groups: Oldstyle Antique, Formal Oldstyle, Informal Oldstyle, Transitional, Modern, and Sans Serif.

The Oldstyle Antique is characterized by knobby or square-cut serifs, bulging beyond the hairlines, and by relatively little difference in weight between hairlines and stems. Modern Roman goes to the opposite extreme, with long, thin, pointed serifs, great difference between stems and hairlines. Intermediate characteristics are displayed by Formal Oldstyle, Informal Oldstyle, and Transitional. For example, the type in this book is Caledonia, a Transitional style. Examine a capital *T* and you will see the typical flat hairline, rounded serifs with vertical sides, and fairly heavy stem.

Sans Serif refers to any font without serifs. Here the distinction between stems and hairlines is apt to be slight or nonexistent. Although rarely seen in body type, this style has many specialized uses.

The difference between one font and another, in the same class of Roman variation, may be difficult to detect if only single letters are compared. But compare masses of type and the difference is obvious. The mass appearance of printed letters is compounded of many small elements—the weight of strokes, the width of individual letters, the angle of serifs, the spacing of words, the total amount of ink on a given area of paper.

How Is Type Set by Hand?

Originally all type was set by hand, and hand setting is still unavoidable for many purposes—odd-size fonts, large display type, "job" work where there is little text but great variety.

For hand-set, a font is distributed in compartments in a large shallow box or *case*. Capital letters are separated from small, and from their position in the early boxes are commonly called "upper case" and "lower case" respectively. Besides letters, numerals, symbols, punctuation, and spaces, the case may also contain some *logotypes*, which are blocks with two or more letters, such as ff, fi, ffi.

The typesetter knows the arrangement of characters in the case, by memory. He picks out the type with one hand and puts it in a *stick* held in the other. The stick is a shallow metal case in which one line of type at a time can be placed. After

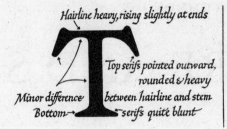

Hairline heavy, rising slightly at ends

Top serifs pointed outward, rounded & heavy

between hairline and stem

Minor difference

Bottom →   ↙ serifs quite blunt

Oldstyle Antique

Hairline lighter, rising noticeably at ends

Top serifs rounded but lighter right serif canted to left

More contrast   between hairline & stem

Bottom serifs →   refined & rounded into stem

Formal Oldstyle

Hairline still lighter, slight rise at ends

Top serifs slant outward and are more pointed

Great   difference   between hairline & stem

Bottom serifs →   refined and more rounded into stem

Informal Oldstyle

Hairline very light & straight across

Serifs sharp, rounded into hairline & nearly upright

Greater difference   between hairline & stem

Bottom serifs →   sharp, rounded into stem

Transitional

Hairline very light and straight

Top serifs much sharper, longer & nearly straight

Greatest contrast   between hairline & stem

Bottom serifs →   straight line to stem

Modern Roman

Hairline equal or nearly so, to stem

No serifs on hairline no difference between the hairline and stem

Little & sometimes

No serifs   at bottom of letter

Sans Serif

the line is complete, the operator transfers it to a *form* on a level table where whole pages of type are assembled.

Look at the right-hand edge of this page of type. You will see that it is a straight vertical line, instead of the ragged line that usually results when you write in longhand. To make all the lines on a page of equal length, called *justifying*, the typesetter has to juggle the spaces between words until they come out right. Justifying is the chief problem of the hand setter, calling for both skill and judgment.

TYPE SIZES IN COMMON USE

FOURSCORE AND S

36-point

FOURSCORE AND SEVE

30-point

Fourscore and seven years ago our

24-point

Fourscore and seven years ago our fathers bro

18-point

Fourscore and seven years ago our fathers brought forth on this

14-point

Fourscore and seven years ago our fathers brought forth on this continent

12-point

Fourscore and seven years ago our fathers brought forth on this continent a new

10-point

Fourscore and seven years ago our fathers brought forth on this continent a new nation,

8-point

Fourscore and seven years ago our fathers brought forth on this continent a new nation, conceived in liberty,

6-point

Comparison of the appearance of body masses set in six Roman classes
The type size of these examples is 12 point

However, a writer that is assigned the task of phrasing printed expressions can bring to it only the attributes that he possesses at the time. His purpose should be to make the most of those attributes, whatever they may be. His proper first step toward
Oldstyle Antique Roman (Bookman)

However, a writer that is assigned the task of phrasing printed expressions can bring to it only the attributes that he possesses at the time. His purpose should be to make the most of those attributes, whatever they may be. His proper first step toward accomplishment of this purpose is to
Formal Oldstyle Roman (Garamond)

However, a writer that is assigned the task of phrasing printed expressions can bring to it only the attributes that he possesses at the time. His purpose should be to make the most of those attributes, whatever they may be. His proper first step toward
Informal Oldstyle Roman (Caslon)

However, a writer that is assigned the task of phrasing printed expressions can bring to it only the attributes that he possesses at the time. His purpose should be to make the most of those attributes, whatever they may be. His proper first step toward accom-
Transitional Roman (Baskerville)

However, a writer that is assigned the task of phrasing printed expressions can bring to it only the attributes that he possesses at the time. His purpose should be to make the most of those attributes, whatever they may be. His proper first step toward accomplishment
Modern Roman (Bodoni)

However, a writer that is assigned the task of phrasing printed expressions can bring to it only the attributes that he possesses at the time. His purpose should be to make the most of those attributes, whatever they may be. His proper first step toward accomplishment
Sans Serif

How Is Type Set by Machine?

As you can imagine, setting type by hand for a book of this size would be a very long as well as expensive business. Practically all body type for books and newspapers and magazines is now set by machinery. The two principal machines are the *linotype* and the *monotype*.

The linotype is so-called because it sets a whole line of type at a time on a single metal *slug*. The operator sits at a keyboard and writes just as you use a typewriter. The font is contained in a metal case called a *magazine*, divided by vertical partitions into a number of *channels*. Each channel contains a number of identical *mats* (short for matrix, matrices). A mat is a piece of brass having the face of a character inset; it is in effect a mold for making a block of type. When the operator punches a key, a gate is opened at the bottom of the corresponding channel, and one mat drops out. The mats are carried along by an endless belt and deposited on a *carrier* in front of the operator, to left of the keyboard. The operator can lift out mats from the carrier and rearrange them, to correct mistakes; he can insert extra

spaces; he sets by hand certain mats for rare characters that are kept in a separate box near by. A sliding stop on the carrier can be adjusted to make lines of any desired length. When the line of mats is complete, the operator pulls a hand lever; this causes the mats to be pushed off the carrier into a holder on the so-called *wheel*. The operator can proceed to set the next line of type while the machine is automatically dealing with the previous line.

One of the keys on the board sets *wedge spaces*. The wedge space is actually two metal wedges linked together in opposite directions, so that the total thickness depends on how far the wedges are thrust toward each other or pulled apart. The operator is careful to put wedge spaces between the words, and to set the line a little short of the full width, leaving some "play." When the line of mats and spaces is transferred to the wheel, the first thing that happens is that a horizontal bar comes up

The linotype machine. At top is the magazine; below it is the slanting way through which the mats pass to the carrier, just above and to left of the keyboard. The toothed rim of the casting wheel is just visible through the superstructure at the left.

from below and hits all the wedges simultaneously. The spaces expand uniformly until the line is full. Next the wheel makes a half turn, bringing the mats in front of a slit in the *casting chamber*. While the mats are pressed tightly against the slit, a plunger in the chamber forces molten lead against them, and so casts a

[665]

Corrections in linotyped matter are made by resetting complete lines and substituting a new slug or batch of slugs for the erroneous lines.

metal slug with the characters for one line of type on one edge. The lead cools and hardens very quickly. The wheel then carries the newly cast slug past a knife that trims the back edge, so that the slug will be of standard height.

Having served to mold the slug, the mats are plucked from the wheel by an arm and are deposited on a kind of worm screw at the top of the linotype machine. This screw carries them along from left to right. Each mat is cut in such a way that it hangs from guide rails until it reaches its own channel in the magazine, whereupon it drops off and is once more ready to be set.

The advantage of casting solid lines of type is obvious. Make-up is much easier with, say, thirty slugs per page than with upward of a thousand separate type blocks. But in one way there is a disadvantage. If a typographical error is made, a whole line has to be reset. For complicated text where absolute accuracy is essential, as in legal documents and scientific reports, it is desirable to be able to correct mistakes letter by letter. The monotype machine is preferred in this field.

The monotype machine casts metal type from brass mats, and is operated by a keyboard, like the linotype, but every character is on a separate slug. Besides the necessary mechanical differences, there is also a difference in the operation. The linotype machine justifies automatically, through the use of wedge spaces. But the monotype operator has to justify by distributing spaces of fixed standard sizes. The monotype mats are made in precise widths of from one to five units, and the so-called *dial* on the machine shows the operator how many units of width remain

The monotype machine. The type-setting keyboard is separate from the type-casting machine at the right, but can be placed adjacent for one-man operation. The illuminated "dial" just above the keyboard shows the operator at every instant how many units in the line remain to be filled.

to be filled in a line. The reading on the dial changes each time a mat is set in place, and when the operator sees that there is no more room for an additional syllable, he distributes the residue of space by increasing interior spaces of the line.

What Is Make-Up?

The arrangement of type, pictures, etc., in a compact mass for printing is called *make-up*.

Type is *solid* if the lines are placed as close together as the metal of the slugs or type blocks will permit. For readability and other reasons, type is often *leaded* by the insertion of spaces between lines. These spaces or *leads* are thin strips of metal or wood. The standard leads are graduated in sizes of even points from 2 points up. Body type in newspapers is mostly solid, while editorial matter is usually leaded.

Flat-bed cylinder press. Paper fed into the machine at the right is carried down to a cylinder at the center, which rolls it across the flat chase of type below. The cylinder then ejects the paper upon endless moving tapes which throw it on top of the pile at the left. This press makes 7,000 impressions per hour.

The effect of leading can be achieved in machine setting without the use of leads. The brass mats determine the size of characters, but the size of the slug on which they are cast is fixed by the slit in the casting chamber. Thus 9-point letters, for example, are commonly set on 10-point slugs, so that the solid type gives the appearance of 1-point leading. The 12-point type in this book is set on 14-point slugs, with the effect of 2-point leading.

Make-up is usually conducted on a *stone*, a heavy table with a level stone surface. The type is placed inside a *chase*, a rectangular metal frame. When the type must be made into a page of fixed size, as is usually the case, the stone worker starts by putting some *furniture* into the chase to mark the depth of the page. Furniture includes metal and wood blocks, strips and so on, necessary for filling spaces between the mass of type and the chase. For final *lock-up,* metal wedges called *quoins* are placed along the inside edges of the chase. After sufficient furniture has been inserted to make the page fairly tight, the quoins in opposing pairs are screwed together by a hand tool so as to lock the type and furniture together rigidly. The type faces must remain aligned in a plane surface against the pressure of the press during printing. The stone worker often tests the page, after lock-up, by raising the chase on one edge and pounding the type with a wooden mallet.

How Do Printing Presses Work?

Printing ink is much thicker than the ink you use in your fountain pen. It has about the consistency of molasses. It is smeared on the type by a hard rubber roller. In a small hand press, there may be only one roller, which swings back and forth between the type and a metal platen on which the operator daubs ink from time to time. But on larger presses there are several rollers, up to about twenty-four in some cases, which pick up the ink from a gutter or *well* and pass it along the line until by the time it reaches the type it is spread with great uniformity.

After the ink roller has passed over the type, a sheet of paper is pressed down upon it. As to the mechanical arrangements for printing, there are many different kinds of presses. We need take account only of the two principal types, the *flat bed* press and the *rotary* press.

The flat bed press is so-called because it prints direct from type, the chase being laid on a horizontal bed. The chase is alternately pushed under a fixed inking roller and retracted under a large cylinder that rolls a sheet of paper upon it. The paper, stacked in sheets, is fed automatically to the cylinder, and, after printing, is snatched automatically off the chase and piled at the foot of the press. In this last move the paper is carried over a line of burning gas jets, which help the ink to dry quickly so that it will not blur.

[669]

The rotary press does not print from type but from a *stereotype* (page 671). This is essentially a reproduction of an entire page, cast on a single plate. The plate is curved so as to fit around a cylinder. This cylinder revolves in contact with another which carries the paper, fed to it from a continuous roll. Since rotary motion can be stepped up to speeds far beyond the reciprocating motion of the flat bed press, the rotary press prints much faster. It is used for all high-speed and large-scale work, such as newspapers and national magazines. The flat bed press now is limited to "job" work and to small-scale book and pamphlet printing.

How and Why Is Printing from Type Avoided?

In large-scale printing runs, such as newspapers and books, printing directly from the type involves extreme difficulties.

Part of a huge rotary press that turns out 42,000 copies of a 52-page newspaper per hour. The continuous paper roll on which all the pages are printed is here led into the machine that cuts and folds it. Finished newspapers emerging at lower left are carried vertically upward to the bundling department.

First, there is the difficulty of keeping intact the locked-up pages. Even if the type remains rigid in the chase against the pressure of printing, the lead type wears away faster than the zinc or other metal used for pictures, and so the printing surface tends to become ragged. Second, keeping all the type for a whole book or a newspaper ties up an enormous amount of metal and requires huge storage space.

Consequently, large-scale printing is done from reproductions of the type, rather than the type itself.

One kind of reproduction is the *stereotype*. A damp sheet of papier-mâché is pressed (at 300 pounds per square inch) upon the type, and it dries as a mold. A reproduction of the whole page is cast in this mold. The metal plate so cast is much lighter than the original type. It may be used for flat printing, but more commonly is bent for use in a rotary press.

General view of the four-unit rotary press. In the foreground is the "flyboy," who examines the finished papers to see that margins are correct, watches the paper "web" and stops the press if it breaks. At the right, a pressman adjusts the flow of ink from a control box.

Another kind of reproduction is the *electrotype*. Wax is pressed upon the type to make a mold. The mold is then used to make a copper-faced plate. (The plate is made by electroplating, not by pouring molten metal into the mold. The wax is coated with a conducting substance and immersed in an electrolytic bath. An electric current causes copper to be deposited on the conducting surface, making a shell of uniform thickness. After this shell is stripped off the copper mold, the back is reinforced so that it will stand up under printing pressures.) Many books are printed from electrotype plates.

Other reproduction methods depend upon photo-engraving, which is discussed in the following sections. For example, in the *photo-offset* or *offset lithographic* process, the type is used to make one clean proof, which is then photographed to make a *planographic plate*. This plate is used for the mass printing, but not directly. After it is inked, the plate is pressed on a rubber "blanket" and then the paper is pressed on the blanket. One advantage of this lithographic method is that the plates last longer than do electrotypes, since they escape the pressures necessary for the transfer of ink to paper. THE MODERN WONDER BOOK OF KNOWLEDGE is printed by this offset process.

How Are Pictures Reproduced?

From the mechanical point of view, there are three ways to apply ink to paper so as to reproduce a picture. These are *intaglio* printing, *relief* or *letterpress* printing, and *planographic* printing.

In an intaglio plate, the lines to be printed are cut below the surface, making troughs and hollows. The ink roller deposits ink in the depressed portions; the surface is wiped clean; paper is laid over it, and when the plate is inverted the ink settles upon the paper. You can often detect intaglio printing from the fact that the ink tends to bulge somewhat over the surface of the paper. The process is often used for calling cards, fine art prints, and the like, but is too costly for long press runs.

A letterpress *cut* ("cut" is the general term for the plate used in printing a picture) is so-called because the lines to be printed are raised in relief over the surface, just as letters and characters of type are raised in relief. The ink roller deposits ink only on the raised portions.

The so-called planographic plate is flat, but owing to its composition the ink roller deposits ink only on the portions that represent lines to be printed.

How Are Cuts Made?

The signature-printing and cloth-decorating stamps of ancient times were mostly carved in relief. But the first method evolved for printing pictures in books was intaglio carving of wood blocks. The art of making woodcuts engendered fine craftsmanship, and engaged the services of many great artists, but it had obvious shortcomings. Wood wears fast under printing pressures. Where fine lines had to be printed, copper or another metal had to be used in place of wood; copper engraving with hand tools is costly and time-consuming. Consequently, in most of the early books the illustrations are few and poorly reproduced.

A revolution came about through the application of photography to engraving. The general method now used to make cuts is as follows: A zinc or copper plate is coated with a light-sensitive emulsion. The picture to be reproduced is photographed, and the negative is laid over the plate to print a positive. (See "The Story of Photography.")

When the print is developed, the emulsion is washed away from the light portions of the picture, while a deposit of silver salts is left on the dark portions. The plate is then bathed or sprayed with an acid that eats away the exposed portions of the metal, leaving the darkened parts raised in relief. (The engraver may complete the work begun by the acid, by *routing* excess metal with hand tools.)

This photo-engraving process suffices for all "line" cuts—pictures formed of lines. The lines may be thick or thin, but all print equally black (or whatever color the ink may be). But many pictures that have to be reproduced are composed of

[673]

Zinc line engraving   *Drawing by W. P. Schoonmaker*

Most line drawings are etched on zinc plates for printing. Zinc engraving suffices when the lines are not too fine nor too close together. A drawing with much detail, and especially with shading effects by cross-hatching and fine parallel lines, requires a closer-grained metal. Such drawings are etched on copper.

Manual engraving of metal plates has been relegated to a fine art, practiced by only a few draughtsmen. For commercial purposes, photo-engraving has replaced hand-tooling.

Copper line engraving   Drawing by W. P. Schoonmaker

masses and gradations of grey, from white to black. For example, take a portrait photograph. The print will show very few hard lines. Such lines as you can trace will be boundaries between different masses of grey.

The commonest method of reproducing photographs is the *half-tone* process. The picture is photographed through a screen, a mesh of vertical and horizontal bars. The effect is to break up masses of solid color (photographing grey in black-and-white photography) into separate dots. The size of the individual dots is determined by the intensity of the color. In any event, the dots are so small and so close that they are not seen separately in the reproduction, but the total amount of ink they spread over a given area is capable of making all gradations of grey from black to white.

The half-tone process. At left is a half-tone reproduction of a photograph. Contrast this picture with the line drawings on the preceding two pages. At right, an enlargement of the picture of the gear wheel shows that it is composed of black dots, varying in size from area to area.

The size of screen used for a half-tone, measured in lines per inch, is determined by the quality of paper on which it is to be printed. Newsprint, having a very rough surface, requires a coarse screen, usually 60 lines to the inch. You can see the separate dots in a newspaper picture by bringing your eye close to the paper. With glossy book paper, the screen is 120 up, and a magnifying glass is needed to detect the individual dots. The photographs in this book are reproduced by half-tone; can you see the dots with the naked eye?

Photo-engraving is applied in many other ways. One way has become a serious rival to mimeographing, multigraphing, and the other methods of reproducing business forms without printing. This is to type the form on a typewriter with a special black ribbon, then photograph it, and print from a plate by the offset method. Conceivably this direct process may in time render movable type obsolete. The linotype operator may be transformed to a typewriter operator, tapping out the final copy without intervention of metal type and proof-pulling. For large-size letters that cannot be conveniently put on a typewriter, the operator may assemble slips of cardboard instead of metal blocks. The camera eye, reducing everything it sees to a single plate, does not care how the image was constructed in the first place!

What Is the Teletypesetter?

The teletypesetter is an ingenious device by which type may be set by telegraph. At the transmitting end there is a machine similar to a typewriter, which perforates a paper tape in code, each group of perforations corresponding to a letter or a numeral. The perforated tape passes on through a transmitter which converts the message into electric impulses for wire transmission (maybe a thousand miles away). At the receiving end these electric impulses are registered on a similar tape. This second tape, now perforated in code like the first one at the sending station, is fed into another mechanism which operates a linotype or other typesetting machine. Electric impulses translate the code into depressions of the keys on the typesetting machine. The copy strip is kept as a permanent record. By means of the teletypesetter, an operator in a New York newspaper office, for example, may control similar typesetting machines in Chicago, San Francisco, New Orleans, and any number of cities by telegraphic connections.

INDEX

Hail, 374-375
Haldane, J. S., 653
Halley's Comet, 354
Halogens (inert gases), 9
Hangars, dirigible, 247
Harbors, dredging out, 632
Haslam, "Pony Bob," 206
Heat insulation, 293
Heaviside, Sir Oliver, 94
Heavy water, 30
Helicopter: 218-225; basic principle of, 218; description of, 221-224; maneuvering of, 224; origin of, 218-221; uses of, 224-225
Helium: 12, 13, 15; for dirigibles, 242, 244, 245; number of neutrons in, 15
Hellot, M., 125
Hennepin, Father Louis, 490
Henry, Joseph, 72, 73, 200
Hero of Alexandria, "aelopile," 163, 182
Herodotus, 417
Herschel, Sir John, 126
Herschel, Sir William, 345
Hertz, Heinrich, 93, 94
Hertzian waves (radio), 35, 43, 93, 94
Hess, Professor Harry H., 55, 598-600
Hibernation, 455
Hickok, "Wild Bill," 206
Hiller, Stanley, "Hiller-Copter," 221
Hillier, James, 65-67
Hindenburg, dirigible, 241, 242, 248, 249
Hiroshima, 1-3, 24
Holladay, Ben, 205
Holland, Clifford Milburn, 452
Holland, John P., submarine, 635-638
Holland, submarine, 635
Holland Tunnel, 452-454
Homer, *Iliad*, 647
Hoosac Tunnel, 442-443
Hoover Dam, *see* Boulder Dam
Hottest place in United States, 101
Huguenots, 324
Hunley, Confederate submarine, 635
Hussey, Obed, 564, 567
Hyatt, John Wesley, 335-336
Hyder Ali, rocket corps, 165-166
Hydrogen: 7; atomic weight of, 8, 9; for dirigibles, 241-242, 244

Ice, dry, 586
Ice cream: 579-581; first made known in America, 581
Ice refrigeration: 577-586; in ancient times, food preservation, 578; artificial ice, first made, 582-583; ice business in America, 580-581; ice harvesting, 579; snow icing, 585-586; varied diet permitted through, 583-584. *See also* Ice cream; Railway refrigerators; Refrigerators

Iconoscope, seeing eye of television, 66-67, 148, 150, 153
Image dissector, 153
Image Orthocon camera, 153
India: cotton, 328; spinning, 328-329; rockets, used by Hyder Ali's army, 165-166
Indian Ocean, 592, 601
Industrial revolution, 329
Industry: use of X-rays in, 50-53; food industries, 51-53; metal castings, inspection of, 50-51
Influenza virus, photographed, 68
Infra-red rays, 30, 38
Intaglio printing, 672, 673
Iodine, as a specific, 85
Ionization, 32
Ions, 32
Ireland, flax and linen, 324
Iron, 7, 602-603; atomic weight of, 8; smelting, 603
Islands, floating, 600
Isotope, 11, 16, 21, 30
Italians, method of cooling liquids, 578-579
Italic type, *see* Type

James I, King, 633
Japan: atom bombing of, 1-2; silk industry, 327, 333
Jenkins, C. Francis, 153
Jet planes (propellerless planes), 161
Jet propulsion: 172-182; advantage over rocket propulsion, 175-176; duct engine, 178; future of, 181; gas turbine, 178, 180; perfection of, 180-181; for helicopters, 182; jet-assisted take-off (Jato), 181; nature of, 173-174; turbo-supercharger, 176-178
Jet propulsion engine, 172
Joachimsthal, mines, 29
Jones, Samuel, "Lucifers," 316
Jupiter, 353

Katanga mine, Belgian Congo, 28
Keefer, Dr. Chester, 89
Keller, Gottfried, inventor of paper from wood pulp, 550-551
Kennelly, Arthur E., 94
Kennelly-Heaviside surface (radio roof), 94
Kenny, Meave, 86
Kepler, Johannes, 228, 344
Kerosene, 508, 518
Key, Francis Scott, 166-167
Kinescope, 148, 152
Kitty Hawk, 219
Klarer, Dr. Joseph, 86
Knoll, Max, 63
Kodachrome film, 129, 130, 131
Kodacolor film, 129, 131
Kodak, 125, 126, 128

Radar—*continued*

first, when tested, 95; distance first measured by, 94; England saved by, 97; Pearl Harbor, warning at, 97-98; radar unit, essential parts of, 98, 100, cathode-ray tube indicator, 98, 100, directive antenna system, 98, 100, microwave transmitter, 98, 100, sensitive receiver, 98, 100; radio "echo," 93-94; signals to moon, 101; uses of, 100-101; warships, first installed on, 96; working of, 98; schematic diagram, 99

Radio: 35; beacons, 256-259; supplanting of wires by, 209; telephone, obstacles to supplanting by, 198; transmitters, oscillators, 40; transmitting tubes, 37. *See also* Electronics; Television

Radio broadcasting (pictures), 138-146

Radio Corporation of America: 66; pioneer radar work, 96; television camera tube (Image Orthocon), 153

Radio "echo," *see* Radar

Radioactivity: 11-12; from atom bomb, 2, 8, 9; discovery of, 14

Radium: 15; discovery of, 11; first isolated by Pierre and Marie Curie, 12, 29; rays emitted by, 12-13, 20, 26, 43

Railroad bridges, earliest, 458-460

Railroading (pictures), 472-484

Railway refrigerators: 583-585; Civil War, 583-584; modern, 584-585, bunker icing, 585

Rain, causes of, 369-375

Rainiest place in world, 101

Rayon, 332-333, 337, 338, 340

RCA, *see* Radio Corporation of America

Reaper, McCormick: 557-574; essential features of, 562-564; farming improved by, 573-574; first, invented by Cyrus Hall McCormick, 557, 560-562; factory, Chicago, 567; first manufactured for sale, 565; honored abroad, 567; improvements in, 569-573; in War between the States, 568. *See also* McCormick, Cyrus Hall

Rectifier, 34

Refinery, crude oil, 516

Refraction, law of, 600

Refrigeration, ice, *see* Ice refrigeration

Refrigerators, ice, 581; "ice preserver," 581

Relativity, Einstein theory of, 14

Relay, Maryland, viaduct, 459-460

Renaissance, 71

Rescue work, use of helicopter in, 224, 225

Richland Village, 3

Roberts, Louis, 550

Robot, 278

Rock salt, 274-276

Rockets: 159-171; bazooka, 167-169, 171; first, made by Hero of Alexandria, 163; fuel for, 160, 162; future use of, 170-171;

Rockets—*continued*

interplanetary travel, 170-171; weather data, 170; launched from planes, 169; principle of, 159-160; vacuum, traveling in, 161; warfare, first used in, 164-170; in World War II, 167-171; V-bombs, 170

Roentgen, Dr. Wilhelm Konrad, 11, 33, 41-45

Roman type, *see* Type

Romans: Atlantic Ocean known to, 588; dams built by, 419; linen manufacture, 326; use of snow for refrigeration, 578; use of sulphur salve, 291

Roosevelt, Franklin D., 3, 429

Roots blower, 531, 533

Rotor, 73, 79, 81

Royal Oak, sinking of, 642

Royal Observatory, Great Britain, 348

Rubber, natural plastic, 335, 337; synthetic, 337, 340, 517

Ruggieri, Claude, 165

Ruska, Dr. Ernst, 63

Russian-Japanese War, 636

Rutherford, Sir Ernest, 12, 18-20

Safelight, photographic, 124

Safety matches, 318-319, 322

Saguenay River, damming of, 438-439

St. Gotthard Pass, tunnel, 444-446

Salt: 272-278, 294; composition of, 7; how much used, 278; mines, mining, 273-276; purification, methods of, 276-278; where found, 273-275

Salt licks, 272-273

Salt springs, 274

Salvarsan ("606"), 85, 89, 90

Santa Fe, New Mexico, 3

Santos-Dumont, 240-241

Satin spar, 283

Saturn, 353

Sauria, Dr. Charles, phosphorus matches, 316-317

Scanner, electrical, 152-153; used in television, 39. *See also* Television

Schilling, Baron, telegraph, 200

Schroeder, Major R. W., 177, 178

Schrotter, Prof. Anton von, 318-319

Schulze, J. H., 125

Scientific American, 568

Script girl, 103-104

Sea water, salt from, 273

Seismograph, 512-513

Senner Dam, Sudan, 432

Seven Wise Men of Greece, 137

Sextant, 360

Shasta Dam, 427

Shenandoah, dirigible, 248

Ships, *see* Steel ships

Sibley, Hiram, 204, 206

Siebe, Augustus, 648

V-bombs, 167-170, 176; U. S. test of, 170
Vacuum tube, invention of, 33. *See also*
Electronics; X-rays
Vail, Alfred, 201-202
Valve, *see* Electron valve; Electronics
Van Buren, President, 202
Van de Graff, Dr. J., 20
Video, 155, 156
Volta, Alessandro, 71, 72
Voltaic pile, 71
Volts, 54

Waksman, Selman A., 90-91
Walker, John, friction matches, 316
Wan-Hoo, 171
War Between the States, 568-569, 635
Warner, Chauncey E., 320
Warships, radar first installed on, 96
Washington, George, 491
Water: composition of, 7; "heavy," 30; why
a stick seems to bend in, 600
Waterpower, 82, 83
Watson, Bell's assistant, 186, 187
Weather: 362-375; air, 362-363, pressure
of, 363-364, how measured, 364-365;
rain and snow, causes of, 369-375; wind,
cause of, 365-368
Wedgwood, "camera obscura," 125
Western Union Telegraph Company, 201,
203, 204, 207; first transcontinental tele-
graph line, 206-207
Westinghouse Company, 155, 176
Whale oil, 508
Wheatstone, Sir Charles, 201
Wheeler, electrical experiments, 200
Whitney, Eli, 330
Whittle, Frank, 180
Wielizka, Poland, salt mines, 274-275
Wildlife, pictures, 386-405
Wilhelm II, 42
William of Orange, 56
Wind, cause of, 365-368
Wireless telegraphy, 35-38
Wise Men of Greece, Seven, 137
Withington, Charles B., wire binder, 571-
572

Women, first taken into American armed
forces, 455
Women Appointed for Voluntary Emer-
gency Service (WAVES), 455
Women's Army Corps (WACS), 455
Women's Reserve of Coast Guard Reserve
(SPARS), 455
Wonder drugs, *see* Drugs, wonder
Wood, electrical experiments, 200
Woodcuts, 673
Wool, 331-332; history of, 331-332; where
produced, 331-332
Woolworth Tower, New York City, 615
World War I: 219, 234, 463; blimps, 241,
convoy by, 249-250; dyestuffs, need for,
502-503; plastics, 337; tractors, 575;
U-boats, 502, 641
World War II: 2, 9; animated cartoons, 121;
atom bomb, 1, 21-24; blimps, 241, 247-
249; commandos, 340; cotton, 330-331;
Diesel engines, 539; drugs, wonder, 85,
86, 88; fifth column, 440; ice manufacture, 583; jet propulsion, 176, 178, 181;
plastics, 337; radar, 147; rockets, 159-
164; silk, 333; television, 156; women in
armed forces, 455
Wright Brothers, 219

X-rays: 11, 13, 26, 30, 33, 39, 41-54; in
dentistry, 48-49; existence made known,
Roentgen's discovery of, 41-43; in industry, *see* Industry; in medicine, *see* Medicine; other uses, 53-54, examination by
means of, 53-54, forgeries exposed by, 53,
to produce plant permutations, 54; how
produced, 43-45; improvement of, 45-46;
in therapy, 49-50

Yerkes Observatory, 40-inch telescope, 341,
348
Young, Arthur, 221

Zambesi Bridge, Africa, 462
Zeppelin, Count Ferdinand, dirigibles, 241-
242
Zworykin, Dr. Vladimir K., inventor of iconoscope, 66-67, 153